The Extraordinary Events of an Ordinary Life

The Extraordinary Events of an Ordinary Life

Jeanne Chaeley

Front and back cover artwork by kind permission of Martin Lawrence Photography:
www.martinlawrencephotography.com

Matador
Unit E2 Airfield Business Park,
Harrison Road, Market Harborough,
Leicestershire. LE16 7UL
Tel: 0116 279 2299
Email: books@troubador.co.uk
Web: www.troubador.co.uk/matador
Twitter: @matadorbooks

ISBN 978 1 80313 499 4

British Library Cataloguing in Publication Data.
A catalogue record for this book is available from the British Library.

Printed and bound in Great Britain by CMP UK
Typeset in 11pt Minion Pro by Troubador Publishing Ltd, Leicester, UK

Matador is an imprint of Troubador Publishing Ltd

To my family

Contents

Prologue	xi
Part One: Maid in Cumberland	**1**
Chapter 1: A Chance Encounter	3
Chapter 2: Football Fever	17
Chapter 3: London	32
Chapter 4: Sweet 16	48
Chapter 5: A Day in the Life	69
Chapter 6: Sarah	86
Chapter 7: The Road to 19	106
Chapter 8: Love, Labour and Loss	122
Chapter 9: The Wedding	140
Chapter 10: Farewell Cumberland	161
Part Two: Seesaw	**185**
Chapter 11: A Happy Accident	187
Chapter 12: The Benefactress	205
Chapter 13: Capital Letters	226
Chapter 14: The Funeral	254
Chapter 15: Life After Death	273
Chapter 16: Between a Rock and a Hard Place	292
Part Three: Water Under the Bridge	**319**
Chapter 17: The Catalyst	321
Chapter 18: The Treehouse	350
Chapter 19: Wild Love	374
Chapter 20: The Icing on the Cake	393
Epilogue	419
Acknowledgements	423

Cast List

Narrator: Victoria (Vicky) Jane Caswell (b. 15.10.1953)

Her parents: Robert and Marion Kelly

Her siblings
Chris (b. 22.09.1948)
Alan (b. 21.01.1950)
Antonia (Toni) (b. 16.03.1951)
Michael (b. 19.07.1952)

Generation X
Sarah, Louise, Scott, Julia, Ryan and Leonie

The Millennials
Sophy, Harriet and Liam

The relatives
Nan – Louisa (Liz) Taylor
Maternal Aunt Gwen and Uncle Roger

Friends and associates
Cumberland/Cumbria
George and Ellen Duffy, Janice and James (next door neighbours)
Anne Cowley and Paul (a local schoolteacher and her son)
Liam Blane and daughter Julie
Dolly Cartwright and daughter Avice
Sally and Robin (Vicky's schoolfriends)
Wendy, Linda, Donna and Karen (Vicky's friends and workmates)
Jason, Joanie, Phil and Jean (Toni's friends)

London and the South

'Uncle' Bill, 'Auntie' Anji, Ruby and Ray (family friends)

Nicky (Vicky's workmate)

Polly

Manchester

Sister Rose Sparks, Leslie and daughter Deborah

Caroline

Amanda (Mandy)

Other characters not listed are incidental and appear only once.

Prologue

It is the 4th of January 1994. As I was driving home down the Vale of Lorton this morning, it snowed, but by three o'clock the sky had cleared and now the lower reaches of Buttermere Valley are basking in the late afternoon sun. The golden shafts illuminate the glistening fellsides and cast lengthening shadows across the white-green pastures that fall away to the lake.

I love this view. In the middle distance, Grasmoor and Whiteside rise, stark and magnificent, from behind the north-eastern fringe of Lanthwaite Wood. I often fancy these genial giants are suspended perpetually in a friendly contest for supremacy, Grasmoor having the merit of its greater height but Whiteside being possessed of a number of far superior vantage points. Between and behind them, Sand Hill looms grey-green against the sky. The glimmering blue smudge is Crummock Water; you can see the boathouse from here. Outside the garden, rocky outcrops, clumps of trees and dry-stone walls are all features of a landscape typical of the lower Lakeland slopes. Sheep dot the fells and birds are plentiful here in our little corner of England.

Inside, a log fire cracks, pops and whistles in the grate, scattering a rosy glow over the whitewashed interior walls of the old stone cottage. The fragrance of wood smoke mingles with the aroma of roast pork wafting from the kitchen. The lilting melody of an old Beatles number called 'Michelle' floats in the air and the kettle is singing on the hob. Two cats adorn the furnishings. Thomasin is sprawling on the crimson hearthrug, like honeysuckle blossom tumbled amongst a carpet of poppies. Little Elfride is perched daintily on the back of the chintz sofa, washing her glossy black coat meticulously.

Minutes later, teacup in hand, I am sitting at my writing desk, gazing out of the window at the serene vista. I put down my cup, close my eyes and try to visualise the monochrome, blurry images of the two tiny human forms revealed to me this morning on the hospital monitor by the miracle of ultrasound technology. I am brought to my senses by the gentle nudge of a velvet nose against my right shoulder. I turn and stroke my small companion's pretty black head. Then I pick up my pen and begin to write.

My name is Victoria Jane Caswell, I am 40 years old and I am intensely happy …

Part One

Maid in Cumberland

Chapter 1

A Chance Encounter

I was born on the 15th October 1953, youngest child of Robert and Marion Kelly of Cinderdale Farm in the Western Lake District. I thought myself a plain child with a fair freckled complexion and non-descript brown hair, neither chestnut nor golden in tone, which descended to my shoulders in a torrent of unruly curls. I considered my mouth rather too large for my face despite the protestations of my mother, who referred to it as "charming" and "expressive" and insisted that it was my best feature.

I longed to look like my sister Antonia who was three years my senior. I envied her for her big dark eyes and long thick lashes, and for the texture and hue of her silky-smooth chocolate-brown tresses which she wore in a style borrowed from Diana Rigg in the Avengers during the 1960s. As if that wasn't enough, she had inherited our mother's tall, slender figure; I was short and square like our father. In my eyes she was beautiful, and even at 15 she was considered 'quite a catch' and was the focus of much attention from the local lads.

My mother's approach to parenthood was 'enthusiastic'; within the span of six years, along with my sister and myself, she gave birth to three fine boys. My father bore it with his customary stoic patience, vanishing off to the fields when the noise and bustle became insufferable. Chris was the oldest, and I looked up to him as some kind of demigod. He was tall, fair and handsome. He was also incredibly kind to me and would spring to my defence whenever Alan or Michael teased me. They never missed an opportunity to remind me of my lowly status as the baby of the family, but Chris never failed to treat me as an equal and would sometimes even seek out my opinion about a song he had heard or a piece of artwork he had created; he had been apprenticed to a graphic design company in Whitehaven when he had left school the previous year. I found this immensely flattering.

Over the years, my own fate and the fate of Chris have been so closely intertwined that I sometimes wonder if our lives are actually governed by a series of random coincidences or whether, in fact, our destinies are preordained. In any event, it transpired that the summer of 1966 was a life-changing one both for my esteemed older brother and for me. At the time, I was 12 and he was 17.

Our home stood at the junction of three minor roads. One branch led north-westwards to the tiny hamlet of Strands a short walk away. The second led south-west towards Santon Bridge and the third eastwards towards Wast Water a good mile away. This route was my favourite. I would often take our labrador Rufus down to the lakeshore. I was shy and cared little for the company of friends, and even if our house had been less remote I think I would have found the attentions heaped on my sister quite irksome. A healthy communion with nature and the occasional company of my brother Michael was sufficient to while away the hours when I was not either at school, pottering about on the farm or ensconced cosily in the room I shared with my sister listening to the Beatles on her second-hand Dansette, usually when she was out.

In many respects, Michael resembled me more closely than any of my other siblings. He was only 15 months older than me and, apart from his hair – which was a few shades lighter, the similarity in our physical appearance was so striking that people often mistook us for twins. In nature we were also alike as children; Michael was quiet and serious-minded. If anything, he was sometimes a little too serious. From an early age, he seemed wise beyond his years and obsessed about environmental issues with an intensity which was unprecedented in a boy of such tender years. He watched the news avidly and would choose 'Farmers Weekly' over the 'Beano' every time. His classmates regarded him as a bit eccentric, but he was well liked nonetheless as he was mild-mannered, pleasant-natured and friendly.

Much later, he told me that he thought his obsession sprung from one of his earliest childhood recollections. It concerned a local event which hit the headlines in October 1957. Michael was five years old at the time.

One Saturday night he was awoken suddenly by a fearful banging on the door. He heard the heavy tread of our father as he descended the stairs, the rattle of the door-chain and then an unfamiliar male voice speaking in gruff urgent tones. Next, the faint rustle of our mother's housecoat and her soft footsteps on the staircase reached his ears. The visitor was admitted. In a state of extreme agitation, Michael crept silently out of the bedroom he shared with Alan and crouched on the landing intent on finding out the cause of the disturbance. The kitchen door was closed, but Michael was able to hear most of the conversation and what ensued filled him such an acute spasm of alarm that its aftermath shaped his perspective and profoundly influenced the entire course of his life.

The Government official (for such he was) could be distinctly heard explaining forcibly to our parents that all the milk on the farm was to be destroyed due to an 'incident' that had occurred eight miles away at the Windscale Nuclear Power Station several days ago. He said that the milk was deemed unsafe because some radioactive vapour had leaked from a cooling tower and contaminated the grass. Michael had no idea what 'radioactive' meant, but he knew what a radio was as Mum had a Bush radio in the kitchen that she loved to sing along to. He also knew what it meant to be active, so he bypassed the innocuous sounding part and became fixated on the ominous portent engendered by the words 'vapour' and 'contaminated'. Because of its relatively close proximity to his school at Gosforth, he had seen the vast concrete and metal structures, monstrous barbed wire fences and 'Keep Out' signs that they called 'Windscale'. Now, the sinister nature of the midnight call and the nightmarish images conjured up in his impressionable young mind by the stranger's chilling discourse wrought his brain to fever pitch.

Soon after, he heard the familiar sound of the sneck lifting and the kitchen door swung open. With his heart racing and his head in a state of turmoil, he hastened back to his room and peered out of the window into the gloom. A pale yellow light spilled out of the open front door into the yard, and he could just make out the bulky form of a middle-aged man in a dark overcoat emerging from the house. He watched the stranger climb into a large, mud-splattered motor vehicle and listened to the whirr and chunter of the engine as it spluttered into life. He watched the vehicle creep slowly forwards. He watched the tail lights disappear out of the gate into the black night. The front door closed softly and the yard was submerged into darkness.

Michael climbed into bed and lay on his back, staring at the ceiling. 'Vapour' … 'contaminated' … what did it all mean? He recalled the large tumbler full to the brim with rich, creamy milk that he had gulped down just before bedtime and felt faintly sick. Presently, his attention was diverted to the low murmurings of our parents in the next room. He couldn't make out what they were saying and eventually he fell into a fitful sleep, but he never forgot the events of that dreadful night.

The next morning dawned, to all intents and purposes, like all the ones before, with one exception – the conspicuous absence of the big white milk jug from the breakfast table. Michael was possessed with an uneasiness that not even two rashers of bacon and a large helping of hot buttered toast could alleviate. Our mum muttered something hurriedly about running out of milk and quickly changed the subject. Our brother Alan was a bright and inquisitive boy and pressed her mercilessly for an explanation as to how a thriving farm with a sizeable dairy herd could possibly 'run out' of its chief commodity. It was clear that Mum was getting flustered, and this had the effect of heightening Michael's anxiety; our parents must be hiding something. He knew it was wrong to eavesdrop so he was compelled to bury his secret and await the consequences of that fateful bedtime drink.

Back in the 1950s, school milk was an integral part of school life along with tapioca pudding, learning by rote and the cane; I remember being milk monitor and handing out the little bottles of milk and paper straws. They didn't refrigerate it so by mid-morning break it tasted awful. That morning, when Michael came in after playtime to discover the milk crate was empty, his relief at not having to drink the ghastly stuff was instantly banished by a renewed sense of foreboding.

Several weeks passed and, to Michael's immense relief, none of the deadly symptoms he had anticipated materialised; he remained hale and hearty. However, he was still plagued with a morbid curiosity centred on the disturbing events that occurred during the night of 12th October. Eventually he came up with a plan. He would ask his teacher, Mrs. Cowley, to explain it to him.

Anne Cowley was a jolly, pink-cheeked woman of 37. She had short, brown, curly hair, twinkling eyes and a rather loud voice. What she lacked in stature, she made up for in personality. She was warm, bright, bubbly and friend to all. Her only fault, if she possessed one, was that she could be a trifle insensitive and overbearing, but she had been blessed with the 'gift of the gab' and could charm her way out of the occasional difficulties that her over-zealous nature got her into. She was a leading light in the local community; she arranged the flowers at St. Catherine's Church in the quaintly-named village of Boot where she resided with her 16 year old son Paul. She baked cakes for countless charities; her resonant voice was audible at every local event that she had a personal interest in – and some that she didn't. Paul, a talented young bowler, was the target of much good-humoured ribbing at the hands of the Cumberland County Cricket Club Youth 11 on account of his mother's wholehearted vocal support. Anne had lost her husband during the Battle of El Alamein in North Africa, when Paul was still in nappies. For the sake of her child, she had strived so hard to 'put on a brave face' that the optimism she evinced had become embedded in her psyche.

On the last Monday before Christmas, Michael plucked up his courage and walked timidly up to Mrs. Cowley's desk. She greeted him with her customary broad smile.

"Hello, little man. What can I do for you?"

"Please Miss," he faltered, "b-but what's vapour?"

Mrs. Cowley gave the question some consideration.

"I expect your mum has a kettle at home?"

Michael nodded.

"Well, you know when the water gets hot and steam comes out of the spout; it's the same thing, see?"

Michael was completely nonplussed. It was impossible to conceive that 'vapour' could be potentially life-threatening; if that was the case, surely people's lives were endangered every time someone made a cup of tea.

His teacher sensed his confusion and tried again …

"Like mist; that's a kind of vapour. You do know what mist is, don't you?"

Michael nodded again. Vapour didn't sound very hazardous. Maybe he had got it all wrong.

"Do you understand now?" she asked gently.

"Thank you Miss, yes Miss … but-but there's something else …" Michael took a deep breath and said, very slowly and deliberately, "What's 'con-ta-mi-na-ted'?"

"Why, bless my soul, child, wherever did you hear a word like that?"

Mrs. Cowley was a thoroughly honest woman whose high regard for the capacity of young minds inspired her to bestow her wisdom without restraint. 'I'll tell you when you're older' was a phrase that had no place in her vocabulary; there was no time like the present.

"When something is contaminated, it means it's dirty. It might have got some germs in it, or something else that could harm you. If your food gets contaminated, it could make you very ill. That's why you should always wash your hands after you've been to the lavatory."

Ironically, his ignorance, which had been the cause of so much discomfiture over the last two months, now became his ally and his fears fell away. In the intervening weeks, his recollection of drinking the milk before bed had receded to such an extent that, in his naïve quest to fill the gaps in his knowledge, he forgot about it altogether and leapt to the conclusion that because he hadn't eaten the 'contaminated grass' and always washed his hands when he came indoors, the chance of making it to his sixth birthday was virtually guaranteed. The Windscale nuclear power station still remained, a spectre lurking in the recesses of his mind, and at a conscious level he found its physical presence menacing and oppressive, but that afternoon he returned home from school lighter of heart. Our parents were pleased that he seemed less preoccupied than of late, but found his absolute refusal to go outside barefoot from that day forward quite inexplicable.

* * *

On Saturday 30th April 1966, Michael and I set off towards Wast Water with Rufus at our side. It was a beautiful bright morning; the lane was dappled with a shifting mosaic of sunshine and shade and birds twittered in the hedgerows. There was a light breeze and the scent of cow parsley pervaded the soft spring air. Half an hour later, we reached the lake where we paused and idly watched the sunlight sparkling on the blue expanse that stretched away into the arms of its great stone cradle in the fells.

Wasdale is sublime. Every time I wind my way up the valley, I am struck anew by the awesome loveliness and drama of the prospect that reveals itself at every twist and turn. It is a place of savage beauty. To the north lies a fine high ridge culminating in the massive bulk of Pillar. On the opposite side, the magnificent screes plunge steeply down to the floor of the lake. Wasdale Head is crowded with mountains: Yewbarrow, Kirk Fell, Great Gable, Lingmell; all impart rough grandeur to this primitive landscape – an ancient volcanic wasteland carved up by vast rivers of ice. Scafell Pike dominates all, the highest mountain in England and a fitting counterpart to the deepest lake, which laps at its feet.

Wast Water fascinates me; when I contemplate the dark, unfathomable depths, I am stirred by conflicting emotions akin to apprehension and wonder. In temperament, she is volatile. In fair weather, she is smiling and benign; in foul, she broods and threatens; but whether moody or magnanimous, she is always enthralling. Today she was in a benevolent humour.

Michael and I continued along the shore at a slow amble. Michael threw sticks into the shallows for Rufus to retrieve, but it was across the shimmering water towards the splendid north face of Whin Rigg that I was compelled to gaze, as here lay a spectacle to which I know no equal. On the opposite side, Wast Water is deep and dangerous. Here, huge fans of loose stone of reddish-grey tumble steeply down, at a near 45° angle, into its secret heart. With its feet submerged in 43 fathoms of water and boasting an immense crown of crags, chasms and buttresses, Whin Rigg, though princely in stature, wears the aspect of a king.

Presently we joined the road. A few minutes later, I noticed the figure of a man in the distance coming towards us. A dog ran a few feet ahead of him. As the pair drew nearer, I noticed that the dog was a border collie – a little smaller than Rufus, and that the man looked quite old and quite tall, with a thin frame and gaunt features. He wore an old brown tweed jacket, faded and frayed, and a flat cap, and walked with a stick. His expression was stern and preoccupied, and this put me into an awkward dilemma. We had been taught by our parents that we should always acknowledge fellow walkers with a smile and a friendly word, but there was something in his closed countenance that caused me to falter.

However, my dilemma was short-lived. All of a sudden, a pheasant rose from its hiding place in the rough grass almost alongside us, croaking loudly and beating its wings, and all hell was let loose. The collie started barking frantically and good-natured Rufus, who was evidently startled and confused, lunged headlong at the collie. The two dogs rolled over and over on the ground, growling and snapping at each other. The man turned on us with a face like thunder.

"You should keep your dog under control, you stupid children!" he bellowed. "That thing's a menace, it wants putting down!"

He brandished his stick viciously at Rufus, who was uppermost in the fray, upon which the poor labrador stopped short, released his grip on the collie's neck, retreated with his head lowered and slinked behind me, whimpering.

I was struck dumb but Michael managed a small, broken apology.

"I-I'm sorry … the bird made him jump … he's a nice dog … r-really, he is."

"He doesn't seem very nice to me," the man retorted savagely. "I suggest you keep him on a leash."

He scowled angrily at us while Michael fumbled in his pocket. After what seemed like an eternity – in fact it was only about a minute – he produced the lead and fastened it shakily to the collar of the abject Rufus.

"Now mind you don't let it off again, nasty animal …"

This was too much for me. My eyes filled with water and tears rolled down my cheeks.

Then the most unexpected thing happened. The stranger's expression immediately softened to one of concern and alarm.

"Oh, my dear, are you all right? I didn't mean to frighten you," he said anxiously. "Would you like a hankie?" He produced a large spotted handkerchief from the top pocket of his jacket and held it out to me. I hesitated, took it shyly and dabbed my eyes.

"I'm terribly sorry," he mumbled.

Now Michael found his tongue. "Look what you've done to my sister, you frightened her out of her wits," he said petulantly.

"Oh dear, that was never my intention. You see, I have rather a hot temper."

His tone was calm and apologetic but Michael was not easily won over.

"Well you did, anyway!"

"Leave it Michael, I'm all right," I said miserably, between sniffs.

The old man held out his hand to me and smiled benevolently.

"Will you shake hands, my dear? Surely you can forgive a crusty old gentleman."

I submitted. His hand was warm and his grip was firm and reassuring.

"Now then, why don't you let that fine dog of yours off the leash? I'm sure he's a nice fellow. What's his name?"

I looked up into the strange old gentleman's face for the first time and noticed that his eyes looked rather sad.

"He's called Rufus."

"Rufus – that means 'red' doesn't it? He's a chocolate labrador, isn't he? You should have called him Bruno," he chuckled.

"Oh, that was my Dad's idea. He's a big fan of Rufus Thomas. He did a song called 'Walking the Dog'. It was his idea of a joke." By this time I had regained some of my composure.

The man clapped his hands. "Oh how delightful! Your Dad sounds like a jolly fellow. This is Shirley." He gestured to the shaggy black and white border collie at his side.

"Would that be anything to do with Shirley Bassey?" I asked tentatively.

"Good Lord no!" laughed the man. "As a matter of fact, I got her when she was a pup from a breeder in Shirley. It's a little place near Solihull, but I don't suppose you've ever heard of it."

"Solihull?"

"It's near Birmingham. Good gracious! What do they teach you youngsters at school nowadays? Would you like to stroke her?"

Michael was growing restless but I was getting just into my stride. I liked making new friends, especially canine ones. I reached out cautiously and rested my hand on the collie's soft white head. She wagged her tail appreciatively so I bent down and gave her a hug and she licked my face.

"She's beautiful," I murmured.

"Now then, do you think Rufus is ready to forgive me?" the man continued presently.

By this time, Rufus had been released by the attentive Michael and had emerged from his hiding place. He was snuffling in the rough vegetation at the roadside.

"Here boy," the old gentleman called in a kindly voice.

Rufus wandered over and the man gave him a friendly pat.

"Well, now our dogs have been introduced, perhaps you'd like to tell me what your name is," he enquired in a manner which was now positively friendly.

"I'm Vicky, and this is my brother Michael."

"I'm Mr. Blane and I'm quite new to the area. I don't have many friends round here. Will you promise to say hello to me next time we run into each other?"

"Yes of course I will, I'd be glad to," I replied, feeling much relieved at the happy outcome to the morning's events.

I glared at Michael, who was standing sulkily a few feet away kicking at the gravel. He walked forward and held out his hand stiffly.

"Pleased to meet you, sir," he said grudgingly.

The man sighed. "I'm sorry we got off on the wrong foot, young man," he said. "It was my fault, entirely. Now run along and have a nice day, both of you. Come on, girl."

The collie sprang to her feet and we parted company, continuing along the road in opposite directions, Michael with his eyes fixed straight ahead while I looked back over my shoulder, smiling and waving.

"He wasn't such a bad old fellow really," I remarked casually, and dropped the subject.

When we got home, I found the blue spotted handkerchief stuffed into the pocket of my gingham dress. I hastened downstairs and recounted the morning's adventure to my mum. To my surprise, she knew something about the man already, but then my mum knew everything.

"That'll be the old man and the girl that's taken the old cottage up at the Head," she said. "It's been standing empty for years, being so cut off an' all. He's a lean old gent, a widower, by all accounts, terribly serious and sober. He's got a daughter works at your old school in Gosforth – he dotes on her. Mrs. Cowley told me; she's such a gossip, you know."

"He *was* a bit scary to start with," I concurred, "but I think he's quite nice really."

"Well, you mind and be pleasant to him. He's a poor, lonely old soul, so I'm told … labouring under some great misfortune, apparently. I've no idea what."

She returned to her baking and I tripped away to the garden.

Three weeks later, I chanced to run into Mr. Blane again when I was out on one of my long, solitary rambles with Rufus. This time I was on my own; Michael was rehearsing for the school play, in which he had a minor part. I was roaming on the lower slopes of Buckbarrow when I noticed my elderly acquaintance proceeding along the lane below with Shirley at his heels. I ran down the grassy fellside, shouting and waving my arms. At first he was oblivious to my presence. He continued to stare straight ahead of him with that same, preoccupied expression that I had noticed at our first meeting. Suddenly he stopped abruptly in his tracks, turned and waved back, and a minute later we were exchanging pleasantries.

This was the first of several happy meetings over the next few months. During the course of the summer, I learnt a lot about Mr. Blane. He was 61, although he wore the face of an older man. He had moved down from Glasgow less than a year ago, having inherited a substantial sum of money. He had been keen to escape from the city to a remote country retreat where he could live quietly with his daughter Julie. Julie was 18 and the apple of his eye. She sang, played piano and flute and taught music to the children at the local primary school as well as a handful of private pupils. Her father extolled her virtues, claiming she had 'the voice of angel and played like a muse'. She was cook, cleaner, carer and companion and he 'would be lost without her'.

Although he was too young to serve in the First World War, he had lived under its shadow, growing up in fear of a prolonged conflict that would deal him the same fate as that of his two older brothers, who were slaughtered at Passchendaele in 1917 at 18 and 21. In 1941, his fear was partially realised; he was called up at 36 years of age and served in World War II, sustaining a shattered knee in the Normandy Landings in 1945, and that was the reason he walked with a stick. However, he didn't 'much like talking about it'. After the War, he went back to work on the railways, but he didn't elaborate about that either. He seemed to prefer talking about his daughter.

I would regale him with schoolgirl gossip. He would listen attentively while I poured forth anecdotes about Toni's endless stream of suitors, Joanie's latest hairdo and Robin's clumsy attempts to date my best friend Sally. Sometimes, he would comment on how much I reminded him of his daughter, and then his face would cloud over.

"Don't worry," I would say soothingly. "Julie will always be there for you."

"If only that were true," he would sigh bitterly. "Nothing lasts forever."

From time to time, Michael would accompany me on my rambles. He was very reluctant to engage with Mr. Blane at first, but eventually he was forced to concede that the 'grumpy old man' did have some redeeming qualities. He would press him with questions about the Moors Murders, Vietnam War and Polaris. By the end of the summer, we were all firm friends and Mr. Blane had regained possession of his spotted handkerchief. In the meantime, however, a national event occurred that, unbeknown to us, was to bring our families even closer together. That event was the FIFA World Cup Final …

Chapter 2

Football Fever

Tension had been mounting within the football fraternity, and across much of the population of England, as the national team powered their way into the 1966 World Cup final. After a mediocre start against Uruguay, Bobby Charlton produced an astonishing goal against Mexico and the lion roared into action. France, Argentina and Portugal all succumbed under the might of the England squad, and so it came to pass that on 30th July, football fever reached a pitch unsurpassed in living memory. For a brief moment in time, everybody fell in love with 'the beautiful game'. It is impossible, through the medium of the written word, to do justice to the extent of the passion that fired up the nation. Suffice to say that I do not think I will ever see the like of it. The people of England, almost without exception, united to cheer on our boys – boys that made history on the glorious day when football truly did come home.

The overcast skies, cloudbursts and intermittent sunshine, so typically English, added piquance to the national flavour of a day already bristling with patriotism. At 3 p.m. the stage was set on which England's footballing heroes would play out their greatest drama before the eyes of the world. A multitude of colourful flags from all four corners of the world decked the packed terraces of the Empire Stadium, Wembley. The British National Anthem had been sung with pride and fervour rarely seen and the crowd had erupted into a vociferous declaration of support. From somewhere high up in the stands, a deep steady boom pulsed around the stadium like a heartbeat, and at the shrill command of the starting whistle, West Germany kicked off.

Dad wanted to watch the match at one of several pubs in the area which had acquired a television set on the pretext of providing an opportunity for the clientele to enjoy the match in the convivial atmosphere of a crowded hostelry, although Mum insisted it was all about selling more beer. Chris and Alan were allowed to go with him, even though they were both underage, and Michael had arranged to watch the match at a friend's house.

Mum, Toni and I were to stay at home. I was devastated. I bemoaned my fate and cursed the lawmakers. In my naïvety, I thought that passing a pleasant few hours with my Dad and elder brothers, sipping lemonade and cheering our boys on, would have been charming indeed. The prospect of staying in with my mum and sister was excruciating and I wished fervently that I was several years older. Toni's primary interest was make-up and Mum's placid forbearance in the face of bad refereeing decisions, or worse still the catastrophe of an England defeat, would be intolerable. Chris pointed out that, with all due respect, it might get rather 'lively'. This did nothing to placate me; it merely served to arouse my curiosity. Eventually Michael told me outright that a rough, noisy pub heaving with sweaty blokes tanked up to the eyeballs was no place for girls, least of all a deluded little chit like me. I was persuaded to relent but couldn't help but feel irritated as I watched them piling into the car, laughing and joking, as they contemplated an afternoon of testosterone-packed action.

Mum did her best to soften the blow. She baked a Union Jack cake, promised to sit down for the entire duration of the match and even invited our nan down from Carlisle. Nan was a feisty old dame with plum-coloured hair, a roving eye and a weakness for red wine. Dad referred to her as the Merry Widow. Her surname was Taylor and she called herself Liz, even though her given name was Louisa. She made an impression wherever she went. She could be relied upon to inject levity into the mix and this afternoon her lively banter was a tonic. She berated the ref, scolded the Germans and applauded the English with gusto usually reserved for the terraces. She was so ardent that we were all infected by her zeal, rose to the occasion and did likewise. Despite an initial pretence of disinterest, Toni deferred the application of her nail lacquer until after the final whistle. Mum wrestled valiantly with her inclination to occupy her time doing something useful and gave us her undivided attention. Contrary to expectations, I had a thoroughly enjoyable time.

We watched it in black and white as it was in the days before colour. The vermillion shirts of the England team looked dark grey and West Germany wore white shirts and black shorts, so it was easy to tell the two teams apart. Both teams started cautiously, with England quickly gaining the upper hand. Then to our dismay, in the 13th minute, Germany went a goal up after a shocking error on the part of Ray Wilson. The battle was on, but it only took England six minutes to find a chink in the German armour. A superb free kick from Bobby Moore found the well-placed head of Geoff Hurst and it was all square at 1-1.

I let out an involuntary whoop and Nan clapped her hands and went to get a bottle of wine. She held out a glass to Toni and me and winked.

"Come on, try a drop girls, it's lovely."

Mum raised her eyebrows.

Toni was quick in her response. "Yes please!" She turned to Mum. "Could I, please?"

Mum sighed and nodded reluctantly.

"Maybe just a tiny drop for me then," I said hesitantly, glancing over at Mum's disapproving face but anxious not to be outdone by Toni.

Nan trickled a thimbleful of the rich, dark red liquid into two glasses and handed them to my sister and me.

I sipped mine gingerly. "Ugh, it's horrible!" I exclaimed. "How can you drink that stuff?"

Toni sipped hers and screwed up her face. I caught her eye and she smothered her barely suppressed reaction with a bright smile.

"Well Toni, what do you think?" asked Nan.

"It's … it's okay. Actually I quite like it." She took another sip, a very small one, and put down her glass. I sniggered; she couldn't fool me.

The rest of the first half was real 'edge of the seat' stuff, with ball and players flying up and down the field and plenty of action at both ends of the pitch. During half-time, Mum made a pot of tea and cut the cake. The warm, sweet tea and freshly baked sponge was hardly sufficient to soothe my frayed nerves but it was a good deal better than the wine. The start of the second half was a tense affair. Both teams looked nervous and played defensively. The crowd grew restless. Then, in the 78th minute, a crucial second goal from Martin Peters put England into the driving seat. I leapt from my seat and jumped up and down on the spot; Nan sprung up, hugged me ferociously, and danced around the room, glass in hand. Mum and Toni clapped and cheered, and Rufus bounded round and round, barking frantically. We were almost home.

The last 12 minutes were painstakingly slow. Then disastrously, in the 90th minute, West Germany struck back. A free kick against Jack Charlton bounced off the England wall onto the foot of the German Centre Forward, who shot it wildly past the mouth of the goal to Weber, who administered a fatal equaliser. Nan leapt up, waving her arms and shouting,

"Hand ball! Hand ball!"

Hot tears pricked my eyes and I felt myself starting to shake. This was unbearable.

By now the conditions on the pitch were appalling and both teams were near to exhaustion. It was a crushing blow for England but they rallied to the 'never say die' mentality of Manager Alf Ramsey and chants and thumping from the massive home crowd which rumbled like thunder round the walls of the great Empire Stadium. Extra time started positively for England but Germany were still flexing their weary muscles and looked dangerous on two occasions. Then in the 98th minute, a Geoff Hurst shot hit the crossbar and dropped into the front of the goal before being headed away by Weber. The England centre forwards appealed for a goal and, while we all held our breath, the referee consulted with the linesman. The crowd roared and clamoured and we looked at each other in disbelief. Then Nan burst forth.

"Look! See! It's a goal, it's a goal, look! He's given it! We're winning!"

We all cheered but mine were subdued by comparison. The fact that it was impossible to establish beyond doubt that the ball had actually crossed the line made me feel uneasy. Victory was virtually in the bag but it was tainted with the stain of uncertainty.

West Germany fought back valiantly and the last 20 minutes of the match were electrifying. As the seconds crawled by, I found myself compelled to cover my face with my hands and peep through my fingers. Then, seconds before the final whistle, a miracle happened. Hurst powered the ball into the top corner of the net and sealed a hat trick. I squealed, all my reservations quashed by this decisive fourth goal. We all shouted and clapped furiously and almost immediately the final whistle blew, dispelling the nerve-shattering tension of the most breathtaking two hours in English footballing history at a single stroke. England were champions of the world!

Soon afterwards, Mum put a loaf of bread in the Aga and, while Toni went upstairs to apply her make-up, I laid the big oak table in the kitchen in readiness for the imminent return of the male members of the household. This table has always held a special place at the heart of my world; it was the hub around which family life revolved. It was the silent witness to our laughter and tears, our hopes and fears, successes and failures, shared over many a family meal. This was the table at which I did my homework, Mum pored over the farm accounts and Chris would make rough sketches of ideas that had sprung into his mind during his leisure hours. It was here that Dad would share a cuppa with his farm labourers while I looked on, sometimes joining in with their conversations. 28 years later, it still stands in the exact same spot – a symbol from the past that continues to unite our family, even in the present day.

Tea consisted of bread, ham, cheese, scones, fruitcake and a range of home-made preserves so impressive that one was reminded of a Women's Institute table-top sale. Mum grew fruit and vegetables in the little kitchen garden behind the house and anything that could not be consumed fresh she would turn into jam, chutney or pickle. She was born in the middle of the 1920s and had grown up during the depression, an era of privation when wasting food was almost tantamount to a criminal offence and nothing was ever thrown away. By the time rationing came to an end in 1954, she was already mother to five children all under six years of age and frugality was deeply ingrained in her nature.

Dad and the boys got home later than expected and when they eventually arrived, Michael was not amongst them. He had decided to stay on at John's house to play Subbuteo.

"Mmm … that bread smells good," remarked Dad, as he threw his coat down on the chair. "Put the kettle on Marion, there's a love. Hello Liz, hello Vicky," he continued, ruffling my hair. "Where's Toni? Putting on her warpaint, I shouldn't wonder!"

"Yes, be a dear and go and get her," said Mum, turning to me.

I pulled a face, scurried upstairs and hammered on the bedroom door. The Rolling Stones' 'Paint it Black' was thumping out for the twentieth time that day and it was getting really tiresome.

She opened the door and I felt a familiar pang of jealousy. She looked stunning, heavily made-up and wearing a tight-fitting electric blue mini dress and go-go boots. By comparison, I felt plain and dowdy.

"What kept them? They're *so* late. Phil's picking me up in half an hour!" she moaned.

Phil was in the year above Toni at school and a friend of Alan's. He was quite the charmer and very popular with the ladies. Toni was flattered by his attentions.

"They're not *that* late," I retorted. "Anyway, you could've come down earlier. Table's laid ... no thanks to you," I added sulkily.

A few minutes later, Toni came downstairs to be greeted by our horrified parents and rather more liberal-minded Nan.

"Good God Toni!" spluttered Dad. "You can't go out looking like that! Go and put some clothes on!"

"Really Toni," added Mum, much more mildly. "You're only 15. What will people think?"

Chris and Alan exchanged a knowing look and raised their eyebrows.

"Oh, come off it, don't be such a stick-in-the-mud!" interjected Nan. "She's a fine looking girl. Why shouldn't she show off her attributes?"

Louisa was not a woman to be trifled with, and Dad clearly had no intention of jeopardising his current euphoric state of mind, thanks to an England victory, by going into battle with his mother-in-law. He shrugged his shoulders.

"Well, you be careful, my girl. Don't go getting up to any mischief, and mind you're home by 11."

Alan was not so easily placated. "Dad, you always give in to Toni. She looks awful!"

Toni threw him a fiery glance and opened her mouth to retaliate.

"Now, now, let's not all fall out over such a trifle," Mum interrupted, with more than a hint of exasperation in her voice.

"It's really none of your business, Alan. It's been a nice day, let's all stop arguing and have tea."

"She'll get herself into trouble and then ..."

"That's enough, young man!" interrupted Dad sternly. "You seem to be forgetting who's boss."

"I think we all know who's boss," Alan muttered under his breath, and helped himself to a hunk of ham.

Chris kicked me under the table and nodded towards Nan but fortunately nobody else noticed. An awkward silence ensued, which was presently broken by Nan, who addressed Toni.

"Where are you going tonight, my dear?"

"We're going to see 'How to Steal a Million'. I'm going with my boyfriend," she said, rather smugly I thought, and with the air of someone who had carried her point.

"Audrey Hepburn; such a beautiful woman!" Nan exclaimed. "You know, you look a little like her," and she was right.

The conversation reverted quite naturally to the topic of the football, still uppermost in everyone else's mind. Dad and Alan were full of it but Chris was quite reserved and quiet, which surprised me. In due course, the talk took another turn.

"You know, I *was* getting a bit worried," said Mum. "You *were* rather late."

"Oh yes, that. Well, we had a bit of an adventure, didn't we boys?"

"Yeah, Chris broke up a fight," chimed in Alan, giving his brother a playful slap on the back.

"Well, I didn't exactly break it up. I just talked the fellows round," Chris explained. "It was easy really. Jason's a mate anyway and he's not a bad guy. It was just the drink talking."

"What happened, Chris?" I asked gleefully. "Tell us what happened. Did anyone get hurt?"

"Victoria, really! Do try and exercise a bit of self-control," Mum interjected.

"Yes, do try to Vicks," Chris mimicked playfully. "Did you *actually* watch *all* the match?"

"Yes, of course I did!" I said indignantly.

"Well, you know that bit right at the end of the second half when the Germans scored and everyone thought it was a handball."

"It was a handball!" declared Nan. "No doubt about it."

"Well, that aside, we were standing quite near a bunch of guys I went to school with who were all a bit the worse for drink. Oh, and there was a girl with them – phoney Joanie, the platinum predator, ha ha!"

Joanie was a school friend of Toni's. She was notorious for her platinum blonde hair, which she wore in a multitude of different styles from beehive to bouffant to bob, her loud, abrasive manner and her free and easy ways. She dazzled and dazed most young men whom she smiled upon, though my brother was not much impressed, but beneath her glossy veneer there was very little substance. It was true that Toni was glamorous too, but she was shrewd.

"Anyway," Chris continued, "when they gave the goal, they all went mad and started shouting all kinds of obscenities and calling the Germans all sorts of names I won't repeat. There was an old guy sitting on his own near the window and after a couple of minutes he got up and tapped Jason on the shoulder. 'Excuse me, young man,' says the old fellow rather stiff. 'I'll thank you to refrain. My mother was German and I find your comments extremely offensive.' Well, Jason turned on him and hurled a load of abuse – words I wouldn't repeat to you, Vicky. I thought the old boy would back off but he just stood there really quiet and calm. Then, when Jase had run out of insults, the funny old gent rolled up his shirtsleeves and said 'Would you like to settle this outside?' I couldn't believe it. Well, I could see he was going to get a pasting, and like I said, Jase isn't a bad lad. So I went over and I says to Jase 'Leave the old codger alone,' and then I took him to one side and I says to him, 'He's probably got a screw loose. You don't want to get arrested, mate.' Then I managed to get the old boy to sit back down and it all calmed down. Then we won and everyone went crazy, jumping up and down and singing. The old bloke must have been coming back from the bar or something and got his arm knocked, 'cause next thing I knew, his glass goes flying, there's beer everywhere and he's steaming into Jason's mate, shouting and wagging his finger. It would have been quite comical if it hadn't been so scary. Then Terry – that's his mate – made a grab for his collar and got him up against the bar. Luckily I was almost right next to them. I managed to get between and then we got them apart; me and Jase. I took the old guy outside and he was really shaken up, started to blubber, so we drove him home. That was all really … there was no bloodshed," he added archly.

"We-e-ell, that wasn't quite all, now was it Chris?" Alan said provocatively.

"Oh, the other thing …" Chris hesitated. "She doesn't want to hear about that."

"About what?" I was on the edge of my seat by now.

"There was a girl," said Alan. "Wasn't there, Chris?"

"Oh, that was nothing," said Chris dismissively, trying hard to sound casual. "We drove the old boy home. When we got there, there was a girl who came out of the house. That was all."

"He's in love," Alan said superciliously. He was being really irritating this evening.

"Oh, lay off Alan!" Chris retorted, his colour rising. "I only said she was nice."

"I seem to recall you said a lot more than that in the car."

"What's your problem, mate?" Chris was getting very defensive, which was quite out of character as he was usually quite laid back.

At that moment, there was a rap. Toni stuffed the rest of her scone into her already full mouth and hastened to the front door. She returned in less than a minute, still chewing and swallowing, and reeking of Tabu. She managed to articulate a somewhat stifled request for "10 shillings for the taxi". Dad sighed, got up and went to the dresser, pulled a small handful of notes out of an old biscuit tin and handed them over with a grunt.

"Blimey, she could buy a house with that lot!" said Alan facetiously.

Toni glared at her brother, then bid us a swift goodbye and swept out, leaving her scent hanging in the air. Fortunately, by this time the boys had forgotten their differences and were both tucking into their second helping of fruitcake.

After tea, Chris and I sat down to watch 'Opportunity Knocks'. Dad went out in the car to collect Michael while Mum and Nan washed the dishes. Chris was preoccupied and uncommunicative and I sensed that his nerves were on edge. I felt somewhat uneasy, as if to ask questions would mean encroaching onto private territory. This was a sensation completely alien to me, and at that moment I suddenly became aware of the five-year age gap between us and the gulf that separated our different experiences. We sat in silence for a few minutes but eventually my curiosity got the better of me.

"What's the matter, Chris? You're not yourself tonight. You're acting weird."

"I'm okay ... just a bit tired, that's all," he said evasively.

"Aren't you seeing Janice tonight?"

"Janice? Oh, Janice ... no ... no, I'm not seeing Janice tonight," he mumbled vaguely. He paused and then added, with just a hint of justification in his voice, "She's gone to a gymkhana; she won't be back till late."

Janice was the daughter of a neighbouring farmer. She was attractive in a plain, 'girl-next-door' kind of way. She had short blond hair, bright blue eyes, a healthy tanned complexion and a lively disposition. She was passionate about horses and what she lacked in refinement she made up for in physical fitness. She was what is commonly called 'the outdoor type'. Chris and Janice had been childhood sweethearts and as they had grown, so had their fondness for each other. I use the word 'fondness' advisedly. They were an item, certainly, but nobody was quite sure whether they actually loved each other. However, they had been going steady for the last 18 months and everyone assumed that they would eventually tie the knot. Chris was considered handsome and reputed to be choosey, and Janice was proud and protective of her status as his girl of choice. For his part, he was loyal and diffident; he was not the sort to succumb to temptation and rarely a target due to his reticent nature and his widely acknowledged 'niceness'.

"Have you had an argument with Janice?" I persisted.

"No, no, it's got nothing to do with Janice," he protested.

"But it's got to do with something. Tell me Chris, please. I don't like it when you won't talk to me."

"Oh Vicky," he sighed. "What am I going to do?"

"About the girl?" I ventured.

"She was lovely … I never saw a lovelier creature. I can't seem to think about anything else," he murmured dreamily.

"Ooh Chris! Describe her to me. What did she look like?"

He smiled wistfully. "She was quite tall, I think, though it was quite hard to tell as I was sitting in the car. She had long hair … and it was brown – quite a light shade of brown. It was wavy and she wore it loose. It was blowing around very prettily. She had great big beautiful eyes … and very fair skin. When she smiled it was like the sun coming out. Her voice was soft and quite low. My God, listen to me, I sound like a love-struck teenager!"

"Well you are one, by the sound of it!" I quipped cheekily.

"She was wearing a red dress," he continued, "and when the wind blew it clung to her legs. When she walked, it was like she was floating. She was slender like a reed … yes, she was very slender," he mused, "… and she was wearing sandals."

"Oh mercy! You're starting to sound like my English teacher!" I teased. However, it was kindly meant. "Are you sure she was real?" I was feeling rather awkward by now; this was a side of my brother I was unfamiliar with, and I was beginning to get a little uncomfortable. "Maybe she was a spirit," I suggested, attempting to make light of a difficult topic. "Or maybe you were drunk. Hey, you're not still drunk, are you?"

"I might be," he said cryptically, lapsing into thought. When he next spoke, it was in a flamboyant, lyrical manner usually confined to the stage, and with a humorous glint in his eye.

"'Oh Helena, goddess, nymph, perfect, divine!

To what, my love, shall I compare thine eyne?'"

The reference to 'A Midsummer Night's Dream' went over my head and I asked him innocently, "Is that her name then? Helena?"

"No, you idiot!" he laughed. "It's Shakespeare. We did it at school. You have to learn quotes. It just popped into my head because, you see, she had an 'other worldly' air about her. However, she was most definitely real. When we pulled up outside the house – right in the middle of nowhere it was, she came running out … actually, it was more like a skip than a run, as she did it so daintily. She must have seen the car from the window. She looked really worried to start with – she was out of breath, but as soon as she saw the old man in the back of the motor her face lit up and she poured forth such a torrent of gratitude. I told her what happened at the pub and she thanked me so sweetly, and when she gave me her hand … it was warm to touch. So she can't have been a ghost, you numbskull," he said, with his tongue in his cheek. He leaned his head against the back of the sofa and closed his eyes, but only for a minute or two. As I beheld him, I thought I discerned a subtle change in his expression, just before he opened them again. "I never felt like that about Janice, never," he concluded, with a note of resignation in his voice.

"Well I expect you'll forget all about her soon," I said soothingly. "Can I get you another beer?"

"Cheers Vicks, you're a brick. Love one." I scurried out to the kitchen and returned with a bottle of Double Diamond.

"She's probably got a boyfriend anyway," he sighed. "I couldn't tell how old she was; she looked about my age, but her eyes looked older … Don't worry about me, Vicks. I'll be fine."

* * *

Over the course of the next month, Alan teased Chris on and off about the mysterious girl, but as his older brother persistently refused to rise to the bait the subject was eventually dropped. Chris only mentioned the encounter to me on one other occasion and that was six weeks later. The two of us were taking Rufus for a walk down the lane in the September twilight. The weather that day had been a mixture of sunshine and showers and the air smelt damp and earthy. A mild autumn breeze stirred the trees and the first stars were showing. He remarked on the loveliness of the evening and then quite unexpectedly opened up on the inner conflict which he had been keeping closely veiled, though not entirely hidden, from the more perceptive members of his family, Michael, our mother and me.

Upon reflection, he was inclined to think that the circumstances in which he had encountered his dream girl had fired his imagination, so that she appeared to him both fascinating and unattainable. As he attempted to describe his experience, a picture formed in my head. The time was early evening; the sun was shining. An abundance of vegetation, deep green in colour and still wet from an earlier shower, filled the cottage garden, providing a perfect backdrop for the gorgeous crimson dress worn by the girl. The solitary note of a blackbird had embellished the scene, adding a delicate touch of romance to the mix. Hidden away in an enclave in the upper reaches of an isolated valley and hemmed in on two sides by fells, the old stone cottage, with its whitewashed walls, infused its lovely occupant with an aura of freshness and purity, while the wild and lonely recess in the hills gave her an ethereal quality she might not have possessed had he met her in a different place and time. After all, he explained, he had been on a high, fuelled by adrenalin and alcohol, at the precise moment when he had been captivated by her. Then he reasoned that Janice really was a nice girl, smart and capable, who was evidently extremely fond of him. Whether it signified that he confined his deliberations to Janice's attachment to him, rather than his to her, was a matter for conjecture.

A week later we celebrated Chris's 18th birthday. We had a sumptuous family meal at the Scawfell Hotel in Seascale to which Janice was naturally invited. She looked chic and pretty in a pink chiffon blouse and white hip huggers – like candyfloss, as I remarked as we sipped our Coca-Cola. She was in fine form and Chris seemed relaxed and happy in her company. My doubts were allayed, at least for the time being.

Chapter 3

London

The advent of November heralded the imminent arrival of another important family event, one that was to have far-reaching consequences. The celebrations were occasioned by our mother's 40th birthday, which fell on the first day of the month.

Every year for as long as I can remember, Mum had tuned into the annual Lord Mayor's procession on television. She loved the pomp and patriotism, the military bands, carnival floats and quaint old horse-drawn carriages, and would marvel at the splendid golden coach from which the new Lord Mayor greeted the flag-waving populace. When I was very young, I would dance in front of the TV crying "Cinderella's coach, Cinderella's coach!" This year would be different for this year we were to enjoy the event at first hand.

It had also long been Mum's especial wish to be reunited with her old school pal Anjali. Auntie Anji had always been a favourite of mine. She was wealthy and generous, and had the knack of selecting delightful gifts which would arrive in exciting brown paper packages every year in October and again just before Christmas. For my 13th birthday, she had bought me a gorgeous silver charm bracelet which I had worn every day since, keeping it carefully hidden inside the sleeve of my blouse when I was at school.

Auntie Anji and Uncle Bill had relocated to London from Carlisle 10 years ago. Uncle Bill was a dentist and they had moved south so that he could fulfil his ambition of setting up his own practice in partnership with an old associate from his university days. This associate was based in Fulham. Although I had talked to Auntie Anji on the phone a number of times, I had no recollection of our last meeting as I was only two years old when they left the area and they had not been back to visit since. My geographical compass did not extend beyond Scarborough, where we would spend one week each year making intermittent forays onto the beach between showers.

I had often thought how splendid it would be to visit our fine friends in London, but now the dream was about to become a reality I contemplated the prospect with a mixture of excitement and apprehension. The difficulty lay in the fact that the Elphicks had two children: Ruby, who was a few months older than Toni, and Ray, aged 14 like Michael. This left me potentially out on a limb, particularly because my confidant and protector Chris and brother Alan were staying behind to mind the farm.

Alan was the obvious choice for successor to my Dad in years to come when he found himself no longer able to manage the day to day running of the farm. He was ambitious, intelligent, versatile and physically fit. Indeed, he possessed all the qualities that were needed to run a profitable business in the face of inclement weather, the threats posed by pests and diseases, constantly changing Government regulations, stiff local competition and exciting technological advances. Alan had left school in the summer with exceptional qualifications, achieving A grades in 'O' level English, Maths, Chemistry, History and PE.

He had, however, shown no inclination to get a job so Dad, seeing his potential, had not wasted any time in initiating him in the basic procedures of running a successful dairy farm. This was invariably greeted with a groan from Alan, who didn't share my Dad's enthusiasm for farming.

On the evening before the morning in question, I hastily threw a change of clothes and a few other essentials into a little canvas suitcase I shared with my sister and we all piled into our Ford Corsair to make the 50 mile trip to Carlisle, where we would be joined by Nan before boarding the train to London. In those days there were a lot fewer cars on the road than there are now, so we could usually do the journey to Nan's in an hour and a half, even in rush-hour traffic. We parked outside her home on Lismore Street which was 10 minutes' walk from the station. When we arrived she was already waiting by the front door with her new colourful Pucci bag stuffed full of make-up and accessories.

Carlisle Station looked impressive after dark. Its many-windowed façade, with huge gaping arches, a mass of turrets and a fairy-tale tower, looked like a palace to a country-bred girl like me, and I would not have been surprised to see Rapunzel peering down from the battlements that topped the tower. Mum hustled me inside the station entrance from where I was standing in a temporary state of inertia gazing up at the spectacle before me. Meanwhile, Toni had gone on ahead with Nan to buy some sherbet bon bons, and when she emerged onto the station platform a few minutes later she shot me a significant look which I completely failed to comprehend until much later on that night.

In less than15 minutes, we were aboard the Glasgow to London sleeper train hurtling through the Cumberland countryside. Toni and I were to share a sleeping compartment. I was very excited at the prospect of sleeping on a train. Mum and Dad ushered us to our berths, whereupon Toni instantly scrambled up the little wooden ladder and flung herself on the top bunk proclaiming,

"This one's mine!"

"That's not fair," I protested.

"No, it's not really fair, is it Toni?" Dad concurred. "I think we'd better toss a coin."

Toni scowled.

Dad reached into his coat pocket and drew out a sixpence.

"Right," he continued. "Heads Toni gets the top bunk, Tails it's Vicks."

The coin jangled to the floor.

"Tails!" I shouted gleefully. This was the icing on the cake.

Toni descended reluctantly and stomped off to the washroom. I climbed up, knelt on the bed and peered through the little round window into the night, but it was pitch black outside so I shut the curtains and settled down to enjoy the next chapter of 'Charlie and the Chocolate Factory'. Lulled by the steady clunk and rattle of the train, my eyes soon grew heavy and I slept.

Much later, I was woken from my slumber by a voice close to my ear.

"Wake up! Wake up! D'you want a bon bon?" It was Toni.

"What? What time is it? Is it time to get up?" I mumbled sleepily.

Toni giggled. "No, it's one o'clock in the morning. Have a sweet." She was perched half-way up the ladder. She leaned towards me and shoved the sweet-smelling paper bag towards my nose.

I propped my head up on my arm and tried to stifle a laugh.

"Shhhh … you'll wake Mum and Dad," she scolded.

"And Nan," I smirked.

"Oh, she won't care," Toni quipped. "She'd probably want one too!"

She clambered up onto the top bunk and we gossiped in whispered tones while we sucked on our bon bons. Goodness knows what Uncle Bill would have thought about the damage we were doing to our teeth. Eventually we started to worry about the prospect of being caught. Toni slid back down the ladder to her berth and I drifted off to sleep, soothed by the gentle, swaying motion of the train and the delicious taste of cherries on my tongue.

"Wake up Vicky, we're nearly there!" I rolled over and rubbed my eyes. Mum's tousled head was framed in a gap between the privacy curtains that extended along the length of the berth. Her face was lit up with the sort of excitement usually reserved for the younger generation.

I yawned, sat up and peeped out of the porthole into the murky dawn for a quick glimpse of our fair capital city. Alas, my first impressions were not favourable. A dismal mass of buildings filled my vision, not handsome like the decorative frontage of Carlisle Station but grey, grim and featureless. Factories and flats huddled together in an attempt to ward off the abrasions of the chill November air. I cast my mind back to the view from my own bedroom window at home; the green fields and copper-coloured woods near at hand and the familiar outlines of the hazy blue hills on the horizon. I shivered and pulled my smart new tartan drop-waisted dress over my head.

At length, the train ceased its rhythmic clatter and with a bump and dragging noise the brakes engaged, signalling that we had reached our destination. As we were jolted into the station precincts, I craned my neck towards the window at which I was standing with my mum and sister to get a better look at the broad highway containing multiple tracks and sidings. I couldn't help but wonder at the train drivers' ability to navigate successfully through such a complex network of tributaries. Finally the great machine slithered to a halt, clanking, squealing and hissing like a big, bad-tempered beast.

We alighted onto a shiny new platform and made our way to the smart, modern concourse. The floor was so smooth and polished that you could almost see your face in it.

Michael gaped. "Wow! It looks like the inside of a spaceship."

Euston Station had just been rebuilt, Dad explained.

"As a matter of fact, it's not quite finished," he said. "Anyone want some victuals?"

We all nodded in assent and followed Dad over to a kiosk where he bought tea and chocolate. Meanwhile, Mum went off to call Anji from the public phone booth and purchase an A to Z.

As I sat on the bench sipping hot, sweet tea, munching on a Milky Way and contemplating the day ahead, I felt a mounting sense of excitement. As soon as Mum reappeared, Michael piped up.

"I'm starving!"

"Me too," said Nan. "Let's go to the Wimpy."

Mum looked shocked. "A burger bar, at nine o'clock in the morning?"

"Don't be such a fusspot, dear," Nan replied briskly. "I expect they do a decent breakfast. I'm for an egg and bacon sarnie. Come along folks! Let's ask that man over there if he knows where the Wimpy is."

"Oxford Street," came the gruff reply from the middle-aged uniformed porter with a rather surly expression. Nan gave him a blank look and opened her mouth to continue while Mum thumbed through the index of her A to Z. "Melton Street exit, head for Warren Street Station, turn left down Tottenham Court Road ... or you can get the Northern line," said the porter curtly.

"Is it far?" I asked timidly.

"Takes 20 minutes," he replied curtly.

"Oh, do let's walk," I begged, appealing to my dad while Mum pored over the A to Z. "There's so much to see."

Dad smiled, ruffled my hair playfully and led the way towards the station exit.

It was a cold, damp morning but that didn't seem to deter the mass of shoppers and sightseers that thronged along the busy street. As I threaded my way down Tottenham Court Road, clutching tightly onto Mum's gloved hand, I was struck by the sheer number and diversity of people, all jostling for space on the crowded pavement and straying into the road. There were men in overcoats and trenchcoats; fashionable ladies wearing pillbox hats and fake fur on their collars and cuffs; girls sporting swing coats and knee-high boots. We passed a dusty tramp crouched in a doorway, staring into space. A gang of youths in anoraks loitered on a street corner, smoking and swearing – my Dad said they were mods. Sometimes I caught snatches of conversation, mostly in English but occasionally in an unfamiliar foreign tongue. An appetising savoury smell wafted from the open doorway of a working men's café and my mouth started to water. Outside the Wimpy Bar, a dishevelled young woman held out a thin, bony hand and begged for sixpence. As we crossed the threshold into the cheerful interior, a blast of warm air hit me in the face.

Soon we were tucking into a delicious breakfast served on white china crockery by a pretty blonde-haired waitress with lipstick as red as her brightly coloured uniform.

"Mmm … this sarnie tastes delicious," said Michael, taking an enormous bite and licking his lips. "Much better than the ones you make, Mum."

Mum sighed. I couldn't help but agree; however I wisely held my tongue. It was certainly exceptionally tasty, but after all I was ravenous and probably not in the best position to judge.

"Mine's rather fatty," complained Toni. "Here, d'you want the rest Michael?"

"Yeah … give it here, I'll eat it." He held out his plate.

Toni was always getting uptight about her weight, her skin and her hair.

I finished my sarnie and gulped down my strawberry Whippsy shake. I couldn't wait to tell my school friends all about it. Most of them lived in little villages and fast food outlets were few and far between in our neighbourhood.

"Let's see," said Dad. "Now, we need to get to Waterloo; that's where we're meeting Bill and Anji, isn't it, Marion?"

It was a short walk back to Tottenham Court Road Station

and we found an underground map on the wall just inside the entrance.

"Looks like it's the Northern Line." Mum pointed to the map. "This way." She herded us towards the ticket office and then we descended down the biggest escalator I had ever seen.

This was my first experience of the tube and I was smitten. I loved the noisy clamour of the train as it thundered out of the blackness; I loved the warm gust of wind that flew in my face; best of all I loved the heady combination of metal, engine oil and ozone which lent the air a unique flavour.

We deposited our bags at Waterloo Station where Mum had arranged to meet Auntie Anji and her family. Here I found a welcome counterpart to the smart modern plaza at Euston, all glossy and glib. The light and lofty interior was reminiscent of a giant conservatory from a bygone era. The elaborate scaffold of criss-cross steel trusses which underpinned the glass-panelled roof was a masterpiece in geometric design. There was a grand stone entrance arch, decorative cast iron pillars dotted along the concourse and a lovely Victorian four-faced clock in the centre, under which we now waited for the imminent arrival of our friends.

All of a sudden, Mum let out a whoop of pleasure and started waving frantically at an attractive middle-aged lady of Asian extraction who was approaching us. Auntie Anji and Uncle Bill greeted us warmly and introduced their children. Ruby was a tall raven-haired beauty. I laughed inwardly at the thought that Toni had finally met her match. Ray was a good-looking boy, slim with a dark complexion, large brown eyes and beautiful teeth – well, after all, he was the son of a dentist.

"I thought we might make our way over to Blackfriars," suggested Auntie Anji. "It's a nice walk across the bridge."

As we wound our way towards the river, Mum quickly fell into easy conversation with Auntie Anji while Dad addressed Uncle Bill with polite enquiries about his business, health and family.

Toni lost no time in throwing herself into an animated discussion with Ruby about make-up, mini skirts and music. Ray made several attempts to draw the taciturn Michael into conversation and I trotted along behind with Nan, looking all about me with the curiosity of a newcomer.

We passed rows of shops, offices and elegant townhouses. They differed much in terms of age and design but they had one thing in common; they were all tall and packed in close together. Trees were in short supply.

"London's so *chic*, don't you think, dear?" said Nan, assuming to read my thoughts. "Look at those townhouses, Vicky. They're lovely!"

"Yes, they're nice but I could never live in a place like this. I just feel … well … hemmed in, I suppose … and there's nowhere to walk a dog."

Nan chortled. "Oh, you're so rustic, Vicky! London's full of green spaces. You just have to know where they are."

At length we turned left onto a broad highway and headed up onto Blackfriars Bridge, leaving the commotion of traffic behind us as the road was closed to vehicles today. I thoroughly enjoyed the walk over the Thames. The familiar combination of water, damp air, open space and relative tranquillity was redolent of home and a welcome tonic for a Lakeland girl. The view from this elevated spot was tremendous. I liked looking down at the pleasure boats, barges and motorboats. Better still, I liked it when Ray dropped back alongside me as I paused to look around and pointed to the landmarks – St. Paul's Cathedral, the Oxo Tower and distant Post Office Tower, the tallest building in London.

From the bridge, we turned right along Queen Victoria Street, crossed over and stopped outside a pub called the Baynard Castle.

"Here's a good spot," said Uncle Bill. "Fancy a beer, Robert?"

Dad and Uncle Bill disappeared inside for a swift pint while Mum and Auntie Anji went off in search of alternative forms of sustenance and returned bearing doughnuts, hot drinks and little

Union Jack flags for us to wave. Then we waited for what seemed like an eternity for the procession to arrive.

At last our patience was rewarded by the strains of a rousing military tune pounded out by persons as yet unseen. I was gripped by a quite unexpected and inexplicable surge of national pride and forgot how cold I had got as I warmly anticipated the start of the show.

For the next hour we were treated to a spectacular display. We waved our flags, shouted and cheered as the procession passed along the street right before our eyes. There was a multitude of marching bands, some of them sporting the famous scarlet coats and busbies of the guards, others wearing dark-coloured uniforms with peaked caps, helmets or berets. Some regiments paraded with rifles on their shoulders. The Cavalry was my favourite; I thought the horses magnificent and the clip-clop of their hooves on the tarmac road delightful. There were vintage cars and vans, brightly decorated lorries and floats packed with musicians, dancing girls and folks in fancy dress. There was a lavish helping of international culture too; troupes of dancers in exotic costumes and two men in Arabian dress eating fire. At last the Lord Mayor rolled by in his glorious fairy-tale coach of crimson and gold pulled by six beautiful white horses.

All this time, I had been becoming increasingly conscious of the dark figure of Ray standing next to me. I had the strangest sensation akin to butterflies in the stomach and found myself struggling to respond coherently to his idle chatter, but I had no desire to move and wished fervently that the procession would go on indefinitely. I was unspeakably grateful when Nan pushed into the row of spectators on my other side. This forced me into closer proximity with Ray, although this came at a price as next time he addressed me I turned scarlet and found myself virtually tongue-tied.

I must have covered up my embarrassment well as when, at the end of the celebrations, Auntie Anji suggested we all walked to Trafalgar Square, Ray attached himself to me and this time it was Michael who enjoyed the dubious honour of escorting Nan.

"How do you like London, then?" Ray enquired casually.

"It's brilliant!" I breathed, keen to impress.

"You wouldn't say that if you lived here," he replied.

The sense of mortification brought about by the realisation that my white lie had completely backfired was out of all proportion with the situation and I tried hastily to retract my bold assertion.

"Well … what I mean to say is that parts of it are nice."

"What parts?"

"Er … Waterloo Station … and the townhouses … and the Wimpy, I liked the Wimpy," I mumbled abstractedly.

Ray laughed out loud. "Is that all? Come, I'll show you Trafalgar Square. You'll like Trafalgar Square. D'you like pigeons?"

"I never really thought about it. I guess I do."

"Mum, Mum, *can* I go to Carnaby Street with Ruby … *please?*" Toni looked imploringly at Mum, who glanced helplessly at Auntie Anji and shrugged her shoulders.

"They'll be all right," said my aunt reassuringly. "Ruby goes everywhere on her own. She knows her way round London like the back of her hand."

Mum gave her assent rather reluctantly on the condition that they were back by four o'clock. Nan stuffed a 10 shilling note into Toni's hand and winked.

"Treat yourself to something nice, love."

Meanwhile, I stood between Michael and Ray with my head thrown back gazing up at Admiral Lord Nelson perched atop his monumental granite column. Michael's attention was focused almost exclusively on the great bronze lions which he described alternately as "smashing" and "awesome", whilst Ray's chief source of amusement appeared to lie in watching the antics of multitudinous pigeons that scurried and flapped. They were smaller and less uniform in appearance than the pigeons back home and a few of the less fortunate ones had deformities.

"We're going to the National Gallery," said Dad. "Would you youngsters like to come in or d'you want to stay out here?"

"We want to feed the pigeons," said Ray in a flash. "Can I have some money, Mum?"

Auntie Anji drew out her purse and Nan followed suit. Then Ray led the way towards a man with a barrow who was selling bags of seed and gave him a coin.

"Hold out your hand." Ray sprinkled a little heap of the birdseed into my palm. "No, flatter." He nudged the tips of my fingers downwards. A tingling sensation rushed up my arm. "Now, wait …"

I didn't have to wait long. They swooped down in droves and in less than a minute the more surefooted ones had taken up residence on my head, shoulders and outstretched arms. Their feet tickled my scalp and I tried hard not to move my head as I gave myself over to a fit of giggles. We spent a jolly half hour in the company of the voracious little creatures; next Ray suggested a trip to a sandwich bar for a hot drink and a snack and then we headed back to the National Gallery ready to embark on the final stage of our exciting day.

As we approached, I noticed that Mum was in the throes of an animated conversation with Toni, who was clutching a small packet. She glanced across at me, then turned back to Toni with a gesture of resignation. By this time, Michael and Ray had discovered a shared interest in volcanoes and were engaged in earnest conversation peppered with traces of one-upmanship. Toni hurried towards me and grabbed my arm.

"Vicky, Vicky, look at these!" She waved the packet in my face.

"Fishnet stockings!" I exclaimed. "No wonder Mum looked cross."

"She thinks they're indecent," declared Toni. "What's more, she thinks the whole shop is indecent! We went to Lady Jane," she smirked.

"What's Lady Jane?"

"Oh really, Vicky, you're such a square! It's only the most *famous* boutique in the *whole* of London. They got arrested for having live models changing in the shop window. Don't you read the newpapers?"

I had to admit that I didn't, and I knew for a fact that she didn't either. She must have been enlightened by Ruby whom I suspected to be a hotbed of gossip.

"Carnaby Street was *amazing*," she went on. "The shops were *amazing* ... and the boys ... Vicky, are you listening?"

I tore my eyes away from Ray's glossy black head bobbing along a few feet in front of me and smiled distractedly at her.

"Sorry, I was miles away ..."

"Yes, and we all know why, don't we?" she teased, and tripped back to Ruby's side.

Just as dusk was beginning to fall, we reached the area of London known as Covent Garden. Carts and crates spilled out of the market into the adjoining streets, and for a pleasant half hour we lingered amongst the fruit and flowers while the adults flitted in and out of the quirky little shops which have long since capitulated under the steamroller of progress.

Back in the 1960s, Covent Garden bore all the hallmarks of a traditional close-knit community of working-class people. Now it is a tourist hotspot boasting slick shops, swanky bars and street entertainers. Then it was a bustling London market fighting to hold its own in a changing world. There was a curious mix of poverty and wealth, of rough and ready trades-people and quaint local businesses; restaurants and pubs serving the theatres and Opera House; all set against a backdrop of shabby warehouses and run-down dwellings. Goods vehicles choked the narrow lanes that now swarm with sightseers.

Barrow boys wolf-whistled at my sister and her glamorous companion as we ambled along. Cigarettes glowed in the twilight and their fumes marked the air. Men swapped coarse jokes in broad

London dialect with fellow traders. Everyone seemed to know their neighbours and there was genuine warmth in their exchanges. It was like crossing a portal into an earlier time and I half-expected Eliza Doolittle to step out in front of me and thrust a posy under my nose.

I began to feel quite cold but a brisk walk along the Strand and over Waterloo Bridge revived me and soon we were snugly packed into the tube train bound for South Wimbledon. All of a sudden Mum let out a shriek, much to the astonishment of the startled passengers who had the misfortune to share our carriage.

"Oh my God, we left our overnight bags at Waterloo Station!"

I cringed with embarrassment, Michael sniggered and Toni glared at her with a face like thunder.

"Well, we all forgot," she added defensively.

"Yes, you can hardly hold your mum responsible," said Dad firmly, shooting the three of us a warning look.

"No need to panic," Uncle Bill said soothingly. "We can easily get off at the next station and go back and get them. Anji, why don't you take the young'uns home and we'll join you later?"

"Good idea," agreed Dad. "Liz," he continued, turning to Nan. "You go with Anji, Marion and I will go back for the bags with Bill."

The Elphicks lived in a smart semi-detached Edwardian villa on a residential street 10 minutes' walk from South Wimbledon underground station. The interior was sumptuous, stylish and expensively furnished. The large L-shaped living-dining area was carpeted from wall to wall in a rich shade of purple with matching floor length curtains. At one end there was a plush five-piece floral suite of khaki and cream. At the other stood an elegant oval dining table made of highly-polished walnut and decorated with a pair of ornate silver candlesticks. An enormous rubber plant stood next to the window.

"Wow, it's like the National Trust," Toni whispered, as Ray ushered us out and led the way up two flights of stairs to a cosy little attic room containing two Z-beds and a collection of boxes, bags and other paraphernalia.

"This is where you and Toni are sleeping. Sorry about the mess," he said apologetically. "Michael, you're sleeping in my room. Would you like to see my collection of stones?"

The boys hastened downstairs. Toni threw off her coat and I did likewise. I sat down heavily on the Z-bed feeling vaguely disappointed that Ray had neglected to include me. Then I chastised myself; after all I was only an unsophisticated country girl. As I was pondering, a gorgeous savoury smell wafted upstairs and I heard Mum's voice in the entrance hall.

Soon we were tucking into a big spread of home-cooked Indian dishes, served in bone china vessels on a tablecloth of fine white linen. Some were so spicy that they made my nose stream and my eyes water. Ray poked fun at me good-naturedly; it was better than being ignored.

"That's not spicy," he mocked, pointing at a bowl of rich, red massala. "You should try this one!"

I shook my head and gulped down mouthfuls of water.

"Seriously Vicky, haven't you even eaten Indian food before?" he continued.

"No, never. We don't eat stuff like this at home."

"Like it?"

"Mmm …". If Ray had offered me a bowl of pigswill, I believe I would have liked it.

After dinner, Ruby and Ray removed themselves to the kitchen to wash and dry up. Theirs was a strict regime and they did not need to be asked. I plucked up my courage and stepped cautiously across the threshold.

"Can I help?" I asked Ray timidly.

"Sure," he replied and threw me a tea towel.

Ruby was first to finish and when she left the room, there was an awkward silence.

Then Ray spoke up. "What d'you want to do next?" he asked politely. "I could show you my stones but you might find them really boring."

"No, really, I'd love to see them," I answered shyly, but inside I was exultant.

I spent a blissful 45 minutes feigning an avid interest in his large collection of rocks and crystals, hanging onto his every word but understanding little and caring nothing about geology. I went to bed that night with my head swimming and a warm glow in the pit of my stomach.

The following morning we had a full English breakfast before saying our goodbyes. Waiting at the front door, I felt my colour rise and a lump form in my throat as Ray stepped over to me.

"Goodbye, Pipsqueak," he said, flinging his arms round me in a mock embrace. "Let's keep in touch. I'm so pleased you liked my stones." He kissed me gently on the cheek and I trembled, unable to reciprocate. I wondered if he had any idea why.

Chapter 4

Sweet 16

One evening towards the middle of December, I was halted in my tracks as I entered the house by the sound of raised voices issuing from the kitchen at the end of the passage. Our family enjoyed relative equanimity so I was surprised, and not a little perplexed, by what I heard. Dad was in full throttle.

"My grandfather built up this business from nothing and my father breathed his last breath on the field out yonder," he bellowed. "This is my farm and I'm not about to let some money-grabbing corporation snatch it from under my nose. Good God boy, you're useless! Your brother's the same with his namby-pamby drawings. A pretty pair of pansies I've bred!"

"I hate farming! I've always hated it and I'll never be a farmer, not if my life depended on it!" Alan cried passionately.

I heard the back door slam and everything went quiet. I sidled half-way up the stairs and waited nervously, fearing discovery, as Dad was evidently in a very bad humour.

Mum spoke next. "Listen, Robert, you have to face facts. You're wrong and you know it. You're driving a huge wedge between you and those boys. Alan's not interested in farming, never has been; nor is Chris. You can't force a square peg into a round hole, you know."

"What's going to happen to the farm when I've gone, that's what I'd like to know?" Dad retorted hotly.

"For heaven's sake, you're only 46; you're hardly at death's door … and there's always Michael."

"Humph … Michael. What use is Michael? He's a big softie just like his brothers."

"That's enough, Robert. I won't have you talk about the children like that," scolded Mum.

I heard the kitchen door opening, tiptoed quickly upstairs to my room and waited for a decent interval, before coming down to the kitchen nonchalantly with my school bag slung over my shoulder.

"Hi Mum," I said casually throwing my bag onto the table and diving in to retrieve my maths textbook.

"Hello, Vicky dear" Mum replied with a forced smile. "Had a good day?"

"Yeah, it was okay," I replied in my customary non-committal manner adopted for most matters concerning school.

For the next hour, while I ploughed through my homework, Mum maintained a thoughtful silence.

When we all gathered for dinner, you could have cut the atmosphere with a knife. I guessed that Alan had taken Chris into his confidence as they came downstairs together making small talk. This implied a cover-up since it was quite out of the ordinary. Dad threw them a cursory glance and sat down with his back turned.

Michael lacked the subtlety of his older brothers.

"What's wrong with everyone?" he complained, helping himself to a large plateful of stew. "Anyone would think someone had died."

Dad cleared his throat. "You may as well know, Alan's determined to abandon the family business. He wants to teach. Much good may it do him."

"Good for him!" proclaimed Toni unexpectedly. "Alan's much too clever for farming."

Dad spluttered and turned crimson with rage.

"Come, come, Toni," said Mum reproachfully. "You don't know what you're talking about. Managing a farm is a very skilled job. It's difficult and complicated."

Chris was the epitome of tact and sprung to Alan's defence whilst attempting to placate Dad.

"Everyone knows farming's a tough call, but Alan's just not cut out for it. It's horses for courses."

Alan was next to take up the reins.

"Won't you at least let me try, Dad? If it doesn't work out, then maybe I'll give farming a go."

However, Dad was intractable.

"It strikes me you don't like getting your boots muddy, boy. Well, let me tell you, that's not what managing a farm is about, not nowadays. It's all about quotas and budgets and what-have-you. D'you think I have time to swan around outdoors? Oh no, too much paperwork ... more's the pity. You're a bright lad. I can give you a permanent position, some responsibility. I'll teach you how to run the place. I won't be here forever, you know."

"You just don't get it, do you? I want to do something worthwhile, something rewarding."

"You don't regard producing basic life-sustaining commodities as doing something worthwhile? Dear oh dear, Lord help us! I had high hopes for you. You've got a good business head on your shoulders. How you can contemplate throwing away your talents on a bunch of ungrateful wretches is beyond me!"

Michael looked affronted and Toni glowered.

"Oh, we're ungrateful wretches, are we?" she declared frostily. "Thanks, Dad."

"Antonia!" Mum intercepted sharply. "You know full well what your Dad means and there's no need for you to make things worse. You've said far too much already. Robert, you're just as bad. Let's put an end to this silly argument. We must agree to disagree."

Dad and Alan maintained an uneasy truce over the next few weeks. Dad was steadfast in his conviction that Alan would come round to his way of thinking and continued to persuade, cajole and entice him with the promise of a fulfilling role, financial security and a satisfying career. Alan was compliant to a point. He genuinely tried to show an interest in the day-to-day management of the farm and took on some of the much-maligned 'paperwork' under Dad's watchful eye.

Then one Saturday morning an official-looking brown envelope arrived addressed to Alan. He opened it nervously and examined the contents. A slow smile spread across his face. He handed the letter to our father, who was standing by the back door with his boots on.

"You've made up your mind then?" said Dad gruffly, trying hard to suppress the emotion that was all too evident in his voice. "Well, I've got to hand it to you, son, you're your own man … I like that in a fellow …" He trailed off, unable to continue.

"I can go then?" Alan pressed him.

There was an awkward silence while Dad continued to stare down at the letter in his hand. Then he flung it down on the wicker chair next to the door in a gesture of defiance.

"Looks like it," he replied bluntly, putting on his coat.

"Thanks, Dad," said Alan, with effort. "I'll make you proud."

"See that you do, that's all," and he stomped off toward the cowshed without a backward glance.

Alan looked crestfallen. He turned to Mum.

"That didn't go well," he said bitterly.

"Give him time, he'll come round," Mum said gently.

Alan continued to help out on the farm but relations were strained and all that winter a cloud hung over our normally happy abode.

* * *

As spring approached, preparations began for an event which was uppermost in everyone's mind, especially mine. The event in question was Toni's 16th birthday. In a moment of weakness, Mum had agreed to allow Toni to hold a party at home. However, it transpired that Mum's motives were not altogether selfless when a few days later she came up with a proposal.

"Toni, how would you like to invite Ruby to your party? I think we can put the family up for the weekend."

I could have jumped for joy as I savoured the prospect of a weekend with Ray with relish, the magnitude of which surpassed all my expectations. Then I began to worry. What if Ray didn't care to come? What if he decided to stay with a friend instead? I mulled over all the possible outcomes for several days with an intensity bordering on obsession until at last I was no longer able to contain my fears and slipped into the kitchen when I knew Mum was there on her own.

"Do you think they'll all come?" I asked innocently, forgetting that she couldn't read my mind.

"What? Who?" Mum asked confusedly.

"Auntie Anji … and Uncle Bill, Ruby … and Ray," I added hesitantly.

Mum looked intently at me and a slow smile spread across her face.

"Yes, they're all coming," she said. "All of them … including Ray."

"Oh … right …" I felt the colour rush to my cheeks, lowered my head and rushed headlong up to the sanctity of my bedroom. Evidently she could read my mind after all.

On Saturday 18th March I woke early. Grey light seeped through the curtains and birds twittered in the trees behind the house. I could faintly hear the voices of the farmhands in the yard next to the cowshed. 6.15. I rolled over, snuggled down and endeavoured to sink myself into a delicious reverie featuring Ray as principal character in a romantic scenario to be played out with me under the stars tonight, but adrenalin surges fuelled by the contemplation of his imminent arrival so upset my equilibrium that my dreamy state was swiftly overtaken by restlessness and nausea. Soon after, I heard Mum descend the stairs. I slithered out of bed, wrapped my dressing gown around me and installed myself in the bathroom for the initial steps in a prolonged make-over that was likely to span the entire morning. Today I wanted to look my best.

At 8 a.m. I emerged smelling of parma violets and setting lotion and scurried back to the bedroom. Toni was sitting up in bed, rubbing her eyes.

"Toni, Toni," I gasped breathlessly. "Will you do my hair? You'll do it so well."

"For God's sake, Vicky, what time do you call this?"

"Please Toni, I want it to look nice for …" I stopped, embarrassed by my inability to suppress the torrent of words that I had carelessly let fall from my lips.

Toni yawned sleepily. "For Ray. Yes, I know, I know. Get the hairdryer … and the curling tongs. It'll look awful by the time he arrives, you know. They won't be here until lunchtime."

"Oh thank you! Thank you! I'll just stay indoors, and I won't move or anything," I added conciliatingly.

"You *have* got it bad," Toni quipped. "I hope he's worth it."

"My, your hair looks nice," Mum said half an hour later as I swept into the kitchen with neatly curled ringlets swaying about my ears. "Isn't it rather early to be styling it?"

"Oh no, not you as well," I groaned. "Toni just said that".

"Well, you won't be able to walk Rufus, you know," she cautioned. "Not if you want it to look nice for tonight. Michael will have to go on his own."

"It's just this once," I said defensively. "Rufus won't care. Anyway I have to stay in and paint my nails."

Mum frowned. "Vicky, you're only 13. Aren't you rather young for nail lacquer?"

"Don't be silly, Mum. All my friends wear it," I lied.

I ate a scanty breakfast. It was hard to entertain a hearty meal at this critical point in my life and I fully expected my preparations to fill up the rest of the morning. After breakfast, I shut myself in my room to complete the transformation I hoped feverishly would impress my heartthrob and earn me a kiss. No effort was spared. I daubed pink on my nails and cheeks and green on my eyelids. I touched up my eyebrows with Toni's pencil, added a sweep of mascara to my eyelashes and applied her pink lipstick discreetly lest I should get found out by my sister or, worse still, incur my mother's disapproval. Then I pulled on my orange sweater dress and matching patent leather daisy shoes and slipped into Mum and Dad's room to admire myself in the full-length mirror. The effect was startling and with my head held high I glided downstairs feeling more like a princess than a farmer's daughter.

"My goodness, you've brushed up well," Chris grinned as I made my dramatic entrance into the kitchen.

"Yeah, like the Ugly Duckling," Alan chimed in.

"I take it there's a compliment hidden somewhere in that statement," I said haughtily.

"Rather," he said. "Look out, Ray!"

"Oh my God, is there anyone who doesn't know *all* my secrets!" I spluttered.

"You should never have told Toni," goaded Alan.

"I didn't," I protested. "She guessed."

"I'll put in a good word for you," he continued relentlessly.

"Don't you dare!"

I scowled and escaped to the solitude of the front room, where I spent the next 45 minutes staring out of the rain-splattered window for a first glimpse of the long anticipated deep brown eyes, raven hair and tanned complexion that occupied my every waking hour.

Eventually I heard the purr of a car in the lane outside and an expensive looking Rover turned into the farmyard. I jumped down from the window seat, ran to the front door and threw it open. Auntie Anji clambered out and hurried towards me with her arms outstretched.

"Hello, sweetheart," she cooed, giving me a hug. "You look different … well, very nice actually. Your hair looks nice."

Uncle Bill shook me warmly by the hand.

"Good to see you again, girl," he said heartily. "Where's your mum and dad?"

"In there," I said hastily, waving them past me into the hall where Mum was standing, tea towel in hand.

Ruby and Ray followed behind.

"Hi Vicky." Ruby held out her hand. "It's really sweet of you all to have us for the weekend. Can't wait for the party."

Finally it was Ray's turn.

"Hello Vicky," he said nervously.

"Hello Ray."

There was an awkward pause. He shuffled his feet.

"You've done something different to your hair. It looks nifty."

"Toni did it," I blurted out, instantly regretting my honesty and inwardly cursing the foolishness that had led me to reveal my lack of refinement within 30 seconds.

"Well, she'd make a great hairdresser," he smiled. "It really does look nice."

Soon we were all crammed shoulder-to-shoulder around the big pine table in the centre of the kitchen. The situation was ripe with a potential that I had not failed to notice and I lost no time in hopping nimbly up onto a stool alongside Ray in which position I could bathe in his body heat and wallow in the sensation of his arm pressed against mine. Mum heaped ladlefuls of rabbit stew into bowls while Dad handed round hunks of home-made bread. Ray nudged me and pointed to the stew.

"Did your Dad shoot the rabbits?" he grinned, his voice low and confidential.

"Not likely; the ones on our farm are much too scrawny. You'd need a whole army of them," I giggled. "Have you ever eaten a rabbit before?"

"Absolutely not! They're pets!" he retorted with a mischievous glint in his eye.

"My dad says they're vermin. You would too if one ate your mum's rubber plant!"

A mental picture formed in my head and I tried to stifle a laugh. However, I only partially succeeded and it exploded like a cough. I grabbed my serviette and stuffed it over my mouth.

Mum looked up. "Are you all right, Vicky?" she said, looking mildly concerned.

I cleared my throat noisily, took a deep breath and mastered the convulsions that threatened to betray my frivolity.

"I'm fine. It was just a bit of rabbit." I grabbed my tea and took a large gulp.

Ray kicked me under the table and winked.

It was still raining after lunch. Toni and Ruby disappeared upstairs to listen to the Dansette. The men donned wax jackets and caps and went off for a tramp round the farm while Mum and Auntie Anji busied themselves in the kitchen preparing sandwiches, cocktail sausages and cheese straws for the partygoers. Michael, Ray and I drifted into the lounge. The lounge was a long, bright room which extended from the front to the back of the house. The floorboards were bare at the edges and glossy with varnish. In the centre were two giant Persian-style rugs which had seen better days. There was an old oak sideboard and a rustic coffee table. A small circular dining table stood in front of the French windows at the opposite end. The sofa was deep orange in colour – large, soft and frayed.

"What d'you want to do now?" I asked Ray. "We could go for a walk down to the lake but it's pouring."

"Never mind," he said. "There's always tomorrow. D'you have any board games?"

"We've got Cluedo," I volunteered. "Michael's really good at it ... aren't you?" I glanced over at Michael, who was idly turning the pages of the morning paper. "He's got a strategy, you know, but he won't tell me what it is. I'm rubbish," I continued.

"Yeah, I've got a strategy too," Ray said coolly, settling himself on the sofa and stretching his long legs out in front of him. "Bet I could beat him, hands down."

"Oh you could, could you?" Michael raised his head, put down the paper and disappeared out of the door.

"Looks like it's game on," laughed Ray. "Bags I be Professor Plum. He's obviously the cleverest. He's a professor."

"Michael's always Colonel Mustard, he says he's the poshest."

"Most posh ... Victoria ... most posh. You can't say 'poshest'; there's no such word". He shook his head and tutted. "What about you then?"

"I'm always Mrs. Peacock. I like blue."

"That's female thinking, that is. My mum bought a car once 'cause it was blue. What about your sister? I suppose she's Miss Scarlett."

"Yeah," I groaned. "That's her all over."

"Same as mine," he grinned. "Only mine's got an excuse ... being called Ruby, that is. Ruby Scarlett ... imagine that!"

Michael returned with the Cluedo and we played three games. Ray won the first and Michael the second.

"Best of three, best of three," cried Michael, waving the dagger and Mrs. White triumphantly in the air.

"Okay, I'll admit it, you're good," conceded Ray. "Better than my sister ... and most of my mates."

"Oh, he's the brainy one in the family, him and Alan," I said. "Chris is just a sweetie but he doesn't have much brains, like me. Toni ... well, she's just Toni."

Ray picked up the cards and started shuffling them absent-mindedly.

"Dad thinks I'm brainy. He wants me to go to university."

"... And will you?" I enquired.

"Yeah, I guess so. I like History. Maybe I'll study that."

Ray won the third game but only by a nose. This time the murderer was Mrs. Peacock.

"Oh my God, I *hate* being the murderer," I said petulantly, as we packed the board away.

Ray burst out laughing. "You're so funny, it's only a game. Come on, let's have a cup of tea. I'm dry as a desert. Got any cake?"

Mum was in the kitchen emptying packets of crisps, twiglets and peanuts into bowls. I filled the kettle and grabbed the cake tin from the shelf.

"Want some cake, Mum?"

"Yes please. I'm sure Anji would like some too. She's just getting changed. The men are in the front room. Would you be a dear and take them some in."

I sighed audibly and set about cutting slices of rich, sticky, sweet-smelling fruitcake.

"Oh … and can you make a large pot?" she added. "We'll all want some tea."

I groaned. "Michael can do that, can't he?" but Michael had made himself scarce, driven, no doubt, by the prospect of pitching in.

While we drank our tea and ate our cake, the men were shunting furniture in the lounge. When we peered in half an hour later, the rugs had been rolled up and the sofa pushed back against the wall. The coffee table was alongside it, buried beneath a large white tablecloth that touched the floor on all sides. Toni's Dansette was plugged in and ready on the circular table in the far corner of the room. Toni stood next to the table with Ruby, discussing the merits of the Beatles versus the Stones.

"The Stones are so *raw*," Toni was arguing. "I like *raw* … like my men."

"Toni, you're *so* rude," Ruby tittered. "I like mine to be rich and sophisticated. I want to be wined and dined."

We exchanged amused glances and retreated into the hall.

"Come and see my room," I said to Ray.

"Sure, love to."

"Hmmm … now let's see …" Ray said archly, looking from one side of the bedroom to the other. "I'm guessing you sleep on the window side."

"Well, duh …" I shot him a playful glance.

The walls were lined with posters. Mick Jagger and the boys dominated the wall adjacent to the doorway, while John, Paul, George and Ringo smiled down at us from the opposite side of the room.

"Go on then," he said confidentially. "Tell me, who's your favourite Beatle?"

"Oh, definitely Paul," I confessed, blushing. "He's so dreamy. What about you?"

"I'm a boy!" he scoffed. "Boys don't have favourite Beatles! Seriously though, I quite like George, I mean musically. He's got a lot of hidden talent, has George. I suppose you like all that sloppy stuff Paul spouts."

"He doesn't spout, he … he … warbles," I said, creasing up at my own joke. "And it's not sloppy, it's romantic, so there!"

"Favourite song?" he continued, strolling over to the window. "My, what a view!"

"Song? Oh … 'Here, There and Everywhere' I guess, with 'Michelle' as close second. I like 'Eleanor Rigby' too. 'Yesterday''s Mum's favourite. I used to love it too but she's overplayed it and unfortunately it's lost some of its magic. Yes, the view's gorgeous; I wouldn't swap it for the world."

"I like 'Love You To' … you know, on 'Revolver'. I like the sitar. It makes it sound, like, kinda Indian. It reminds me of my grandma." He picked up the dog-eared copy of 'Second Form at Malory Towers' from my bed and turned it over disdainfully. "Can't say I think much of your taste in fiction," he continued, throwing it back down. "No, wait a minute …" He walked over to the bookshelf. "You've got 'The Hobbit'."

"The Hobbit?" Just in time, I recollected that Michael had lent me the book a few months ago. "Yes, I've got 'The Hobbit,'" I said casually.

"Ace! Have you read it?"

"No, not yet." I hesitated. "Would you like to borrow it?"

"Oh, can I? Fab!" he exclaimed, pulling it down from the bookshelf. "Are you sure you don't mind?"

"No, it's fine … only don't tell anyone." He looked at me quizzically and I fumbled for an explanation. "Mum hates me lending my books."

He replaced it carefully and shrugged.

"You can have it tomorrow," I qualified, "… only I don't want anyone seeing it."

There was a moment's silence. I took a deep breath.

"Ray, I … I've got something for you," I said falteringly.

"Really?" He raised his eyebrows.

I felt my colour rise. I walked quickly over to my bedside cabinet and rummaged in the top draw. "Here it is. Shut your eyes and hold out your hand."

Ray did as I bid.

"There. Don't look yet, just feel."

He closed his hand around the small, hard, round object.

"It feels cold. Is it a stone of some sort?"

"Oh my gosh, you guessed," I said, feigning surprise.

"It wasn't exactly difficult. Can I look now?"

"Yes, yes of course. I found it on the lakeshore. It's for your collection."

He gazed at the pretty, grey and white pebble twinkling in his palm.

"Oh Vicky, that's so sweet, it's lovely!" He looked into my face. "I shall treasure it."

He leaned forward and gave me a friendly peck on the forehead. My legs were trembling so violently that I was forced to steady myself against the cabinet with one hand. He stepped away awkwardly and we fell back into conversation, both acutely aware of the possibilities smouldering beneath that innocent gesture.

Janice was first to arrive. She was an hour early. I could see her blonde head clearly from the upstairs window, bobbing across the east pasture.

"There's Janice," I cried. "Hey, we'd better go downstairs. Mum'll wonder what we're up to." The words tumbled out before I could check them, and for the third time that day I would gladly have scooped them up and swallowed them. At least I had managed to hide the identity of the true owner of the book. I smothered my embarrassment with a nervous laugh and hurried Ray out of the door and down the stairs.

Mum was sitting at the kitchen table. Presently Janice hopped over the stile in the corner of the garden, strode across to the back door and breezed in. She swept across to me, folded me into a fond embrace and pressed her cold rosy face against my warm one.

"Watcha Vicks," she said cheerfully. "Gosh, you look peachey."

She bounced over to Mum, leant over and planted a kiss on her cheek.

"Hello Mrs. K. How's tricks? Hello, who's this?" She tugged off her muddy boots and deposited them in front of the Aga.

"This is Ray, he's visiting," I replied.

"Hello Ray. Pleased to meet you." She grabbed his hand, shook it energetically and then stripped off her coat and scarf. "Where's Chris?"

"Oh, upstairs I think ..." Before Mum could continue, Janice was out the door and bounding up the stairs.

Ray looked after her incredulously.

"Oh don't mind Janice," I explained. "She's like one of the family. She's a bit of a whirlwind. She never walks anywhere," I laughed, relaxed once more.

Not long after, Phil appeared at the door with two packages tucked under his arm. Phil had been dating Toni for several months. He was tall and slim with a long, lean face and dark collar-length layered hair. Mum said he looked like Keith Richards.

"Hi Phil, come and meet Ruby".

Toni ushered him into the kitchen where I was popping corn with Ray. Phil surveyed Ruby artfully and a provocative smile flew from his face right into the path of my sharp-eyed sister's suspicious gaze. Toni glared at him and snatched the presents. She ripped the paper off the first one and squealed.

"Oh my God, the Troggs! I *love* 'Wild Thing'!" She tugged at the wrapping of the second package. "Milk Tray? Oh Phil, how *could* you? You *know* I'm dieting. You *know* chocolate gives me spots. Honestly Phil, what were you thinking of?" She dumped the chocolates unceremoniously on the table, grabbed the bemused Ruby by the arm and marched out, clutching the LP.

Phil swore under his breath and followed them out.

Next to arrive was Joanie. She was draped on Jason's arm, chewing gum and reeking of cheap perfume. She wore a pink mini skirt, tight-fitting sweater and fake eyelashes. Her platinum blonde hair was piled high on her head. I didn't like Joanie. Jason was a good-looking guy and I used to wonder why he wasted his time on her, until my sister reminded me that she was a fully paid-up member of the permissive society. They came bearing three carrier bags loaded with Watney's Red Barrel and Babycham that rattled and clinked inauspiciously all the way down the length of the lounge to their resting place outside the French windows.

"Quick, hide them down there!" Toni whispered conspiratorially. "Mum and Dad'll kill me if they find out. We'll have to be careful about the empties."

Soon the party was in full swing. Mum had put me in charge of the music and I sat in the corner next to the Dansette sipping Tizer with Ray at my side. Just before 11 o'clock, I noticed that Phil had been missing for at least 10 minutes.

"I wonder where Phil could have got to," I said to Ray at last. He scanned the room and I saw a shadow pass over his face.

"Yeah … I wonder where my sister is."

I looked wistfully first at Ray and then past him towards the garden. My thoughts flew back to 100 moonlit rendezvous', rehearsed in my head in the spaces between night and day.

"Let's go outside … to look for them," I qualified, my eyes shining and my heart pounding in my chest.

We slipped out through the French windows into a pool of soft yellow light. Tonight there was no moon. The darkness was intense and the air was mild, damp and restless. The trees whispered and murmured like waves on a beach. This sea of darkness harboured tantalising opportunities with force to cloud my judgement and make me rash. Fascination, tinged with foreboding, was drawing me irresistibly into a current bound for Paradise or Purgatory, with only a kiss wanting to make the difference. Were my wild notions divine or deluded? The compulsion to find out was overwhelming. I took him by the hand.

As we stole down the garden, the opening riff from the Doors' 'Light my Fire' trickled into my ears and the Lizard King delivered his lines with a cool, sultry air.

Ray was first to speak. "I can smell something."

"It's the damp earth," I said dreamily. "It always smells like this at night."

"No, it's cigarette smoke." His tone was matter of fact. "It's coming from over there."

He veered off to the right, pulling me with him, stopped abruptly in front of the hedge that bordered the lane and put his lips close to my ear. I felt my knees give way but managed to remain upright.

"Listen," he whispered.

The sound of soft voices and muffled laughter could be plainly heard in the lane. I waited on in silence, hypnotised by the rhythmic, lilting bass line and the roaming passage of the jazzy organ along its length. The effect was intoxicating.

Eventually, Ray plucked a stick from the hedge, snapped it

audibly between his fingers, grinned and tugged me towards the bottom end of the garden.

"There," I said softly. "Let's hide over there by the barn."

We darted across the grass into the shadows and stood close together, our backs pressed against the cold steel. I leaned into his shoulder, taking exquisite delight in the smallest changes in pressure.

Presently the French windows opened with a faint click and a tall figure emerged, smoking a cigarette. Almost simultaneously, I discerned a female form clambering over the stile at the opposite corner of the garden and stepping lightly towards the house.

"Oh my Lord! It's Joanie," I said with unrestrained glee. "I thought it was your sister!"

Ray's relief was physical; instantaneously, I felt his whole body relax.

"Oh, thank Christ."

"Wait a minute, though," I said, craning my neck towards the patio to get a better view. "That's Jason."

"And …?"

"Well, if that's Jason," I continued, "who was behind the hedge with Joanie?"

Ray shrugged. "Does it matter?"

"Of course it matters!" I said, feigning exasperation.

"Well, Sherlock?" he said archly.

"Come … Ray, I've got a plan. We have to keep Jason talking."

In a trice, my quest for a kiss was forgotten. I grabbed his hand, walked briskly down the garden and stopped on the patio in front of Jason, who had wrapped his free arm around Joanie's trim waist. He looked from me to Ray and raised his eyebrows.

"My, you're a dark horse, Vicks," he said drolly.

"Jason, this is Ray. Ray, meet Jason," I said hurriedly. "Um … Ray's come up from London, haven't you Ray? Joanie, have you seen Phil? We've been looking for him everywhere," I continued, without pausing for breath.

Joanie turned a fetching shade of crimson and glared at me.

"I don't know what you're talking about, Vicky," she said icily. "Why would I know where Phil is?"

"Well … we thought we heard voices. We're sure we did, didn't we Ray?"

She tossed her head impatiently.

"Can we go inside now?" she said irritably, addressing Jason. "I'm freezing."

"No, let's stay out for a bit … can't we Jason?" I looked at him imploringly. "It's a lovely night … and Mum doesn't like smoking in the house … and I know everyone's doing it but … oh, please Jason. Ray doesn't want to go in yet, do you Ray?"

By now, Jason's suspicions were well and truly aroused. He turned to Ray.

"Um … I think I'll wait out a bit. What part of London d'you come from, mate?"

The boys slipped into easy conversation. Joanie shuffled her feet awkwardly, visibly perturbed. Eventually she tugged peevishly on his arm.

"For God's sake, Jason, come inside!" she said crossly. "I'm running out of patience!"

At that moment, Phil came out of the darkness, strolling casually down the garden from the stile corner. I looked pointedly at Jason, who broke off talking mid-sentence, turned on Phil and glared at him with a hostile expression on his face. Phil opened his mouth to speak.

Jason took a step forward, disengaged himself roughly from Joanie's clutching fingers and clenched and unclenched his fists. Then he threw off his jacket, strode across to Phil, grabbed him by the lapels, threw him sideways and pinned him to the wall. Joanie screamed and I shut my eyes hard. I heard the French windows open with a crash and Toni's voice crying, "Jason! Jason! Oh my God!" I opened my eyes.

Jason hesitated and stepped away, right into the path of the panic-stricken Toni, who squealed and tottered backwards. He spun round coolly and scooped her up. There was a moment's stunned silence.

"Now, hear me out." His tone was imperative and his face was close to hers.

Toni submitted meekly, as I knew she would. Her partiality for Jason was no secret to me. He picked up his jacket, placed it over her bare shoulders, put his arm around her protectively and took her inside. Ray took me by the hand, looked at me reproachfully and we followed them indoors.

"Well, that didn't go quite according to plan," I said abjectly. "I didn't bargain for his temper."

Ray smiled and handed me a Tizer.

"It might not turn out as bad as all that," he said reassuringly. "Look!"

Toni was seated close to Jason on the sofa, looking like the cat with the cream.

Much later, when we lay in bed comparing notes, I put the question to Toni.

"Well, did he kiss you?"

"Who? Jason? Of course he did! What about you?"

"Oh … I blew it," I said resignedly. "I got sidetracked."

"Never mind, Vicks, there's always tomorrow. Goodnight, sweetie."

Sunday morning dawned bright and clear. I woke early, feeling nervous and expectant. I had to make today count. Unable to relax, I washed, dressed and descended to the kitchen. Mum was feeding Rufus.

"Did you have a nice evening, love?" she said, looking up and smiling.

"Yeah, it was good. When are they going?"

"About midday, I believe. I'm doing a cooked breakfast and then I thought you might like to take Rufus for a walk. You can show Ray the lake."

The instant the words were out of her mouth, that familiar fluttery feeling welled up inside me. I trotted over and flung my arms round her neck.

"Oh, Mum, can I?" I cried passionately.

"Silly girl! I wasn't born yesterday. I'll see what I can do." She smoothed back my wayward hair and kissed me lightly on the head.

She was as good as her word. The moment the last piece of bacon had been devoured, she looked conspicuously at the clock on the wall.

"Michael, your father needs you. He's got some firewood wants shifting. Vicky, dear. Would you mind taking Rufus out this morning? You can take him down to the lake. Perhaps Ray might like to go with you. Do they have time, Anji?"

"Yeah, sure."

Michael opened his mouth to protest but Mum was ready with an answer.

"Now, don't argue Michael," she said firmly. "Chris has some drawings he needs to finish and Alan's seeing to the calves. There's no-one else can do it."

We tramped down the lane under a cloudless sky. A fresh wind blew from the east, chilling my face, tousling my hair and frolicking amongst the shambling avenue of assorted trees we passed between, which creaked and rustled in response. In a distant field, sheep bleated, a dog barked and a shepherd whistled his commands. The sun played amongst the overhanging branches, making patterns on the tarmac. The earth smelt damp from yesterday's rain. Soon we reached the lake.

"Wow, this is amazing!" Ray said, gaping in wonder at the glorious vista.

I pointed across the beautiful, blue water at the screes beyond.

"That's Whin Rigg," I said proudly. "Isn't it grand? You can climb right up it, not up the face of it of course; there's a path, you know."

"Have you been up it?" he asked, clearly impressed.

"Yeah, loads of times," I lied. Actually I had only climbed it twice. "You can walk along the bottom too. You have to be careful though. The water's very deep and it's a bit of a scramble. The rocks are bigger than they look from here; mostly boulders, like this one." I stepped lightly up onto an enormous rock at the water's edge and balanced on the highest point with my arms outstretched, showing off.

He surveyed the shingle, bent down and picked up a reddish-coloured stone.

"This one's pretty," he called across. "Would you like to see it?"

He mounted the boulder and dropped the stone gently into my palm but instead of retracting his hand, he held it aloft, alongside mine. As I passed the stone back he caught hold of my fingers. I started and wobbled. In an instant, his arm was round my waist.

"That was a neat stunt your sister pulled last night," he grinned.

"What stunt?" I said weakly, struggling to regain my composure and rueing my ineptness at such a critical point in my life.

He pulled a serious face and put on a deep, manly voice.

"Now, hear me out ..."

As I exploded into hysterics, he stopped my mouth with a long, lingering kiss – my first.

That night, as I lay in bed, Toni put the question to me.

"Well, did he kiss you?"

"Mmm ..." I said sleepily. "It was heavenly."

I closed my eyes and drifted off with a warm, fuzzy feeling in the pit of my stomach.

Chapter 5

A Day in the Life

Cinderdale Farm,
Strands, Seascale,
Cumberland.

2nd December 1967

Dear Ray,
I hardly know how to begin, I am so distraught. My two older brothers have both deserted me and the gap they have left is indescribably huge. I hardly ever see my sister anymore. She left school in the summer and got a job at the Scawfell Hotel in Seascale. She's always at work. When she's not, she's either painting her face or painting the town with Phil. They've patched up their differences following that awful business at her birthday party and Jason has gone crawling back to Joanie like a big fool. Michael is no consolation. He spends all his spare time with his head buried in his books. I HATE being the youngest. It's too bad

being stuck here at home while everyone else is off having fun.

Alan has turned his back on farming, left home and gone to a college in Lancaster. You'll remember that he had a fall-out with Dad last year. Dad thought his determination to become a PE teacher was nothing more than a case of 'jumping on the bandwagon'. There's a big drive in the North West at the moment to recruit teachers. I don't know if it's the same in London but it's all the rage up here. They're offering all sorts of incentives – money and suchlike – but I really do think Alan has got what it takes to make a success of it and it's not just a whim on his part. He's taking History as his second subject, which will impress you no doubt, being a keen historian. What will you do when you leave school next year?

At least Dad and Alan appear to have buried the hatchet (as I knew they would) and I do believe that Alan's success in the swimming arena in the spring made a difference.

I sighed, put down my pen and took a sip from the mug of hot, sweet tea at my side on the writing desk, nervously twisting the dainty silver-plated 'V' which hung around my neck on a fine chain and finding some solace in the comforting presence of this treasure which Ray had bestowed upon me on my 14th birthday last month. I gazed out of my bedroom window into the void that separated me from my two dear brothers. The mountains were silhouetted against the darkening December sky and the wind moaned around the old stone walls of the farmhouse.

* * *

Alan was a talented swimmer. Throughout his youth, he had been an enthusiastic and dedicated member of the Egremont Amateur Swimming Club. He practised three evenings a week and always did well in local competitions run by the Cumberland and Westmorland Swimming Association, lifting several cups and trophies. This year he had surpassed himself. His skill and speed in backstroke had won him a place in the finals of the North West Region Youth Championships, which were held in Liverpool in the spring. I had never been there before and could hardly contain my excitement before the event at the prospect of visiting the home town of the Beatles.

During the month of May, while Chris stayed at home to oversee the farm and Toni was working, Mum, Dad, Michael and I had made the trip to Liverpool with Alan to watch him compete. Since the venue was nearly three hours' drive away, we travelled down by car the night before. At 7.30, we checked into a small hotel on the outskirts of the city, dropped off our bags and then found a cheerful little fish and chip restaurant where we feasted at tables draped with red and white plastic tablecloths to the sound of Freddie and the Dreamers. We were served by an attractive, easy-mannered redhead with a Mary Quant haircut who announced herself as Caroline. While Alan stared with undisguised admiration at the flame-haired waitress, I pondered on the likelihood of Paul McCartney stopping by for a bite to eat, and put the question flippantly to Mum. She said he was probably touring. At 10 o'clock, I retired to my delightful little room on the first floor and snuggled under the pretty Paisley floral bedspread of yellow, salmon pink and olive, musing over the possibility of encountering Paul the following day at the Austin Rawlinson Sports Centre.

The next morning, after an early breakfast of bacon, sausage, eggs, fried tomatoes and buttered toast, we pulled up in the car park outside a smart new leisure centre that looked like a giant shoebox, situated in a suburb of Liverpool called Speke.

Inside the foyer, we parted company with Alan and made our way to the poolside seating area. After what seemed like an interminable period of time but which was, in reality, only about 45 minutes, the competition swung into action. Alan was competing in two events, the Boys 17/18 Years 100 metre Backstroke and Freestyle. To amuse ourselves while we waited for his turn to come, Michael and I tried to predict the outcome of each heat, awarding ourselves three points if we successfully guessed the winner, two points for second place, one point for third place and a deduction of one point if our 'man' came in last. Michael approached the game with customary scientific reasoning, choosing first and foremost the tallest competitor with the longest stroke length, then the thin swimmers based on the effect of streamlining, and if in doubt selected the competitors in the inside lanes due to the impact of water turbulence on the outside lanes. On the other hand, my predictions were typically subjective, based on the overall attractiveness of the male participants and the costume colour of the females. It goes without saying that Michael scored significantly higher than I did, my forfeit being the purchase during the break of the winner's prize – a Cadbury Picnic bar, which Mum made him share with me anyway.

At last Alan emerged from a doorway situated at the far end of the pool area and took his place in lane four.

"Ooh, look! He's on the inside," chirped Michael, waving his hand in the air in a vain attempt to catch his brother's attention.

At length a whistle sounded and they were off. Alan's backstroke was a force to be reckoned with in the eyes of the local swimming fraternity and as he made the first turn he was comfortably in front, maintaining a convincing lead down the whole of the second length. However, at the second turn he faltered, losing precious ground, and the competitor in lane two gained swiftly on him, overtaking him two-thirds of the way down the third length. Alan made a perfect flip turn a second or two behind the leader and the two swimmers raced down the pool towards the finishing line close to where we were seated, Alan advancing inch by inch until he was alongside his rival who was evidently beginning to tire. I held my breath while my heart beat wildly in my chest. At the halfway point they were neck and neck with 12 metres to go. Moments later, he had edged back into first place and won by a nose. We all clapped and cheered as if our lungs would burst. He hauled himself out of the pool, red-faced and panting hard, made his way over to us, flung himself against the barrier fronting the terraced seating area and grinned up.

"Nearly messed up," he gasped. "Lost it at the second turn ..."

"You're in the final!" I squeaked, bouncing up and down in my seat with unrestrained glee.

"Yeah ..." He paused, gulping down mouthfuls of air. "Won the battle ... not the war though, not yet."

Half an hour later, he was back at the poolside, this time competing in the 100 metre Freestyle event and hoping to duplicate his previous inspirational display of the finest backstroke in the competition so far. This time he was in lane six.

Michael groaned. "He'll have a tough time on the outside ..." His jaw dropped. "Oh my God, look at the size of that guy! He's gigantic!"

"Oh, don't be such a pessimist, Michael," I scolded. "Alan will be fine."

He did make a terrific start, holding second place for the whole of the first length, but he was no match for the leader, the incredibly tall youth whom Michael had already earmarked for a place in the final on the basis of his height alone. It transpired that his front crawl was as formidable as his stature and he flew through the water like a cruise missile, quickly gaining a sizeable lead. The end result was never in any doubt. Alan came in third, having been overtaken during the latter half of the race by the hunk in lane one, to whom I would have given my unadulterated support (as well as my heart) had it not been for the presence of my esteemed brother on the opposite side of the pool. Alan scrambled out of the pool, skirted round the end and leant heavily against the barrier beneath us, his chest heaving. He smiled up at us ruefully.

"Can't win 'em all," he said breathlessly, with an air of good-humoured resignation. "As soon as I saw Lurch over there, I knew it was probably a lost cause."

Soon it was lunchtime. We bought tea and sandwiches in the cafeteria and afterwards Michael and I resumed our game. This time I lost by a much smaller margin. As luck would have it, my Adonis won second prize in the 400 metre Freestyle event and, in two other events, the girls with the prettiest costumes came in first.

At around 2.30, the six finalists in the Boys 17/18 Years 100 metre Backstroke mustered at the poolside. This was Alan's only remaining race and his success in today's competition hinged on the outcome. He clambered down into lane two, an air of intense concentration on his face. The starting whistle pierced the air and he took off like a rocket.

"Look! He's first!" I squealed, half-covering my face. "I can't look."

He maintained his lead down the whole of the first length and we held our breath while he made a flawless first turn, but the competitor in lane three was beginning to close the gap and drew level as they approached the opposite end. At the second turn, his opponent performed a stunning flip turn and gained the advantage. Alan upped the stakes and temporarily regained first place but it was evidently costing him dear and as the two swimmers approached the final turn, there was nothing to choose between them. I perched on the edge of my seat with my feet suspended in the air, my shoulders hunched and my hands clasped tightly together, willing him to win. The synchrony with which they made their final flip turn would have been quite beautiful to witness in another situation. Alan gained the upper hand with 20 metres to go but looked spent. Then, to my utter dismay, the other boy streaked forward with a final burst of energy, overtook Alan during the closing seconds of the race and won by a hair's breadth.

Although I clapped and cheered dutifully, the applause had a hollow ring and I was overwhelmed with a sense of mortification. Hot tears pricked my eyes and I felt the corners of my mouth quiver as I threw Alan an encouraging smile; not that he was looking. He had remained in the pool with his head bowed, looking listlessly down into the water. After a minute or two, the winner strolled over, reached down and tapped him on the shoulder in a gesture of friendship. Alan looked up, nodded and scrambled out. The two boys approached our corner of the stand.

"Hi, I'm Richard. He's a great guy … brilliant!" he panted, slapping Alan on the back. "He's got the makings of a champion." He grinned at Alan. "One day you'll do something amazing."

Alan smiled weakly and thanked him but his eyes were red and puffy. I had never seen a boy cry before and I was at a loss as to what to say, so I reached over the barrier and stretched out my hand towards his. He took it gratefully and his shoulders shook with suppressed emotion. Eventually I found my tongue.

"You were fantastic", I said shakily. "Really you were. Second best in the whole of the North West …you'll be the best next time."

He sighed heavily.

"I don't think there'll be a next time. I've come to the conclusion I'm not a good loser." He yanked off his swimming hat and wiped his face with his arm. "Never mind," he added unevenly. "I got silver. That's good."

"It's more than good," I concurred, in spite of myself.

Dad descended to the poolside.

"Well done, lad," he said, shaking his son heartily by the hand. "You've made me the proudest dad in England!"

As Alan drifted back to the competitors' area, I shed a few silent tears. Mum leant down from the row behind.

"It's not the winning; it's the taking part," she said sympathetically. "Now, dry your eyes. We all need to be positive, for Alan's sake." She handed me a tissue.

"Yes, I know Mum, I know," I conceded, acutely conscious of this small act of kindness on the part of my mum, which made me cry all the more.

By the time the medals were presented, Alan had regained his composure and looked genuinely proud as he stood alongside the benevolent Richard, a worthy champion. I cheered myself hoarse, not just for Alan but also for the gorgeous guy who beat him into third place in his heat of the 100 metres Freestyle event, went on to gain a Bronze medal in the 400 metres Freestyle final and remained uppermost in my mind for at least a week afterwards.

* * *

I chewed thoughtfully at the end of my pen, trying hard to recall the face of the handsome young swimmer. It was just a distant memory now. Mum was listening to 'Sergeant Pepper' and the strains of 'A Day in the Life' drifted upstairs. I contemplated the chaotic orchestral bridge and bizarre vocal loop in the inner groove with apprehension, finding them both compelling and disconcerting.

* * *

Thursday 1st June 1967 was the day that changed music for this was the day that the magic of the Beatles' groundbreaking 'Sergeant Pepper's Lonely Hearts Club Band' LP was revealed to an expectant public. The launch of the Beatles' eighth studio album was almost tantamount to a national event and Chris was determined to secure himself a copy on the first day of release. He told me that morning that he had arranged to leave work early so he could make the trip into town to buy the LP. I eagerly awaited his return in a state of high excitement. What would the Fab Four come up with this time? In any case, it was bound to be good.

By dinnertime, there was no sign of Chris. Mum began to fret but Dad was unperturbed.

"He's probably met a mate for a drink," he said, "or got a flat tyre! Serve up, Marion."

I tried to cover up my disappointment but eventually it found its way to the surface.

"How could he do this to me?" I said sulkily. "He *knows* how much I was looking forward to hearing it. How am I going to face Sally tomorrow? Her dad got it this morning."

"For goodness sake, Vicky, stay up and listen to it later, if you must … only stop fussing. I'm sure he'll be back soon," said Mum in a brisk, offhand manner which belied her true state of mind.

Eight o'clock came and went, then nine o'clock and still there was no sign of Chris. At 9.30 Mum sent me upstairs to get ready for bed. By this time she was pacing the floor in a state of distress. Dad maintained a stoic calm, reasoning that there must be a perfectly simple explanation. After all, the pubs were still open.

Just before 10 o'clock, I heard the sound of the key in the door with infinite gratitude, rushed downstairs and flung my arms round my big brother's neck.

"All right, Vicks, don't smother me," he said with a hint of impatience in his voice, pushing me gently back. His eyes were bright and his face flushed.

"You've been drinking! Oh Chris, how *could* you?" I felt my temper rise.

He shrugged. "I guess I just got carried away." His voice lacked its usual warmth. I put it down to the effects of alcohol.

"You promised …" I cried petulantly.

"Yeah … well … things happen," he said indifferently, skirting around me and heading off towards the kitchen.

I burst into tears and ran upstairs, sobbing. He turned on his heels, strode up behind me and caught hold of my arm as I reached for the handle to my bedroom door. I wriggled free and averted my face.

"Oh Vicky, I *am* sorry, really I am, but I couldn't help it. Something came up. I'll explain later." He gave my shoulder a friendly squeeze.

I sniffed and wiped my eyes on the back of my hand.

"Can we listen to it now, please? Mum said I could."

"All right, come on," he said indulgently. "Only don't expect me to be much company. I'm feeling rather tired."

In actual fact, I had never seen him looking so alive, but I wisely decided not to overplay my hand.

The following night, Chris was in high spirits again. He hummed tunelessly, made small talk with the farmhands and laughed outright at Dad's bad jokes.

On Saturday morning, when I arrived in the kitchen at breakfast time, he was in conversation with Mum.

"I'll be out all day. I have to work."

"Oh, that's a shame dear," said Mum complaisantly. "What time will you be back?"

"I … I don't know … quite late I should think … before dinner."

"It's ridiculous, Chris," I said peevishly. "It's your day off! Can't you at least work from home?"

"Sorry, Vicks. They need me at the office." He smiled wryly. "I guess I'm just … indispensable." He grabbed his jacket. "See you later, sweetie. By the way, good morning costs nothing," he added, kissing me on the forehead on the way past.

"Urgh … you're wearing scent," I exclaimed, screwing up my nose.

He winked and hurried out with a feverish air, which seemed incongruous in a man with such a placid and easygoing nature. I sat down thoughtfully.

"You know, Mum, he's confusing me. He's acting all peculiar."

Mum looked perplexed. "He does seem to be behaving rather oddly." Then she brightened. "I'm sure it will pass. Perhaps he's in line for a promotion."

Chris was true to his word and just before dinner he arrived home with his files tucked under his arm wearing an air of suppressed excitement. This time, he tried hard to mask it but I was convinced that he had something up his sleeve. With characteristic honesty, I tackled him in the kitchen over a late evening cocoa.

"Chris, where have you been today?"

"I've been at work … I told you."

"That thing you were going to explain … what was that, then?"

"Just work, that's all."

"But you were drunk!"

"No I wasn't, silly! Just tired."

"Chris …"

He cut me short. "Vicky, leave it, right! It's just work, okay?"

Something in his bearing warned me not to overstep the mark.

"Pardon me, sorry I asked," I retorted, under my breath. Snatching up my cocoa, I stomped upstairs moodily and shut myself in my bedroom to ponder on the sudden fluctuations in his usually even temperament.

Over the next few weeks, Chris came home late regularly, usually on a Tuesday and Thursday, and spent most Saturdays 'at the office'. He took great pains over his appearance. He was touchy and irritable when questioned on the subject of his whereabouts. He hardly saw Janice at all. At the end of June, he made a shock announcement that he and Janice had decided to have a temporary break from each other while he 'got his head straight'.

One Tuesday evening in early July, when I was bemoaning his absence from the dinner table again, a chance comment by Michael tapped into a memory and provided the catalyst.

"You rely on him much too much, Vicky," he teased. "You'll have to get used to living without him one day, you know. He'll fall in love, get married and then what will you do?"

The instant the words were out of his mouth, my mind raced back to the events of World Cup night when Chris had revealed a part of his nature which I had never seen before or since. I recalled the girl in the garden who had bewitched Chris and who had been the cause of his odd humour and dismissive attitude towards Janice. The pieces of the puzzle started to fall into place and I determined to have it out with him that night.

To divert my parents' suspicion, I went to bed at the usual time and then lay awake for what seemed like an eternity waiting for his familiar step on the stairs. When at last my patience was gratified, I crept out of bed, slipped on my dressing gown and quietly opened the bedroom door.

"Chris, Chris," I hissed. "I need to talk to you."

"What? Now?" he said, shaking his head wearily.

"Yes now!"

"As you wish," he said briefly, shrugging his shoulders.

I tiptoed across the hall and followed him into his room.

"Chris, I know what's bugging you …"

"No you don't," he interjected, cutting me short. "You don't know anything."

"I know what it's like to be in love."

"What, with Ray? That's a crush," he laughed bitterly. "That's not real love."

I felt piqued at his irreverence and want of tact but I was determined to keep hold of my advantage.

"Aha, so you admit it then!" I crowed triumphantly.

He looked at me in blank astonishment.

"You've fallen in love." I pressed my case home remorselessly.

His hesitation was telling.

"I'm in love with Janice, if that's what you mean," he said eventually, without a morsel of conviction in his voice.

"Oh Janice! You've barely spoken to her for weeks. I don't think so!"

His colour rose. "Don't try my patience," he said in a voice steeped with quiet authority, which I chose to ignore this time. I crossed my fingers firmly inside the sleeves of my dressing gown.

"No, not Janice; the other girl, the one at the cottage," I declared recklessly.

The instant the words were uttered, his face was transformed. Defiance gave way to surprise, which melted into dejection. The picture was complete. He sat down heavily on the bed and his eyes glistened. For the second time in a matter of months, I found myself face to face with a crying man. I sidled up alongside him and leant my head against his shoulder.

"How did you know?" he asked, his voice wavering.

"I didn't. I guessed," I said simply.

"I met her in the record shop on the day I was late home. It was an accident. I'd almost forgotten her. We were both buying Sergeant Pepper's." He smiled wistfully. "I thought 'now's my moment'. I knew I had to act. I might never see her again and I reasoned 'oh well, it's fate'. I told her I thought I'd seen her somewhere before, which must have sounded really corny, but it worked. She didn't remember me at first but then when I reminded her that I brought her dad home from the pub on World Cup night she said she remembered who I was. I asked her if she wanted to go for a drink, there and then like. She said no at first but then I pressed her and she said she'd stay for just one. We talked and talked and talked. Then it got quite late and she started to panic. She called her dad and told him her car had got a flat battery so she'd decided to stay in town for something to eat and come home later. Then we went for a meal."

"You liar, you said you were working!" I said, in mock indignation, my overwhelming sense of relief gaining the upper hand over my mortification at having been kept in the dark for the last five weeks by my cherished confidant. "I shall never believe you again!"

"So we agreed to meet again on the Saturday," he continued.

"... and all the other times you said you were working, I suppose ..."

"Yeah, that's right."

"Why all the secrecy?"

He hesitated. "It's complicated."

"What's complicated about it? You like her. She likes you. Janice ... oh no, wait a minute ... she's not married, is she?"

"Crikey, no!" He laughed out loud, then resumed a melancholy cast. "It's her father. He won't like it, you know. It's not his fault, he has his reasons. She's all he's got and he's not getting any younger. He puts an awful lot of pressure on her, not on purpose, but he does. She told him she's been doing private tuition – she's a music teacher so it was easy – but I don't know how we're going to broach it with him. It really is hopeless. Maybe we should just forget it."

Somewhere in the back of my mind, another light went on.

"Did you say she's a music teacher? What's her name?"

"Julie."

"Oh my goodness, I know her Dad!"

Chris stared at me in utter disbelief. "*What*?"

"I know her Dad," I repeated. "He's a poppet."

"Definitely *not* the same person," Chris said in a tone of finality.

"No, it is really," I insisted. "They live up at Wasdale Head."

"Well, I'll be damned."

"Oh, I admit, he was a bit scary at first," I said with a knowledgeable air, casting my mind back to our first meeting, when Rufus and Shirley nearly came to blows, "but he's nice really. I'll talk to him … if you want."

"Don't you dare!" His face hardened as he uttered these words of warning; then became mellow again under the countereffect of his mild and trusting nature. "I guess it all depends whether you're trying to steal his daughter from him," he said sadly. "There's the rub."

"So, what are you going to do?"

"Oh Vicky, I don't know. I don't even know what I want. Here, you won't tell anyone, will you?"

"Why not? You've got nothing to hide."

"I promised Julie, that's all. If her dad finds out, there'll be hell to pay. Please, Vicky."

"Oh all right, I'll keep your secret," I sighed reluctantly.

"That's settled then. Now go to bed and don't worry about me; I'll be fine." He hugged me tight. "Janice does have her horses," he added, in deference to his former sweetheart, for whom he felt genuinely sorry. "She'll be all right."

I got up and walked towards the door. As I reached for the handle, I stopped and turned.

"Thanks, Chris," I said, feeling a lump rise in my throat. "I'm glad we cleared the air. If there's anything I can do ..."

He shook his head.

July and August rolled by in much the same manner as June. Chris maintained the pretext of a project at work while I feigned an attitude of complete ignorance. At first it was hard to uphold the subterfuge, especially when forced to witness my parents' misdirected conjectures on a regular basis. It was harder still to feign an air of indifference when Mr. Blane complained, on one of our rambles, that he never saw his daughter anymore because she was always out doing private tuition. Eventually, the dust settled and Chris and Julie's frequent absences from the family home became commonplace and unexceptional. Mum and Dad put Chris's mood swings down to nervous strain brought on by overwork and advised him not to 'overdo it'.

In early September, Alan packed his suitcase and departed for St. Martin's College in Lancaster, where he had rented lodgings. It was a sad day, but nothing could prepare me for the sadness I was to experience less than three months later.

During the autumn, Chris announced his intention to go to the UK Package Tour featuring the Jimi Hendrix Experience, Pink Floyd, the Move, Amen Corner and the Nice and compered by Radio One DJ Pete Drummond. The show was coming to Blackpool on the 25th November and he planned to travel down with a 'mate' and stay overnight in a guesthouse. Alarm bells clanged in my head like harbingers of doom and I shot him a meaningful glance, laden with disapprobation.

10 minutes later, I was at his bedroom door, tapping urgently.

"What d'you want?" he called out frostily from the other side, guessing correctly at the motive for my intrusion.

I opened the door, slipped inside his room and closed it softly. He was lounging on his bed, reading a book.

"You're sleeping with her!" I said angrily.

"She's not a '*her*', her name is Julie," he said acrimoniously, without looking up.

"You're mad!" I persisted.

He threw me an exasperated look and continued to read.

I marched across the room, grabbed the book from his hand and threw it on the floor.

His face darkened. "Vicky, I'm 19 years old. I don't need my kid sister telling me how to run my life," he said, his voice taut with constraint.

My eyes smarted at the rebuke. I walked over to the window and stared out vacantly at the blurry landscape, too upset to leave the room. The ticking of the bedside clock marked the lapse of several minutes. At length, he came and stood alongside me and put a protective arm round my shoulder.

"I know what I'm doing. It's all sorted out." He spoke with tenderness and compassion.

"What d'you mean, sorted out?" I mumbled, miserably.

"You'll see. We'll be careful."

His remark was well meant but ill-judged. It bore an implication that left little in doubt and for the first time I was forced to confront the baser elements of my revered brother's nature. Tears welled up in my eyes and trickled down my cheeks.

"Don't cry, love," he said soothingly. "I don't understand why you're so upset."

"I thought you were different but you're just like all the rest!" I burst out. "It's all about *her!*"

He looked at me incredulously. "Vicky, are you jealous?"

"Of course I'm jealous," I wailed, leaning round and throwing myself sideways into his chest.

He wrapped me up in his arms and held me close.

"Silly girl! You'll always be my favourite sister. Nothing can change that."

In the early morning on Saturday 25th November, before I woke up, Chris left the house with a small suitcase. During the night that followed, I slept fitfully. On Sunday I felt tense and edgy, wishing away the hours while I awaited his return. Late in the afternoon, I heard the familiar sound of the key in the door with infinite relief. I leapt up from the kitchen table and ran to the door. Chris swept me up and covered my face with affectionate kisses.

"Vicky, there's someone I want you to meet," he said breathlessly, grinning broadly and dragging me outside through the front door by the arm.

The car door opened and a tall, brown-haired girl stepped elegantly over to me. She held out her hand, smiling.

"This is my wife, Julie."

Chapter 6

Sarah

"Your wife?" Mum said shrilly, staggering backwards and clutching at the edge of the kitchen table to steady herself. "Your wife?" she repeated in a tone of utter disbelief, staring open-mouthed at the nervous young woman who stood meekly at Chris's side with her hand outstretched.

Chris took a step forward.

"Yes Mum," he said evenly. "We were married yesterday." She looked at him mutely. "*Mum?*"

She started, held out her hand mechanically and clasped the fingers of her daughter-in-law in an awkward handshake.

"Gracious, I must tell your father," she mumbled, turning away and heading absent-mindedly towards the back door, but stopping short. "Oh dear, where are my manners?" She turned back and advanced towards the newlyweds, smiling stiffly. "I'm sorry, Julie. Would you like a cup of tea?"

"Yes please, Mrs. Kelly, I'd love one." Julie's intonation was soft, low-pitched and musical.

"Sit down, I'll put the kettle on."

"Thank you, that's very kind of you … if it's no trouble," replied Julie in a voice that was hesitant and apologetic.

Mum pulled out a chair and there was an uncomfortable silence while she fumbled with the tea things, visibly shaken but doing her best not to reveal the extent of her discomfiture.

"Did you have a good journey?" I volunteered helpfully, acutely conscious of both Julie's embarrassment and my mother's high agitation.

"Yes, we had a good run, didn't we, Chris?" Julie answered, brightening. "We drove up from Blackpool this afternoon. It only took two and a half hours."

"Do you have a car?" I asked, not really caring either way but anxious to prolong the conversation and thus eliminate the possibility of another uneasy pause.

"A small one … a Hillman Imp …but I haven't got it with me, it's at home."

Mum pricked up her ears. "Where's home?" she asked more kindly, valiantly suppressing her perturbation and seeing an opportunity to put at ease the unassuming young bride, whose apprehensive and deferential bearing she found rather touching, in spite of herself.

"I live up at Wasdale Head … with my father."

"Oh! Then you'll be the young miss who teaches music at Gosforth Primary," Mum exclaimed. "Your father's a great favourite of Vicky's … isn't he, dear?" she said, addressing me.

I grinned self-consciously. "Oh yes, he's absolutely charming."

Julie and Chris exchanged significant glances.

"He speaks very highly of you too, you know, Vicky," Julie smiled. "He spends an awful lot of time on his own and he really appreciates your company. You really are so very kind to him … I'm a peripatetic teacher, you know, Mrs. Kelly," she continued, turning round in her seat to speak to my mother. "I don't work just at one school, I work at lots of different schools.

I travel about … hence the Hillman Imp," she added, with a nod towards me.

"That's nice. What do you teach? I mean, what instrument?"

"I teach piano and violin mainly, and a little singing."

"I used to play when I was a little girl … the piano, that is. I wasn't very good though," continued Mum conversationally. "Do you have a favourite piece?"

"I love Rachmaninoff's Second Piano Concerto, but it's quite difficult to play … and doesn't sound very good without the orchestra!" she laughed. "I prefer to listen to it. The second movement is exquisite." She paused thoughtfully. "I like to play Chopin Nocturnes on the piano; my favourite is Opus Nine, Number Two. It's a beautiful piece."

"Yes, beautiful," echoed Mum, pleased to have found a little common ground with her new daughter-in-law. "Quite beautiful! Do you like the Preludes?"

They continued in this vein for several minutes, while Mum prepared the tea.

"Sugar?"

"No thanks, just milk please."

Mum passed a cup of hot, steaming tea to Julie, her hand still quivering from the effects of Chris's shock announcement.

At length, Mum turned her attention towards her son. "You'd better break the news to your father. He'll not be best pleased. No offence, Julie, but this is all rather sudden. Chris has never even mentioned you before and now you're … well … part of the family. Clearly you're a nice girl but … well, it's going to take a bit of getting used to, that's all."

"Mum, please don't blame Julie." Chris looked beseechingly at our mother. "It was entirely my idea. I'll explain everything later. Where's Dad?" he added glumly.

"Oh, out the back somewhere," said Mum vaguely, waving towards the back door. "You'd better tread carefully. He likes to have his own way. You know all that trouble we had with Alan and the college. I'm sorry, excuse me, girls." She averted her face and made a hasty exit.

"Oh dear, I think we might have upset your Mum," said Julie anxiously, as soon as Mum was out of earshot. "I feel terrible."

"She likes you," I said reassuringly. "I'm sure she does. Have you told your dad?"

Julie swallowed hard. "No, not yet; I'm going to have to break it to him tonight. It's probably best if I go on ahead on my own. Chris can join me in the morning."

"Join you? Why? Where are you going? Where are you going to live?" I hadn't even thought about that.

"With Father, of course, I can't possibly leave him, it's out of the question," she said candidly. "He'd be devastated. He couldn't possibly cope without me."

A few minutes later, Mum came back in, red-eyed but looking more composed, and we drank our tea. Julie told Mum of her intention to return home on her own that evening and about their plans to live up at the Head with her father. After a while, she looked at her watch.

"Gosh, is that the time! I have to be getting along soon, Father will be worried, but I'd really like to meet Mr. Kelly before I go."

"Yes, of course. Where has that son of mine got to? Vicky, would you be a darling and go and find them?"

I scurried out and tried the cowshed first. Then I headed towards the barn. As I approached the open door, I was arrested by the sound of my brother's voice.

"Come on Dad, you might at least come and say hello to the poor girl," he was pleading, barely able to conceal his frustration.

"I'll come when I'm good and ready, and not before," Dad retorted gruffly.

I entered coyly, baulking at the prospect of my Dad's likely reaction to the purpose of my errand. His face was red and angry.

"Oh, it's you," he said severely. "I gather you're a part of this conspiracy. Why didn't you tell me about it before? Do you have an inkling of what your conniving has led to? You're a very silly girl! He's married now and it can't be changed. Oh well, he's made his bed, he must lie on it, I suppose."

My eyes filled with tears. "Oh Dad, how *could* you? Weren't you ever in love with Mum? Or was it so long ago, you've forgotten what it feels like?" I cried passionately. In my mind's eye, I saw Ray perched alongside me on 'our rock', his face close to mine.

Chris walked over and put his arm round my shoulder protectively.

"Don't lay into Vicky. I swore her to secrecy. She's had a terrible time keeping stumm."

Dad scowled and shook his head disapprovingly. "Well, what do you want?" he barked.

"Julie needs to go soon," I mumbled. "She wants to meet you ... but if you're too busy ..."

"Oh all right, all right. I suppose I'd best meet the woman since we're stuck with her!"

He threw down his shovel. "Well go on, what are you waiting for? I said I'd come."

I looked despairingly at Chris, tugged on his arm and we left the barn. As soon as we were out of earshot, I opened my mouth to speak but Chris intercepted me.

"I'm really sorry, Vicky, I never meant to let on. It just came out. Now he's angry with you too."

I shrugged.

"I've made a real mess of things," he continued despondently.

"No you haven't, it'll be all right, you'll see." Deep down, I was a romantic soul who found it hard not to believe in the notion that love conquers all.

A few minutes later, Dad stomped indoors without a word, pulled off his boots and surveyed the visitor critically. She rose and approached him timidly. He responded with a rough handshake and a cursory greeting, excused himself and disappeared upstairs.

"Don't mind Robert," said Mum, seeking to reassure the bewildered girl, whose pretty manners and refined tastes had already made a strong impression on her. "He's rather crusty, I'm afraid, but he's a good man."

"Just like my father," smiled Julie, putting on her coat. She bid Mum a cordial adieu and floated out, kissing me lightly on the cheek and leaving the sweet scent of lily of the valley in my hair.

I wondered at the remarkable contrast between this delicate young thing and the spirited and irrepressible Janice, and hoped my brother had made the right choice.

"Why did you do it?"

Chris was in his room packing his belongings into an old, brown trunk. Dinner had been a tense affair, during which the subject of his marriage was barely touched upon. There had followed a prolonged discussion between Chris and our parents in the privacy of the front room.

"Shut the door, Vicky." He beckoned me over and we sat down side by side on the bed.

"Why didn't you marry Janice? She's so friendly and easy-going. I mean … I'm sure Julie's very nice but … oh, I don't know … she's different."

Chris shook his head impatiently. "I could never have married Janice. She's a great girl but she's *so* overbearing. She'd suffocate me."

"But why did you *marry* Julie? It's so … final."

"Lots of reasons; Janice for one. Mum and Dad were dead set on the match. I don't know what they hoped to gain by it, probably Duffy's farm, but maybe I'm being too harsh. Anyway, every time I expressed any reservations, and believe me I had plenty, they just shouted me down – 'oh but she'll make a great wife – she's such a good cook – she's so capable – you've known her all your life – she *really* likes you!' When we broke up back in the summer, Mum insisted it was only temporary and even went so far as to tell the Duffys I'd be round to make it up with their daughter in less than a week! They'd never have agreed to my marrying Julie. It would have been a case of 'Are you sure? Have you really thought about it?' Man, they've been asking me that for the last hour and I'm already hitched! They're *so* intractable, Dad especially. Take Alan. It took months for Dad to come round after the fiasco over college; in the end it was only when Alan got a place that Dad agreed to it. It was a 'fait accompli', just like my marriage."

"They only want what's best for you," I said defensively.

"Oh I know that, but they don't *know* her. She's *amazing*."

The superlative stung and the half-filled trunk intensified the feeling, a mixture of anger and grief.

"You might have tried," I said sullenly.

"Oh, but that wasn't the only reason. You see, Julie's dad is ludicrously possessive and no man can ever hope to be deemed good enough for his prize. This way, he can't argue. He *is* on his own and … well, he's been married twice. Life hasn't been kind to him, he's embittered and takes a dim view of relationships generally. He'd never have agreed to it. She hasn't told him anything about me yet. She'll have to do it tonight though; I'm moving in tomorrow." He smiled wryly, then reached forward and hugged me impetuously. "Thank goodness for you!" he said warmly. "You'll certainly soften the blow. I don't know that I could have done it without you to back me up."

"*Back you up!*", I cried, horrified.

"Well, not as such. It's my problem, but you being my sister will certainly take the edge off it. He adores you!" He hesitated. "And then there was the other thing." His colour rose and he twisted the gleaming gold band on his finger back and forth abstractedly. "Julie doesn't believe in sex before marriage and … well … a man's got needs. I'm certain she's the girl for me … and I couldn't wait. Neither could she, for that matter," he added smugly.

"Oh Chris, you *really* didn't need to tell me that!" I exclaimed in mock astonishment.

"We *have* been rather rash, I suppose," he conceded. "It was a spur of the moment decision three weeks ago. We had a bit too much to drink and thought, well why not? So we gave notice the very next day and got married on Saturday because that meant we could stay overnight at Blackpool after the roadshow."

"Well, at least you got married first," I said with an air of resignation. "I thought … well, you know what I thought."

"Yes, I remember," he chuckled. "You were mortified by what you thought was my lack of propriety but, you know, sometimes I get tired of conforming even though deep down I'm a traditionalist. To be honest I got a bit of a kick out of doing something outrageous but entirely proper at the same time. I wanted to pull off the ultimate stunt."

"It was a cruel stunt," I said doggedly. "I wanted to be a bridesmaid."

"Never mind, there's always Toni," he quipped. "She'll be married before she's 20, and you can bet there'll be a sprog in the frame!"

"Now Chris, that's wicked!" I slapped him playfully on the leg and rose to take my leave.

* * *

Wasdale Head is a pocket of stark contrast. When the weather is fine, it is serene. Loveliness abounds, evinced in the diversity of the pastoral landscape, the soft chatter of Lingmell Beck, the twitter of birds and the bleating of the Herdwick sheep. Conversely, its location on the western fringe of the Lake District makes it highly susceptible to the caprice of the climate and the threat of inclement weather is never far behind. In a breath, this eden can be transformed into a grim and inhospitable place. When the rain hisses mercilessly down and an ill-tempered wind moans over the col at Beck Head, the prospect is unremittingly bleak.

At the head of the lake is a parking area popular with hikers and beyond it the lane traces its way amongst lush, green water meadows where sheep and cattle graze in the lee of the fells. The valley is flanked to the west by Yewbarrow with Kirk Fell behind, and to the east by Lingmell, but it is the omnipresent Great Gable up ahead that commands the view. It soars skywards, an immense pyramid of volcanic rock carved by the primitive hands of nature. It is a many-faceted beast, its lower slopes amiable and verdant, its upper face sheer, harsh and uncompromising and its apex a delightful little plateau bearing a crown of naked rock. It is undisputed lord of Wasdale and gatekeeper to the uplands. The road heads north east, ascending gently and terminating at its foot.

In this remote enclave, under the shadow of Kirk Fell and tucked behind the broad shoulder of Lingmell, is an old rectangular stone dwelling. This is Lingmell Old Stead. It is a pretty place, symmetrical in design, with whitewashed walls, forest green window frames and a grey slate roof, which set off the profusion of flowers and foliage that crowd the little front garden and encroach onto the path. The property is bordered on all four sides by moss-covered dry stone walling and is entered via a small porch protruding from the centre between the two downstairs windows.

Chris's reception into this, his new home, was lukewarm at best. My prior acquaintance with the frosty personage of Mr. Blane must have helped a little, but it would be a long time before the reckless effrontery with which the young upstart had gained a place at the old man's hearth would begin to recede in the mind of Julie's father, who would persist in regarding him as a usurper of his daughter's affection for many months to come. A few days after his departure, I received an invitation from Chris, begging me to come and partake of lunch the following Sunday. He hinted that it might provide a welcome respite from the censorious gaze and disparaging comments he had been subjected to by the remorseless old fellow.

Chris looked careworn, but dinner passed pleasantly enough and Julie was evidently a great homemaker. After dessert I joined her in the kitchen to help with the washing up, leaving Mr. Blane dozing by the fire while Chris went out to chop wood.

"I'm sorry about Father," Julie said gravely. "I feel I ought to tell you the reason we did what we did, and why he's taken it so hard."

"I don't want to impose."

"It's all right. It's no secret, just not something we talk about much. It all happened a long time ago, some of it a long time before I was born. Dad was the youngest of three boys and when he was 12 he lost both his older brothers within a short space of time in the Great War. He idolised his brothers and he was devastated. His father died a year later, of a broken heart they say, and that just left him and his mother, who was German, just to complicate matters. He was devoted to her but it didn't win him any friends, as you can imagine. He got married in his mid-twenties, 1930 I think it was, and he had a son soon after that but his wife and child were killed in the Blitz. Sometimes he says he wished he'd died at home with his family rather than survived on the front line. I don't think he's ever completely got over it. During the conflict, he was shot in the knee and ended up in a military hospital where he met my mother. She was a nurse, 20 years younger than him and very pretty. They got married at the end of the War and that's where I come in … but she's gone now."

"Gone?"

"Yes, just gone. Let's talk about something else."

There was an awkward silence while I fumbled for something to say. Julie didn't appear to notice. She seemed to be lost in thought.

"How did you come to live here?" I enquired, eventually.

"We came down from Glasgow at the beginning of last year after my grandmother died, that's the German lady. We'd been living with her up there for a couple of years and she left Father everything she owned. He sold the house and bought this place. He liked the isolation. He doesn't mix well and seems to view most of the human race with a mixture of hostility and scorn. It's a shame his perspective is so narrow; he's his own worst enemy in that respect. However, once you've won him over, there's nothing he won't do for you … apart from sanction your marriage," she added with an uneasy laugh. "I think it's time I introduced him to your family."

"Yes, that would be nice," I concurred. "I'll talk to Mum."

Christmas being only three weeks away, it was decided that Julie's father might be persuaded to spend Christmas Day at the Kellys with his daughter and son-in-law. The alternative was altogether too awful for my poor, harangued brother to contemplate. Under the combined force of his persevering daughter and myself, Mr. Blane finally capitulated and I waited for the big day with a good deal of excitement tinged with not a little foreboding. Alan arrived home a week before Christmas, extolling the joys of college life, including an introduction to the Queen Mother who attended the official opening of the college in November and planted a commemorative tree in the grounds. Toni managed to get Christmas Day off.

The guests arrived around midday and Dad poured everybody a drink. Mr. Blane looked dapper in tweeds and Julie wore a white peasant dress which lent her the aspect of an angel. We made a cheerful little party.

"Please call me Uncle Liam," said Mr. Blane to me as he sipped his port. "Of course, I'm not a real uncle but you're one of the family now, so let's drop the formalities, shall we?"

I coloured and said I would try.

Presently, Alan breezed in brandishing an empty glass.

"Top up, Dad, make it snappy!" Quite suddenly, he stopped in his tracks and, devouring the pretty countenance and sylph-like figure of his lovely sister-in-law, he gave a low whistle. "Oh …er … hi Julie. Well, well, Chris. You've hit the jackpot. My oh my, d'you have a sister?"

The instant the words were out of his mouth, he perceived that he had made a blunder of catastrophic proportions. Julie's face froze, but only for an instant. The glass she was holding fell from her hand and smashed to pieces on the floor. She recovered herself, breathed an apology and looked over at her father, who was trembling visibly. Chris walked cautiously across to his father-in-law, patted him on the arm and offered him a means of escape via the back door, signalling to me to follow him outside. Then he escorted his shell-shocked wife out of the kitchen and upstairs to the sanctity of his old room.

The day was bright, crisp and sunny. From where I was standing, I saw Uncle Liam cast his watery eyes to the crystal clear heavens and the words formed on his lips … "Oh, Sarah, Sarah." I crept to his side, wrapped my arms round his thin frame, stretched up and pressed my cheek against his neck.

"Who's Sarah?" I whispered.

"Sarah was my daughter, Julie's sister," he murmured. "She passed away five years ago. She was only 10. She succumbed to a rare strain of meningitis. There was nothing they could do. I do so miss her." He leaned back and looked into my face. "You're a lot like her, you know. She was bonny too. She would have been about your age."

I looked back down the years at the trail of devastation that had plagued the life of this troubled soul and wondered, not for the first time, what had happened to Julie's mother.

"Oh, you poor old man," I blurted out, my voice brimming with pathos. "You had a son, too, and …" I checked myself, not wishing to trespass onto unchartered territory.

"Yes, I had a son. His name was Oliver. He would have been 34 if he'd lived."

"Well, you've got another one now," I said soothingly, in a clumsy attempt to console him.

"Yes, I know all that, but the capacity to love has been beaten out of me by life's ravages. Every shred of trust in me has been destroyed. She's all I've got left and she needs protecting at all costs." He waved his hand towards the house. I took hold of it and gave it a squeeze.

"You're freezing. Come inside and warm yourself by the fire."

"I'll try to love him," he said ruefully, as we reached the door.

We went indoors and presently the young couple came downstairs, Julie looking calm and relaxed. The rest of the day went without a hitch. We had roast goose with all the trimmings and sang carols around the piano, which Julie played with skill and passion that Mum could never hope to emulate. Then we opened our presents. Uncle Liam loved the photograph of his dog Shirley which I presented proudly in a roughly constructed frame fashioned from small pieces of driftwood I had found on the beach at Seascale. He gave me a stylish red beret, which he had clearly sent his daughter out to choose. We played charades before tea and watched the Ken Dodd Christmas Show on TV after it. At 10 o'clock, Uncle Liam drained his glass and turned to Mum.

"Well, Marion, that was the best Christmas Day I've had for as long as I can remember. Thank you for making me so welcome. Come along youngsters, I'm for my bed."

The fairer sex were all rewarded with hugs, even the unsuspecting Toni who met his advances with a combination of amusement and alarm. The men received a warm handshake and Uncle Liam took pains to ensure that Alan was relieved of the guilt he so plainly felt on account of his sledgehammer wit.

* * *

After that, I became a frequent visitor at Wasdale Head, forming a strong attachment with my new sister-in-law, whom I discovered to be an affectionate, equable and self-possessed young woman. In the spring in 1968, Julie announced that she was expecting a baby at Christmas. Mum's joy was unbounded, whilst Dad greeted the news with dubious pleasure. During the summer, relations between Chris and Uncle Liam improved, assisted by the exciting prospect of the new arrival, the developing ability on the part of both parties to exercise some degree of magnanimity and forbearance and Julie's excellent mediatory skills. Chris bent over backwards to make himself useful and Uncle Liam was eventually forced to concede that it was hard to find fault with him.

Michael passed his 'O' levels with flying colours and became the first family member to embark on 'A' levels, gaining a place at the local sixth form college. By now, Dad had abandoned all hope of passing on the farm to his errant sons and let Michael have his way. Michael's plan was to specialise in Biology, Chemistry and Geography, win a university place and pursue a career in environmental science.

Meanwhile, I entered fourth year and started my 'O' level studies. On my 15th birthday in October, Ray sent me a Parker fountain pen and a Fidji eau de toilette miniature.

* * *

On Saturday 21st December, I set off in the morning on foot to pay a call on my brother and sister-in-law at the Head, wearing a stout pair of walking boots, duffle coat, scarf and the beret that Uncle Liam had given me last Christmas. There was a stiff breeze blowing from the west, the cloud hung low over the fells and snow was expected, but I was wrapped up warmly. I tripped along, feeling light at heart. School had finished, at least for the next fortnight, Alan would be home tonight and Ray had recently made a promise to visit next summer once his 'O' level exams were over and the pressure was off. The five-and-a-half mile journey was completed without incident and the snow held off. I was greeted at the door by a heavily pregnant Julie who looked radiant and happy.

"Hi, how's things? How are you feeling?" I asked, discarding my outdoor gear and warming my hands by the log fire.

"Terrific, thanks," she replied gaily, "only I do wish this baby would hurry up and put in an appearance. I've still got a week to go and everything's such an effort."

"Careful what you wish for," grinned Chris, leaning over the bannisters.

She sat down heavily. "Oh sorry, would you like some tea?"

"I'll do it, you stay put." I hastened to the kitchen, where I found Uncle Liam putting on his wax jacket with Shirley scampering at his feet. "Hello Uncle," I said cheerfully, reaching for the kettle. "Off for a walk?"

"Yes, the young lady's getting restless, aren't you, m'dear? Morning Vicky." He gave the dog a friendly pat and pecked me lightly on the cheek.

I knelt down and hugged Shirley, who proceeded to smother my face with canine kisses.

"Aargh … get off, Shirley! Is that my brother wielding the hoover upstairs or have you acquired a live-in maid?"

Uncle Liam laughed. "I expect he'll want some tea for his pains. Cheerio."

When Uncle Liam returned, we ate a lunch of cold ham, cheese and Mum's home-made pickle with crusty bread and butter. As Julie rose to gather up the dirty crockery, she gave a little gasp.

"Oh crikey, I think …" She hesitated, then scurried up the stairs. A few minutes later she re-emerged in a highly excited state, crying, "Chris, Chris, can I borrow you for a moment?" and disappeared again.

He got up briskly. "This is it!" he called back over his shoulder as he scooted upstairs. They were back down within minutes.

Julie spoke first. "I don't know quite how to put this, but … well … to put it bluntly, my waters have broken. That means the baby could be here in a few hours. I think I'll call for the midwife. Oh my gosh, I'm a bit scared."

She hurried out and came back looking perplexed.

"They said she's on another call but they reckon I've got ages to go yet. They told me to call again when the contractions come every five minutes. Here comes one now, I think …" She winced, took a series of long, deep breaths, then relaxed.

"Sit down, do," her father fussed.

"No it's all right, Father. They told me it's all right to carry on as normal … I think it speeds things up a bit," she added, with a mischievous smile.

For the next three hours, the contractions continued. During the afternoon we had a light snow shower and at four o'clock I telephoned Mum.

"Please can I stay?" I begged. "Julie's in labour. Please Mum!"

"Good Gracious! Yes, of course you may. How exciting!"

By teatime, the contractions were five-minutely.

"I think I'd better ring the midwife," Julie said, finally.

"Mrs. Saxilby? …… Barbara …… Yes, can you come now? ……What? ……Well, what shall I do? …… But suppose …… Okay …… Well, there's Dolly Cartwright, I guess …… Yes, I'll do that …… All right, thank you, see you later …… Bye." She put down the receiver with a bang.

"Well, can you believe that?" she said tetchily. "She said the snow's so bad, she can't come right now. It's not that bad out there. I can't see what the problem is. Oh, I wish she'd come earlier."

"She was on another call, if you remember," said her father patiently.

"Oh yes, I forgot. Well it can't be helped. Chris, can you run down to the Cartwrights and get Dolly. She's got six kids so she ought to know a bit about childbirth. We might need her if the midwife doesn't make it on time."

Chris grabbed his coat and opened the front door.

"Julie, have you seen this?" he exclaimed. "I thought you said it wasn't that bad."

The snow was falling thick and fast and settling on the ground at an alarming rate.

"Well, it wasn't before," she said moodily. "Hurry up, Chris!"

He tramped off into the whiteout and we waited with growing concern.

40 minutes later, to the immense relief of our little party, the front door opened and Chris appeared on the threshold.

"I couldn't bring Dolly, she was out," he explained, "but I've brought her daughter. This is Avice." He ushered in a swarthy, plain-faced girl of about my own age and bid her take off her wet things. "Dolly had most of her children at home, I gather, and Avice sat in on the last one."

"Not that I did anything," said the poor, flustered girl apologetically. "I was just … well … there."

"Oh, you'll do," said Julie bluntly. "Oooh … ouch …" She inhaled deeply and we waited while the pain passed. "I need to be getting upstairs, I think. This pain's getting unbearable. I think the baby's on its way. Vicky, Avice, you must hold my hand … well, both hands," she laughed nervously.

Julie installed herself in her bedroom and I was charged with telephoning the midwife again.

"She knows exactly what to do," Mrs. Saxilby reassured me. "I've been over everything with her, she's very good at the breathing and she knows what to expect. Tell her to get ready and then you must wait until you can see the baby's head. On no account must she push until you can clearly see the baby's head. Do you understand?"

"Yes," I answered meekly, "but …"

"No 'buts', now listen. Once the baby's head is engaged, she must push. She will want to push so just tell her to go ahead, only not too hard, mind, until the baby's head is nearly out."

"Yes, all right," I said uncertainly.

"Once his head is out, you must feel to check that the umbilical cord is not wrapped around the baby's neck. Do you understand?"

"Yes, I understand. Please, I can't do this!" I started to cry.

"Someone's got to do it. She can't give birth by herself!" she said impatiently. I let out a stifled sob and mercifully she sensed my panic and continued in a kindlier tone. "Giving birth is the most natural process in the world. How do you think cavefolk did it?"

I heaved a sigh. "I'm sorry, I'm really scared."

"Naturally, but you'll be all right. Now, in the highly unlikely event that the cord is constricting the baby's neck, just loop it over his head. They're tough little cookies, it won't hurt him."

"Okay."

"You might need to ease the shoulders out, one at a time, but it's often not necessary. The rest is plain sailing. The baby will slide out easily and all you have to do is catch him in your hands. All right, dear?"

"Yes, I think so," I mumbled.

"Avice is a capable girl. She will help you. Now, do you remember everything I've told you so far?"

"Yes, I remember."

"When the baby is born, make sure his mouth is clear. It might take a minute before he starts crying so don't worry. Then you can give him to his mother to hold. Then there's the afterbirth."

"Oh God, not more!" I wailed, feeling completely overwhelmed.

"Yes, it will be messy, I'm afraid. Julie will have a few more contractions but she won't need your help by then. You won't need to do anything else until help arrives. The cord will need to be cut but you can leave that to the experts. All right, dear?"

"Yes, all right, I'll do my best," I said, in a tone of weary resignation.

"I'll try my hardest to get there, but I suggest you ring for an ambulance. Ambulance men are occasionally called upon to deliver babies, you know."

I put down the receiver and telephoned for an ambulance.

When I went back upstairs, my worst fears had been realised. Julie's contractions were very strong and frequent and she lay on her back with Avice at her side, crushing the poor girl's fingers with a vice-like grip. I quickly relayed the midwife's instructions to Avice, fearful that I would forget a crucial step.

"Are you going to deliver my baby?" asked Julie, in astonishment.

"I don't know, probably. It'll be fine," I said shakily, trying, but not succeeding, to sound confident. Fortunately, she was so wrapped up in pain that she failed to notice my voice quavering.

The birth progressed at a rapid rate and half an hour later my new baby niece dropped into my trembling hands. I burst into tears.

"Oh my God, my baby!" screamed Julie.

"No, no," I squealed. "The baby's fine, look, it's a girl."

I prized open her tiny mouth, just as the midwife had told me, and she greeted me with a thin cry.

"My baby, my baby," cooed Julie.

"I handed over the little bundle and sat down on the bed, feeling queasy and lightheaded. There was a rap on the door.

"Oh, thank God," I gulped. "Avice, please would you mind …"

The kind-hearted girl scampered out and the thump of boots on the staircase signalled the arrival of two burly ambulance men.

"Looks like we've missed all the fun," chuckled one. "Now, let's have a look at the little mite." Julie handed over her daughter reluctantly. "My, she's bonny." He checked her over whilst the other man reached into his kitbag.

"You're as white as a sheet!" he remarked, regarding my blood-stained hands and clothing with a nod. "Come along, child."

He helped me up and escorted me to the bathroom. When I returned, they had clamped and cut the cord. A rather squeamish Chris was invited in to meet his new baby daughter and then Avice was charged with washing and dressing her. When I felt better, I went downstairs to telephone Mum.

"What was it like?" she asked, with undisguised admiration in her voice.

"I don't really remember, it was all a bit of a blur … but it was wonderful … Mum, I want to be a midwife," I blurted out.

By the time Mrs. Saxilby arrived, there was nothing left for her to do but assist with the cleaning up.

"Well, Vicky, you did an incredibly brave thing today," she winked. "Well done!"

I blushed. "And Avice," I said, beaming at the girl. "I don't know what I would have done without her. Thank you so much, Avice." I gazed proudly at my new baby niece. "What are you going to call her?" I asked Julie.

She smiled. "We would like to call her Sarah, if that's okay with you, Father." She looked at her father who was standing at the bedside in a state of rapture.

Tears of joy welled up in the eyes of the old man and he nodded in mute approval, bent down and kissed the sleeping child on the forehead. "Hello Sarah."

Chapter 7

The Road to 19

"I passed! I passed!" I bounded into the kitchen clutching a large brown envelope and flung my arms round my mother's neck in an ecstatic hug.

"Well I knew you would, dear," she said mildly, plying my back with a series of maternal pats. "Well done you!"

It was the summer of 1973 and I was midway through my three-year training to become a qualified nurse. This morning I had learnt the results of my intermediate exams and hastened home to share the happy news with my family. The shy, gawky novice had developed into a smart, accomplished young woman of 19, at least, that was the view proffered by Sister Mason in her report. When I say 'grown', I use the word in its loosest sense as, at a diminutive 5 feet 2 inches tall, my growth had been confined to my mental faculties, and even that was a source of constant doubt to me. In my head, I still felt like the clumsy, emotional girl who had brought into the world the pretty, fair-haired four-year-old child sitting at the kitchen table. I had retained my impetuous, artless and impressionable nature and, despite a few knocks along the way, still upheld an unshakeable belief in the ability of good to triumph over evil. I championed the philosophy of basic human kindness and strove to perform my role as a student nurse with devotion, energy and enthusiasm. I had made it my mission to find a small piece of good in each and every person who crossed my path and my positive outlook had touched the hearts of my seniors and won me high praise.

I skipped across the room to my little niece, who was looking up from her colouring book with a quizzical expression on her face.

"Look Sarah, these are my exam results!" I panted, waving my report in the air and bending down to kiss her upturned face. "Soon I'll be a real nurse."

"You're a real nurse already, silly," she giggled. "You've been a nurse for *ages*."

"No, no, I'm just a student. I go to school, like you; only I don't go to a nursery school, I go to a nurses' school." I chuckled at my own joke and Sarah burst out laughing.

"You're too big for school!" she exclaimed merrily.

"It's a school for grown-ups, where they teach you how to be a nurse."

Sarah shrugged her shoulders and returned to her colouring. From the corner of the kitchen, her little sister squirmed in her pram and started to bleat plaintively. I hurried over, bent down, picked up the crying infant and nestled her against my shoulder. Louise was a month old and bore the name of her great-grandmother in its more contemporary form. Nan had celebrated her 70th birthday on the 21st June, three days before the birth of Chris and Julie's second child. She had been deeply touched by the tribute paid to her by her oldest grandson and toasted her great-granddaughter's health with copious quantities of red wine. Some things never change. Louise was an exceptionally pretty baby with a full head of thick, nut-brown hair and large, round, hazel eyes rimmed with long dark lashes. She bore little resemblance to either of her parents but the likeness she shared with my sister when she was a tiny infant marked her out as a beauty.

* * *

As I reread my results slip, I found myself reflecting on the three year journey that had seen me transformed from a nervous beginner to a proficient student nurse. I had left school in the summer of 1970 armed with modest 'O' level passes in English, Maths, Biology, Home Economics and Drama, together with a letter of introduction written by the man from the Ministry of Labour Youth Employment Office, who came to our school during our final year to talk to us about job options. As there was no direct route into midwifery, it was necessary to become a fully-qualified nurse before embarking on the additional training needed to practise as a midwife. An interview at North Lonsdale Hospital in Barrow-in-Furness was duly arranged, and after a brief but nerve-racking interrogation by a sour-faced middle-aged woman called Sister Grimshaw, a person whom I would quickly learn to fear, I secured a position as a cadet nurse. If I proved competent, in the course of time I would gain a place on the three-year programme leading to accreditation as a state registered nurse.

On our first day, each new cadet was issued six new uniforms consisting of a functional yellow dress, a yellow apron and – yes, you guessed it – a yellow belt.

"Oh God, it's awful … look at it, it's nearly down to my knees!" That was the verdict of my newly acquired friend Linda, as she pressed the dress against her, peered down disdainfully and compared it unfavourably with the hem of her suede mini skirt.

We were also provided with a brown cloak. Then we were all given a large piece of starched white material on which we had to perform a complicated sequence of folds and tucks which would have tried the patience of a skilled origamist, as Linda remarked later over tea and biscuits in the hospital dining room. The result was a huge cap which fell off with the slightest puff of air as well as every time I bent over or passed any of the young male porters in the corridor, who made a sport of flicking them off the heads of the trainees. My difficulties were multiplied tenfold by the profusion of springy curls that adorned my crown, which were perpetually engaged in a continuous battle against gravity and would often cause my cap to leap from my head without the slightest provocation. This usually happened when Sister Grimshaw happened to be passing.

It was during my 18 month stint as a cadet nurse that I learnt the meaning of the term 'errand girl'. At the end of every shift, I would return to my lodgings with cries of "Cadetti!", "Canary!" and "Primrose!" ringing in my ears, for this was how our seniors addressed us. They barked out an unremitting succession of orders which had us scurrying hither and thither with the efficacy of despatch runners under the scrutiny of an exacting military commander. I often hankered after the peace and tranquillity of my old school classroom and quickly learnt to appreciate the value of sensible lace-up shoes.

The culture within the National Health Service saw the lower orders labouring under a hierarchical regime that bordered on tyranny and the cadets were at the bottom of the heap. We generally only spoke to our immediate superiors and, even during our breaks, we had to mind our 'p's and q's'. On one occasion early on in our initiation, Linda had the audacity to vacate her seat in the dining room before Staff Nurse Rushworth had finished her meal. Poor Linda incurred the wrath of Matron and got a dressing down for insubordination.

"Could've been worse," she remarked gaily, as we ambled back towards my temporary home on the outskirts of Barrow one wet and windy August evening. "I thought I was fodder for the Grim

Reaper … Imagine that! She'd have eaten me alive!" Next to Sister Grimshaw, or the Grim Reaper as she was known amongst the junior staff, Matron took on the aspect of a lamb.

The cadets worked a five-and-a-half day week including Saturday mornings for £5 16s 6d per week, that's about £200 a month in today's money – barely a living wage. As North Lonsdale Hospital was situated 30 miles from my home at Wasdale and a good hour by car, even had I been wealthy enough to possess one, I lived at the home of my Auntie Gwen and Uncle Roger in Flass Lane during the week. Auntie Gwen was Mum's older sister. She had met and married Uncle Roger, a shipbuilder and resident of Barrow, relatively late in life, and having no children of their own, my youthful presence was something of a novelty to them. I was very nervous at the prospect of living away from home but they proved to be kind and generous hosts. Auntie Gwen indulged me with pin money for odd small luxuries – bangles, an Ali MacGraw hat and a pair of Dr. Scholl's sandals. Often on a Saturday, Uncle Roger would drive me back home to the farm, where I spent most weekends. When Askam United were playing away, Chris came to pick me up. Dad drove me back very early on Monday mornings so that I could continue to enjoy the traditional Sunday evening tea that was such an intrinsic part of my heritage.

During my first year as a cadet, I moved from department to department and although I didn't feel I was accumulating much knowledge, I actually learnt a great deal. For the last six months before I started my official training, I was allocated to the Orthopaedics ward, which was one of the busiest in the hospital – and one of the hottest, for the outside wall was made up entirely of south-facing windows. When it got really busy, they would place extra beds down the middle. This was to be my first real taste of nursing – or so I hoped. In reality, I found myself at the beck and call of everyone, even the student nurses. Everything had to be kept spotless – the bedframes, the curtain rails, the lockers. Then there was the sluice room, where we washed and polished the bedpans, bowls and bottles. The dirty linen confronted me in mountains more daunting than the ones I had grown up amongst.

Some of the senior staff were not entirely without a sense of humour and occasionally they amused themselves by sending us on fools' errands. Linda wasn't the most attentive of students when it came to lessons, so when she was sent by Sister Mason to fetch a bottle of amniotic fluid I could hardly contain my mirth as I watched her tripping off to central stores. The boot was on the other foot a few weeks later though, when one of the student nurses sent me off to collect a consignment of mercury sticks for the thermometers.

My working week also included two days at a local college, where we studied Human Biology. I looked forward to college; it was a welcome relief from the gruelling daily schedule on the ward. Nursing can be a thankless task and some of the cadets left to work in offices or factories where the pay was better and the demands less. Others, like Linda, Wendy and me, were finally accepted into preliminary training school (or PTS) to take up the State Registration training in January 1972.

It was not without a twinge of sadness that I packed my belongings and bid a fond farewell to Auntie Gwen and Uncle Roger. All student nurses had to live in the nurses' home during the whole of their first year of training and often their second. That way, Matron could ensure that we were tucked up in bed by 10.30 when they locked up, got up by 6.30 and ate all our vegetables. My lodgings were on Church Street with Wendy. Linda's were on Albert Street. Linda thought this was very unfair. The nurses' home comprised a row of old terraced houses which had been knocked through. The rooms were unbelievably cramped and a far cry from the relative luxury I had enjoyed in my smart and spacious bedroom in Flass Lane. Everything was small – the bed, the wardrobe, the chest of drawers, even the sink. Worse still, my room was situated right alongside the morgue and every so often I could hear the sound of trollies being wheeled across the yard just outside the window.

For the first six weeks, most of our training was done in the classroom at the new School of Nurses across the road in an old building that used to house the bank. We had already been issued with new uniforms – a lilac over-the-knee dress and a warm navy cloak with green lining. Boy, was I grateful for that cloak to ward off the interminable cold. On the first day, we had to show our nails. Mine were bitten short but Linda's were long and painted lilac, and would have looked stunning with the dress if nail lacquer had been permitted. As it was, she was ordered to remove it and hastened off to the cloakroom with a petulant toss of the head. Jewellery was not permitted, our hair had to be tied back and only the smallest hint of face make-up was tolerated. The silver-plated 'V' that Ray had given me for my 14th birthday had long since found its way onto a cheap neck ring choker as the chain had broken and I couldn't afford to replace it. This made it impossible to conceal so I never wore it at work.

At PTS, they taught us how to make a neat bed, lift patients and give them a bed bath. We learnt how to administer an injection by poking needles into oranges. Occasionally they would let us loose to practise our skills on real patients. I was terrified the first time I had to give an injection. The old rogue must have sensed my fear or noticed my hand trembling, for he slipped me a knowing wink and chuckled "Well done, sweetheart," when the job was successfully done. We had to watch a post mortem and learn how to lay out a body. Luckily I'm not particularly squeamish but Wendy nearly passed out. Sometimes the porters would play pranks on the student nurses. They would hide in the morgue, turn out the lights and then pounce on unsuspecting victims, including sassy Linda who was not so full of funk after her encounter with the Marauder of the Morgue.

At the end of our six weeks' initial training, we sat exams. Wendy came top and got the PTS prize. I came third. Linda scraped through. Then they issued us with new caps, collars, aprons, bibs and belts. The first year students wore caps with a single red line on them, the second year students' caps had two lines on them and the third year students', three. The starched white collar was held in place by a metal stud which practically choked me the first time I put it on, but at least I finally looked like a real nurse and I wore my uniform with pride.

On the wards, the daily routine was made up of an endless succession of rounds – cleaning rounds dressing rounds, bedpan rounds, drinks rounds, blood pressure rounds, and so on. All the nurses were given different jobs to do and the first years generally got given the most mundane tasks which more often than not involved the use of copious quantities of disinfectant. No wonder we all smelt of the stuff. Our shift patterns were irregular and I found them physically and mentally draining. Shift work plays havoc with the body clock and I still find it the hardest part of my job. Sleep deprivation can be akin to torture and I would often find myself staring at the ceiling at any given hour of the day or night in a failed attempt to snatch a precious few hours' sleep. At the start of each shift, we had to report to the ward sister's office for a rundown on the latest admissions. They would besiege us with complicated medical terminology which we would pretend to understand and then talk about amongst ourselves later. We learnt a lot from each other, including the ability to look confident in the face of total bewilderment.

We worked incredibly hard, but we played hard too. Once or twice a week, we would go to one of the local pubs or to my favourite bar, the Dreadnought in the Majestic Hotel, which was named after the UK's first nuclear-powered submarine constructed at Barrow's shipyard in 1960. Most of the young men were employed at the shipyard or at the small steelworks on the west side of town. You can imagine the banter we were subjected to when we announced that we were student nurses. If I had a pound for every time a local Romeo asked for the kiss of life, I'd be a millionaire by now. They would gape at us in disbelief when we told them about the 10.30 curfew. We were allowed one late pass a week – until 11 o'clock. Latecomers had to report to the night sister to collect the key, along with a severe reprimand. Any student who was persistently late got hauled over the coals by Matron or, worse still, the Grim Reaper. Linda was constantly late. She would drink too much, dismiss the consequences and land herself in trouble.

She was worse when she was with Donna. Donna lived with Linda on Albert Street. She had an olive complexion and a mane of beautiful, jet black hair, although we suspected she used dye to enhance the colour. She was part-Italian, which accounted for her name. It sounded exotic and I was rather envious until 10cc scored a smash hit with a record of the same name later in the year and the local boys surpassed themselves. Whenever she walked into the Dreadnought, they would burst into a falsetto chorus which creased us up every time. She took it on the chin for a few weeks until eventually she snapped and threw a half-pint glass of shandy in the face of the chief culprit, an apprentice steelworker called John. After that, they left her well alone.

Wendy and I were more careful about timekeeping and usually got back by the skin of our teeth, not that we were angels by a long chalk. We would creep along the corridor into each other's rooms after lights out for some girly chat, especially if one of us was feeling blue. I can still recall many a whispered conversation about the boys we came into contact with and the men we adored. We would debate on the relative merits of Marc Bolan versus David Bowie, and of Roger Moore versus Tony Curtis, a.k.a. 'The Persuaders'. My feet were in the Bowie/Curtis camp. We laughed together, cried together and built up a lifelong friendship that would sustain me through many a dark hour. I missed Ray awfully and Wendy's cheery presence steadied me whenever I was tempted to dwell upon the fact that most of my girlfriends were getting hitched, while I was turning down offers on account of a tacit arrangement with an undergraduate from London with whom I exchanged letters across a gulf more than 300 miles wide.

I missed my home too and rued the march of time which will inevitably divide the family unit into so many separate strands, like branches of a tree growing in different directions: Chris with his Julie up at the Head; Alan, now a qualified teacher at a school in Stockport 100 miles away; Michael currently living at Lancaster and whispers of a union between Toni and her long-time beau Phil – whispers which found a voice in March 1972 when Phil popped the question on the day of Toni's 21st birthday party.

This magnificent event brought the whole family together for one glorious evening. A function room had been obtained at the Scawfell Hotel at Seascale at a heavily discounted price, for Toni had been working there ever since she had left school. Toni wanted Ruby to come and magnanimously extended an invitation to all of the Elphick family, although I strongly suspected it was Mum's idea. I couldn't wait and spent weeks planning my outfit – a backless shift dress of turquoise crepe with matching chunky-heel strappy shoes.

After breakfast, Dad came to pick me up from the nurses' home. I could barely eat due to butterflies in my stomach, but with the beady eye of the home sister on me, I dared not leave a scrap. Lately, I had been increasingly troubled by misgivings. Ray was a promising scholar with high aspirations and I worried that the rustic farmer's daughter might have lost her appeal in the eyes of the ambitious young geologist. I contemplated his arrival with mounting anxiety and by the time the car pulled into the drive, my knees were weak and I was shaking. My fears proved groundless, however, as the minute he was through the door he swept me up and smothered my face with kisses. After lunch, Mum drove us to the Scawfell Hotel and we decorated the room with banners and balloons. Then we went for a walk along the seafront before returning home to eat and put on our glad rags.

Phil arrived at teatime. His face was flushed, his manner betrayed an uncharacteristic restlessness and agitation and he wanted to wait on his own in the front room for Toni, who was upstairs getting changed, instead of joining us for a snifter in the kitchen. Clearly he had something up his sleeve and it wasn't long before we found out what. In a little while, Toni appeared at the kitchen door with Phil on her arm, glowing with pleasure and pride.

"I'm engaged … look," she purred, holding out her bejewelled left hand. We all cheered, clapped and tried our best to look surprised. We had arrived at the same conclusion 10 minutes ago.

We partied into the night in company with T. Rex, Slade and the Rolling Stones – no surprises there. Mum baked a splendid cake and we drank to the health of my bright and beautiful sister and her dashing Mr. Diall. I was still susceptible to an occasional pang of jealousy and habitually evaded the spotlight in case I should look frumpy by comparison. Tonight, however, though she sparkled like the diamond on the third finger of her left hand, as I stood alongside Ray, his hand clasping mine, no such notion entered my head and I shone like a pearl.

The following morning, Ray and I walked briskly down to the lake with Rufus. Earlier it had rained and a stiff breeze at our backs propelled us along. The wet tarmac glistened in the spring sunshine and the pale yellow light played on the dancing leaves, making the hedgerows shimmer. Every now and then, a gust of wind would shake the leaves of the trees as we passed under them, splashing us with droplets of water and bringing the scent of freshly mown grass. Against a backdrop of murmuring wind, swishing trees and the drone of a distant tractor, Ray expounded on the freedom of life on campus while I lamented the constraints of the nurses' home. Soon we reached the lakeshore and stood idly watching Rufus trotting in and out of the shallows.

"You don't like Phil very much, do you?" said Ray, with a penetrating look.

I shrugged. "She likes him, that's all that matters," I replied, with genuine warmth. Then I felt a cold blast of damp air, looked behind me and, noticing a bank of cloud approaching from the west, hoped it wasn't portentous.

"We'd better make tracks," I cautioned, but we lingered on for another 10 minutes so that on the way home, when the heavens opened, we only had ourselves to blame. The rain lashed down and the wind flew in our faces, whipping at our hoods and beating them down. Our waterproofs proved ineffective against the deluge but as I splashed home through the puddles, getting soaked to the skin, my joy knew no bounds.

After an emotional farewell, I shut myself in my bedroom for a good cry. Not long after, Toni came up, gave me a hug, loaded Bowie's 'Hunky Dory' into my Philips portable cassette player and then brought me up a cup of tea, but I had no appetite for lunch. For the next few days, I felt dull and listless and complained frequently to Wendy that I had nothing to look forward to. Even an eagerly anticipated weekend trip to Blackpool Pleasure Beach on Linda's 18th birthday in April temporarily lost its appeal. I knew the feeling would pass. It was that transient state of melancholy commonly experienced at the end of a 'high'.

Michael, in the meantime, was in his second year at Lancaster University, where he was reading Environmental Science. From time to time, he would come up to Barrow for the weekend with a couple of university mates from the area and meet up for a drink. Donna loved rock music, the heavier the better, and the first time she met Michael she was besotted. By now, Michael's hair was past his shoulders. He had a sizeable collection of vinyl, wore a denim jacket, smoked cannabis and went to festivals.

"He looks just like Ozzy Osborne," she would coo.

"He wants a good wash, and he smells of pot!" I would retort.

Donna was the kind of girl who wore her heart on her sleeve. She would single him out for conversation, look directly into his eyes and flirt outrageously. Michael was shy and told me in confidence that he wished she would stop but he didn't have the heart to tell her. Eventually fate intervened and, although her hopes were temporarily dashed, she bounced back quickly in true 'Donna' style and fell in love with the new barman at the Strawberry Hotel.

Michael was an avid campaigner for CND and in March 1972 he went 'awol' from university to join a 56 mile Easter march from London to Aldermaston in Berkshire. Dad was livid and threatened to slash his monthly allowance. The four-day demonstration started with a rally in Trafalgar Square and culminated in what was described as a 'peace festival' featuring the likes of Hawkwind, Roy Harper, Graham Bond and Pete Brown. The protestors carried plaques and banners, daffodils and 27 coffins which they left outside the main gates of the atomic weapons research unit. Michael explained earnestly that these coffins represented one for each year since the bombs were dropped on Hiroshima, while Donna hung fervently on his every word. During the demonstration, it would appear that he had befriended a young female campaigner from Swindon called Polly and fallen for her head over heels. Later he confessed to me in private that he had some doubts about the extent to which his ardour was reciprocated, but they had swapped addresses and he was hopeful that her feelings would grow. This provided Michael with precisely the ammunition he needed to fend off the zealous attentions of his impassioned admirer. He openly declared his devotion to Polly, proclaiming her to be the love of his life, and applied a liberal dose of varnish to her part in the affair. The pill was a bitter one for Donna to swallow but the cure was effective.

As well as North Lonsdale Hospital, which was quite small and mainly handled medical and surgical routines and emergencies, we worked at several satellite hospitals around the town during our training. During my first year, I worked at Devonshire Road Children's Hospital and the gynaecological and geriatric hospital in the old workhouse at Roose. Roose Hospital was perched on top of a hill in pleasant grounds, overlooking the town on one side and the shipyard on the other. It was a large and imposing clutch of buildings which could be rather creepy, especially the upper floors which, according to local legend, were inhabited by the ghost of a young woman. Formerly Roose had been an institution for the mentally ill and a few of the old folks had lived there most of their lives. I don't think they were very happy and it seemed to me that their capacity to exercise free will had been effaced by a system based on Victorian values, which incarcerated the weak and the wayward. Some of them had funny little routines or catchphrases; some just sat with a vacant expression, humming or rocking. Some clearly had a mental impairment which today would be recognised as autism; others were merely 'institutionalised'. All deserved a place in the community which had been denied them before enlightenment transformed our thinking. I felt desperately sorry for these lonely old people and administered liberal doses of sunshine as I went about my daily business, but nothing I said or did seemed to make a difference. It was a dismal place. Eventually it was time to move on, and after a brief spell back at the School of Nurses, I did a short placement in the private nursing home at the back of North Lonsdale Hospital where well-to-do mums-to-be would pay for a bed. I loved working at the PNH and was one of the lucky students who got the opportunity to assist at a birth.

One of the highlights of the year was the staff Christmas ball held in the town hall. It was the one occasion when hierarchy was swept under the carpet and we could mix with our superiors in rank on an equal footing. All the ladies wore evening dresses and the men wore suits. I wore my turquoise dress, my hair long and loose and lashings of silver eye shimmer. We danced to a live band, rubbed shoulders with some of the local dignitaries, including the mayor, and flirted with our young male colleagues. Linda was a bubbly blonde with an hourglass figure and easy charm that never failed to hit the target, but the night belonged to Wendy, for she won the heart of a junior doctor called David she had met during her placement on the ENT ward who shared her passion for old movies and French cuisine.

Alan came home at the end of term with news of his blossoming attachment to an English teacher called Caroline at the school where he worked. On Christmas Day, Julie revealed that she was expecting her second child in June – the same child whom I now cradled against my shoulder as I contemplated my exam results with a proud heart.

* * *

For all that, Christmas 1972 had been a tense affair which was soonest forgotten. Notwithstanding the forthcoming happy event, Chris and Julie bickered incessantly. Michael was sulking because he had sent Polly a hand-made necklace made from shells and a lace-trimmed chiffon scarf and received only a card in return. To cap it all, Phil was two hours late. He failed to turn up at teatime, which put Toni into a bad humour during the early evening. He eventually arrived at half past eight, cursing his ill luck at being inconvenienced by a flat tyre on Christmas Day. I thought his words had a hollow ring, but then I always found him unconvincing.

Meanwhile, we moved up into our second year. The New Year started with a block of schooling which necessitated a change of residence. Our new home was in Monks Croft, an old Victorian mansion outside town next to Furness Abbey, in large grounds surrounded by fields. It was quite a spooky place at night. In the evenings, we would congregate in Linda's room and drink Hawaiian Punch laced with a dash of cheap gin which Linda kept hidden in the back of her wardrobe. Then we would play 'Haunted House' (a hilarious kids' board game, for those who don't remember it) and tell each other ghost stories into the small hours, in which the Grim Reaper often played a starring role. The housekeeper at Monks Croft wasn't as strict as the night sister at Church Street. She probably knew all about our clandestine parties but she chose to turn a blind eye.

We were allowed to stay out until 11 o'clock and the last one back had to lock the door and turn off the outside lights. I only got locked out once; that was enough for me. I had rather foolishly struck up a friendship with an apprentice builder from Millom called Keith whom I had fallen into conversation with during a night out – well, anyone can make a mistake. He had a silver tongue, a gold motorcycle and tickets to see David Bowie at the Guildhall in Preston on the last leg of the 'Ziggy Stardust' world tour. Wendy thought I'd taken leave of my senses; she probably had a point. Fortunately I saw through him before any irretrievable harm was done. In a moment of madness, I allowed myself to be persuaded to take a midnight ride on the pillion of his Kawasaki Widowmaker. It wasn't long before I realised I was not only completely out of my depth but in danger of losing my life, and I begged him to take me back home. Eventually he relented and, in a fit of pique, deposited me unceremoniously at the bottom of the long gravel drive in the rain and sped off into the night. It was one o'clock in the morning, pitch dark and I was cold, frightened and filled with remorse. My frenzied pounding on the front door would have woken the dead. After what seemed like an eternity but what was, in reality, only a few minutes, several of the girls came down simultaneously to let me in. I cried myself to sleep and swore I would never again fall prey to some dark-eyed Lothario in leathers. Later it transpired that the Bowie tickets were a complete fabrication.

For my placement, I found myself back in the Orthopaedics ward where I had worked as a cadet under Sister Mason. That was a stroke of good luck. The next eight weeks were crucial to my success or failure in the intermediate exams, as they would culminate in a report from the ward sister, and experience had taught me that Sister Mason ruled with a firm but kindly hand. I completed my placement without a hitch.

* * *

In the course of time, I was issued with a new blue uniform, which was the prerogative of all the student nurses who had passed the intermediate exam. I was halfway to the finishing post.

Chapter 8

Love, Labour and Loss

In the summer of '73, we rented a cottage on the outskirts of the beautiful spa town of Bath. Our party of seven was made up of Mum and Dad, Chris and Julie, my two little nieces and myself. Michael had just finished university and started a job with the Cumberland River Authority. Toni was working and Alan had made his own plans with his new girlfriend, Caroline. It was a poor turnout, I would reflect with an occasional pang of bitterness but mostly with sadness at the inevitable parting of the ways that marks the passage into adulthood.

Dad hired a Volkswagen T2 and left Walter in charge of the farm. Walter was an experienced farmhand who had been working alongside Dad for more than 25 years.

Our excursion into the lovely county of Somerset was mainly as a consequence of Sarah's adoration of cats, which did not stop with the small domestic type. Her fascination with felines was all encompassing, even extending to an imaginary leopard which she kept in an imaginary cage at the bottom of the garden. In

1966, the Lions of Longleat had achieved national fame as the star attraction of the first drive-through safari park outside Africa. Sarah badly wanted to go and what Sarah wanted, she usually got if it was left to her father. Bath was decided upon because of its proximity to Longleat and its abundance of historic parks, gardens and buildings, including the famous Roman Baths. Its royal, artistic and literary connections were plentiful and interesting and included Jane Austen, whose novel 'Pride and Prejudice' was a particular favourite of mine. There were shops, restaurants and tea rooms selling local fare such as the famous Sally Lunn bun and even a farmers' market which I recommended archly to Dad as a cure for homesickness. You can imagine his reaction.

Although I knew I was being irrational, as the holiday drew near I became consumed with resentment at the prospect of being the single component within our family party of three neat pairs plus one. I saw myself trotting behind with my two little nieces whilst Mum and Dad ambled along reminiscing or talking about things that didn't interest me and Chris and Julie walked arm in arm, making the most of every opportunity to foist the children off on me. Naturally Sarah would gravitate towards 'Auntie Vicky' as small girls do towards indulgent relatives. It wouldn't be much of a holiday for me. It made me snappy and irritable but I couldn't help myself.

Fortunately, help was at hand. Mum, with her razor-sharp insight and uncanny ability to read my mind, came to my rescue one Saturday afternoon in mid-July.

"I've been wondering if you'd like to invite Ray down to Bath for a few days, as long as he doesn't mind sleeping in the box room. I do understand how you must be feeling. It can't be nice for you being the odd one out."

"Oh Mum, *can I*?" I gasped, tears of gratitude welling up in my eyes. "You've no idea how miserable I've been!" As usual, I found myself unable to suppress my natural inclination to exaggerate whenever my feelings got the better of me, acquired through years spent trying to make an impression from the bottom rung of the family ladder.

"Oh, I think I have," she replied with a knowing smile. "You can't hide much from your mother!"

So the thing was arranged. Ray would join us at the start for two days and return on Monday morning to Portsmouth University, where he had a summer job as a research assistant. After that, my misgivings receded into the far distance and I fell into a delicious state of anticipation, under the influence of which I obsessed over Ray with an intensity that was emotionally draining.

On the first night of our holiday, I barely slept. Ray's bedroom was opposite mine and he was so much in my thoughts that his presence was almost tangible. I wondered if he was thinking about me.

When Sunday finally dawned, the sun was shining and a fresh breeze blew from the south west. We ate a cooked breakfast and drove out to Cheddar, where we climbed the 274 steps up the side of the gorge and then another 48 up to the top of the lookout tower. As we strolled along the clifftop hand in hand, Ray found much to enthuse over. The view was impressive but my perception was clouded by the bigger picture, and alas the towering cliffs and crags of naked rock dotted with weather-beaten trees and patches of rough grass, and the distant Cheddar reservoir, lost a little grandeur seen through eyes that had beheld beauty altogether more raw. My mind flew back to Wasdale; to the mighty ring of mountains at its head, to the immense screes along its steep, southern flank and to the lovely lake within, glimmering like a jewel in a stone casket.

Near the head of the gorge, we scrambled down the bank and ambled back along the lane. Sarah was soon impatient for an ice cream so the rest of the family forged ahead while we lingered on, gazing up at the walls of limestone in search of caves, combing the verges for pretty rocks and stones and discussing the merits of various plants and flowers we happened upon. Soon Ray's arm was around my shoulder and we walked on close together in silence, my hip brushing against his thigh, causing my body to tingle and my stomach to flutter. At length, he broached the subject that had been playing on my mind.

"We've known each other for a long time now …"

"More than six years," I replied, my voice light and tremulous.

"… And yet we never seem to get any closer. I mean, we do things together, go for walks and stuff like that, but most of my mates with girlfriends … well, they've …," he hesitated, fumbling for words, his colour deepening.

"Go on, it's okay," I murmured, with mounting excitement.

"They've … what I mean is, it's 1973 and you don't have to be married to … well … I think you know what I mean."

The instant the words were out of his mouth, I felt a fiery warmth rise from the pit of my stomach. My temperature rose several notches and my legs started to shake. I clutched tightly onto Ray, who had stopped walking and held himself rigid. Clearly he was terrified lest he had offended me. My heart went out to him and I took a deep breath.

"Oh Ray, I thought you'd never ask!" I cried fervently. "If only you knew how long I've dreamed of this."

His whole body relaxed, he released his tense grip on my arm, folded me in an embrace and kissed me passionately.

"Let's do it!" he whispered, with a note of urgency which was telling. "Let's do it tonight, while your parents are asleep."

I giggled conspiratorially. "Yes, of course, lets … oh, but what about the risks?"

"You mean the risk of your mum and dad finding out, or the other risk?" he said mischievously, planting a kiss on my neck. "Well anyway, I've taken care of the *other* risk."

"Oh Ray, how *could* you?" I exclaimed in mock anger, backing off and slapping him playfully on the arm. "What kind of girl do you think I am?"

At 11.30 that night, I ascended the stairs, set my alarm clock for 2 a.m., tucked it under my pillow and attempted to sleep. Instead, I spent the next two-and-a-half hours doing battle with adrenaline-induced nausea, requiring the consumption of at least three glasses of water. This entailed a couple of trips downstairs to the kitchen and several more to the toilet. It transpired that the alarm was surplus to requirements. On the stroke of two, I slipped out of bed, tiptoed quietly across the landing and stealthily opened the door to the little box room. Ray was sitting up in bed, his chest bare and his dark hair ruffled. I closed the door soundlessly. He stretched out a lean, brown arm, took me by the hand and pulled me towards him. I thought my heart would burst. He wrapped himself around me and held me tight. Then, very gently, he laid me down and I closed my eyes. When I opened them again, I was a girl no more, but a young woman cradled in the arms of the man who had shared my journey across the threshold. At five o'clock I crept back to my own room to savour the moment again and again, while the morning sun climbed over the distant rim of the North Wessex Downs.

After breakfast we bid each other a loving farewell, both acutely aware of the invisible bond that cemented us together and confident in the capacity of this bond to add strength and permanence to our relationship. All that day, I walked on air, smiling freely, laughing often and heaping affection on everybody I came into contact with – sightseers, vendors, waitresses, even a lonely old tramp in a shop doorway.

"That visit of Ray's evidently did you good," Mum said breezily, over tea.

I nodded enthusiastically, my mouth crammed full of quiche, trying hard to maintain an air of innocence and hoping she hadn't guessed the truth.

Much later, I recalled the revulsion I had felt when I had held the mistaken belief, at the tender age of 14, that Chris and Julie had been intimate before their marriage. Was I a hypocrite or was it just a sign of the changing times? Either way, it didn't seem to matter anymore.

During the course of the week, it became obvious that Chris did not share my rosy outlook and I witnessed an alarming deterioration in the relationship between my brother and sister-in-law of which I had been hitherto unaware. Chris was an indulgent father, while Julie's feet were firmly in the 'spare the rod and spoil the child' camp. This placed the couple at odds, and although both tried hard to compromise, it appeared to be a frequent source of friction between them. They bickered every day, Chris becoming sullen and desultory and Julie righteous and tetchy. Julie invariably won the battle and took control – just like her father, I thought ruefully.

The situation came to an ugly head on Thursday. Fine weather was forecast. Mum and Julie made sandwiches while I packed pork pies, sausage rolls, crisps, cake and fruit into a large picnic basket. Then we all piled into the van, bound for Longleat. Less than 10 minutes later, a small voice interrupted the easy flow of conversation.

"Mummy, I need the toilet."

"Oh for goodness sake, Sarah, I told you to go before we left?" Julie retorted crossly.

"I didn't need it then. Mummy, can we go back?"

"Don't be silly, of course we can't go back. You'll just have to hold on."

"But I can't, I'm desperate," wailed the unfortunate Sarah.

"Oh, come on love, we're only a few minutes down the road," put in Chris. "Can't we just go back?"

"She needs to learn. She'll never learn if we pander to her," said Julie impatiently. "You'll be fine Sarah, just think about something else."

"Well, I think it's mean," muttered Chris. "Have it your own way. If she has an accident, you can clear it up!"

As Julie had predicted, the journey was completed without

any mishaps. However, she couldn't resist a little gibe as soon as the children were out of earshot.

"I *told* you she'd be all right," she crowed. "*I* spend much more time with her than *you* do. I know what she can and can't do *and* all about the little games she plays."

"Oh give it a rest, Jules. God, you can be irritating!" he barked, stomping off to look at the park plan.

Worse was to come when it was discovered that Sarah's sun hat had been left at the house.

"I told you to pack it," complained Julie.

"No you didn't, you told me to pack the sun cream. You never mentioned the hat," argued Chris.

"Well, I'm sure I did. It's common sense anyway. Why would you pack the sun cream and not the hat?"

"I thought you'd packed the hat," Chris said curtly.

"I can't do everything, I was making the sandwiches. Here, give me the sun cream." She snatched the bottle from Chris's hand.

Chris turned red, clenched his fists and inhaled deeply.

"God, give me strength," he cursed audibly. Sarah was watching and started to cry. He bent over and picked her up. "I'm sorry, sweetie," he mumbled, placing her on his shoulders and walking across the grass in the direction of a small herd of giraffes who were munching at some acacia trees. "Come and see the giraffes."

Julie made a move to follow but then thought better of it. However, less than five minutes later, Chris was back.

"Here, Julie," he said stiffly, depositing Sarah at the feet of her mother. "You'll be wanting to put the sun cream on."

Throughout the rest of the morning, they barely spoke and at lunchtime, as we started to unpack the picnic basket, tempers flared again.

"Can I have an ice cream?" begged Sarah, looking up at her father with imploring eyes.

"Yes, of course you can, honey," he smiled, reaching into his pocket for his wallet.

"After lunch," Julie cut in.

"I don't want sandwiches, I want ice cream!" Sarah said petulantly, grabbing hold of her father's hand and eyeing up her mother slyly.

"I'll get her an ice cream," Chris said, with an air of resignation. "She can eat her sandwiches later, or just a pork pie or something. It's supposed to be her day."

However, Julie was not so easily overruled. She marched over and extracted Sarah's hand from the grasp of her adoring father.

"Now Sarah," she said firmly, kneeling down in front of her. "Sit down and eat something sensible first and then you can have an ice cream. I've made you a ham sandwich, your favourite."

Chris shrugged, wandered off and sat down on the opposite side of the picnic blanket with his back turned. Julie held out a sandwich, Sarah sat down reluctantly and munched at it sulkily.

"Good girl," said Julie cheerfully, when Sarah had finished. "Now would you like a pork pie, a sausage roll or some crisps?"

Sarah brightened, ate some more lunch and then skipped over to her father.

"Can I have my ice cream now, please?" she asked, her eyes full of pleading.

"Of course; come on, poppet," he said, getting up from the ground, taking her hand and walking over to the nearby ice cream kiosk without a backward glance.

After lunch, we got back into the van and took our place in the queue of vehicles awaiting entry to the lions' enclosure. It was an exceptionally warm afternoon and the van was hot and stuffy. Louise started to cry.

"She's hot," Chris fussed. "You need to take her dress off."

"I know, I know," snapped Julie. "Talk about stating the obvious!" She wrestled with the squealing infant while Chris looked on impotently. Eventually she turned on him angrily. "You might do something to help. Here, look after these;" she deposited the tiny socks and shoes into his lap, "and don't lose them!"

No sooner was Louise settled than Sarah began to squirm and wriggle in her seat in the back next to me.

"I'm hot," she whined. "Can't we open the window?"

"No we can't, I'm sorry Sarah," said Julie, turning round. "There's a sign just up the road that says we have to keep them shut because of the lions." Julie pointed towards a large notice board a few car lengths in front.

Sarah hopped off her seat, craned her neck forward and peered between the heads of her grandparents.

"Don't be ridiculous, Julie," Chris said irritably, flinging open the window. "We haven't reached the sign yet."

"Chris, what the hell d'you think you're doing?" She leapt up, spun round, plonked Louise into my lap and reached across Chris to make a grab for the handle.

"I can't take much more of this!" he fumed, pushing her hand away roughly and throwing open the door. "I need some fresh air." He jumped out, strode forward and stopped a few feet away, his shoulders rising and falling with the effort of self-restraint.

Louise started to cry. Julie caught sight of the little white shoes and socks that had toppled off her husband's lap into the road. She scooped them up and fell back into her seat, clutching them tightly, her lip trembling. Dad turned off the engine.

"There, there, Julie. I know you mean well," said Mum kindly, rising, turning and stretching out her hand towards her daughter-in-law.

"I'm sorry Mum," she whimpered. "I try, really I do. I can't help my temper … oh, what am I talking about? I don't even have a mum."

"Well, I'm your mum now. I'd love you to call me Mum." She squeezed between the seats and kissed Julie gently on the forehead. "Now stop crying and let's make the best of it." She leaned out of the open door. "Chris, don't be silly. Come inside and give your wife a hug. She needs you."

Chris trudged back, climbed into the van, shut the window and gave Julie's knee a half-hearted squeeze.

Fortunately, Sarah was a resilient girl and seemed more interested in an opportunity to see the Lions of Longleat than in her parents' differences. She was not disappointed.

That evening, while Julie was putting the children to bed and Mum was washing up, I sought out Chris. He was reading 'Watership Down' on a folding chair in the back garden. Dad was there too, reading the newpaper.

"Chris?" He looked up absent-mindedly. "What are you reading, Chris?"

"Well, I *was* reading that." He put the open book face down on the ground and sighed. "What d'you want?"

I grinned. "It's a kids' book."

"Humph ... ruddy rabbits," Dad grunted, glancing down at the book. "Nothing but pests, only fit for the pot!"

"Come here, Chris, I want to show you something."

"It's actually not a kids' book," said Chris, rising. "As a matter of fact, I wouldn't read it to my kids if it was the last book on earth."

"Over here." I beckoned, walking off towards the bottom of the garden.

"It's about ... politics," he continued, coming up alongside me. "Power struggles and suchlike."

"You mean, like the one you're having with Julie?" I suggested as soon as I was sure we were out of earshot, grasping eagerly at the connection. "What's going on? It's like you hate each other."

"Oh, don't ask! I've tried, believe me I've tried Vicks, but she gets more like her father every day. Now, what did you want to show me?"

"Well ... nothing actually. I just wanted a chat," I said sheepishly.

"You really need to learn to mind your own business, Vicky. I *knew* you were about to quiz me. You're *so* predictable."

"Well, I can't help being concerned. Now, you were saying ...?"

"She's much worse since Louise came along. She's so wrapped up in the kids, sometimes I feel like I don't exist. Half the time she only talks to me when she wants me to do something for her. I'm not sure how much longer I can stand it. She's driving me mad, her and her father."

"That's terrible, I had no idea. What will you do?"

"I don't know. Put up with it, I guess. I'm not the quitting type. Don't get me wrong; when it's good, it's great … but it's not great very often … well, hardly ever, if I'm honest."

"You know, she can't always help herself," I replied tenderly. "She got really upset today, after you stormed off. I think she's got real mother issues. She actually called our mum 'Mum' today. I don't think she meant to. It just, kind of, came out. Interesting, don't you think?"

"She could try being a bit more open. I know she's been hurt but she flatly refuses to talk about her own mother … ever," he said peevishly. "God knows what that's all about. Her father's just as bad; it's like a conspiracy of silence; skeleton in the closet. It'll never get any better until they let it out."

"It must be really hard for you, living with both of them," I said, sympathetically.

"Oh, you don't know the half of it. They gang up on me, I swear they do, and set the children against me. That's why I spoil Sarah. I know I do, but I can't help myself."

I shook my head. "I'm sure they're not doing it on purpose. Julie seems such a nice person and she *is* a good mother, and Uncle Liam's really quite sweet on the inside. It can't be all that bad."

Chris turned crimson. "Jesus Christ, have a care, Vicky," he spluttered. "It's intolerable! He blames me entirely for seducing his daughter and coercing her into marriage. Well, let me tell you, she's every bit as culpable as I am but she's too spineless to own it to her father, so he hates me for a blackguard, though I've tried to win his approval … God knows I've tried. And you tell me it 'can't be all that bad'?" He drew in his breath and clenched his jaw. "If you want to try living with them, be my guest! I'm in sore need of an ally." He struck his foot against the fence angrily.

"You make it sound like war. You should talk to her."

"*Talk* to her? Have *you* tried talking to her?"

"Well I'm really worried, that's all."

"Don't fret, Vicks. I won't do anything rash. Maybe it's her hormones. I don't want to discuss it anymore." He turned and started to walk back up the garden. I hesitated. "Forget it, there's nothing you can do," he called softly over his shoulder.

All things considered, the latter part of my stay in Bath was not without its moments of sunshine, but the deepening rift between my brother and his wife cast a shadow over our family to which only Sarah seemed oblivious; or perhaps she was simply used to it. Ironically, my premeditations, in which I had pictured myself as the odd one out, proved to be groundless. I suspect Julie felt it more keenly than I did.

* * *

It was almost a relief to get back to work, which served as a distraction as well as giving me plenty of opportunities to offload. Wendy was a good listener who never failed to remind me that attempting to mend my brother's marriage was not in my remit. Now that we had passed the intermediate exams we were given much more responsibility, including accompanying the junior doctors when they did their rounds. The hierarchy was such that we held them in awe and found it quite daunting at first, until we found out that the doctors were even more terrified of the ward sisters than we were of the doctors.

My next placement during the autumn was at Risedale Maternity Hospital. This was the placement I had been looking forward to the most as it embodied the whole rationale behind my training. Risedale was pretty spartan by today's standards and the auxiliaries brisk and austere. The inmates – and I use that word advisedly – were forced to eat 'to keep their strength up', even during the advanced stages of labour and immediately following an exhausting birth. The regime was harsh and visiting hours strict. The babies spent the night in the nursery and we would wheel them in after breakfast. I loved watching their mothers' eyes glaze over and stole many an opportunity to shower congratulations, compliments and kindness upon these lucky ladies and their offspring, even though I knew this practice was frowned upon by most of the nurses, who never missed a chance to dish out advice. "You'll make a rod for your own back," they would tut, whenever a new mother plucked a crying infant from its crib.

During my final week, a very singular event occurred. One morning, I was summoned to the examination room to prepare a bath for a young woman in the early stages of labour, while the nurse carried out a preliminary examination. A girl lay on the couch, her platinum blonde hair dripping over the sides, but it was the harsh ring of her voice that stopped me in my tracks.

"Ouch, that hurts," she hissed. "Can't you be more careful?"

"For goodness sake, Miss … what was your name again?"

"Barker … B-A-R-K-E-R!"

The girl on the couch was Joanie – the same girl who wore trouble like a badge of honour; the one who was always present at the centre of every local scuffle. Here lay the girl who had witnessed the fracas in the pub on World Cup day and probably had a hand in it, an incident which had cut the old man to the quick and still pained him whenever his thoughts took a dark turn. Here lay the girl who had tried her hardest to come between Toni and her fiancé at that memorable house party and more recently, for all I knew. Phil was often late and his excuses were often lame.

"Come along, nurse," scolded the auxiliary, casting a sharp glance in my direction.

I scurried into the adjoining bathroom with my head lowered, ran a shallow bath and made a hasty exit. One thing was clear. Professional etiquette as well as moral duty demanded lenience, and there and then I made a pledge to drop my prejudices and regard her as a reformed character. Still, I couldn't help wondering who the father was – probably Jason, silly besotted boy that he was.

The following morning, Joanie was in the advanced stages of labour. By the time I entered the delivery room, she had consumed copious amounts of gas and air and didn't seem to know or care who I was. She swore like a trooper and landed me a hefty kick on the shoulder while I was attempting to administer pethidine into her leg for the pain. During the early afternoon, she delivered a healthy, eight pound baby boy.

"Oh, he's beautiful!" I breathed, handing over the tiny infant to his mother. In the heat of the moment, I had totally forgotten that she was not yet aware of my presence in the delivery room.

She looked down at her child and then at me.

"Vicky! Jesus Christ! What the hell are you doing here?" she shrieked, the colour draining from her face.

"I work here," I said simply. "Sorry Joanie, I would have told you earlier, but you didn't seem … well … compos mentis."

The auxiliary in charge glared at me. "Nurse Kelly. Please remember your place. You are to address the patient as Miss Barker."

I gulped and turned crimson. Joanie sniggered.

"Have you decided on a name, Miss Barker?" I asked, awkwardly.

She burst out laughing. I waited patiently for her fit of giggles to subside.

"Dunno, don't care," she drawled. "I'm not keeping it. It's going up for adoption."

"But the father … your husband? Perhaps when he sees your baby you'll both change your minds." It was the standard response. A lot of parents changed their minds.

"Pooh … *I'm* not married. Chance'd be a fine thing."

"Oh, I *am* sorry."

"I'm not," she said impassively. "Not really. Marriage is for losers. You'd better take the boy. I'm knackered." She winked. "Can't afford to get attached, you know."

I placed the poor child back in his crib while Joanie slept off her ordeal.

The next day, visiting was in the afternoon. As I straightened out the last of the beds, the proud fathers startled to trickle in. I watched with mounting curiosity. If Joanie's unexpected appearance on the scene had given rise to a tremor, the realisation of my worst fears had the impact of a magnitude 10 earthquake. In sauntered Phil, cool as a cucumber, brandishing a huge bunch of dahlias which he deposited on Joanie's bed before bending over to give her a hearty kiss. I gripped the end of a bedstead which I was fortunate enough to be standing next to, quickly averting my face and swallowing hard to stave off a sudden inclination to vomit. A minute later, tears stinging my eyes and legs trembling, I made a swift exit, without looking left or right, and shut myself in the toilets where I could sob unreservedly, but only for 10 minutes as this was usually the maximum time allowed before the auxiliaries sent out a search party to extract erring students from the cloakroom.

Through the veil of tears I envisaged the face of my sister. Sooner or later the truth would leak out and her heart would be broken. Phil was a dangerous animal, with the capacity to thrill but the potential to destroy her. I wanted to tell her, to expose him as a cheat and a liar. Then I remembered that I was bound by patient confidentiality. A breach could mean instant dismissal, a risk I couldn't afford to take.

Resolved to act but without any clear plan in place, I dried my eyes, adjusted my uniform, re-entered the ward, marched smartly up to Joanie's bedside and stood directly behind Phil. Joanie's face froze and she gave a significant jerk of the head. Phil turned round and peered up at me. His jaw dropped. I don't care to reiterate the language that issued from his lips; suffice to say that the words conveyed unmitigated alarm.

"I'd like a word with you now, if you please, Mr. Diall," I said, my intonation hard and my countenance stony.

"If you don't mind, Miss … er … Miss Kelly," he retaliated, his voice laden with sarcasm, "I'm visiting my friend here. Do you have a problem with that?"

"It's 'Nurse Kelly' to you, and yes I do have a problem. This way please."

He got up slowly and deliberately, smoothed his hair, straightened his cuffs and accompanied me out of the ward at a leisurely pace with an easy expression smeared all over his deceitful face.

"Do you have your car with you?" I asked coldly, hardly knowing why I did as he was far too arrogant to travel by bus.

"Sure," he replied, with an affected air of amiability.

I followed him into the street, praying I wouldn't be spotted from any of the hospital windows and branded a truant. He ushered me into the passenger seat of his MG Midget and sat down heavily in the driver's seat. As soon as I reached the comparative privacy of his car, my courage failed me and I began to blub helplessly.

"Lord, give me strength," Phil muttered under his breath, diving into the door panel and retrieving a packet of tissues. "I can't abide snivelling women!" He pressed a hankie into my hand and then lit a cigarette and stared out of the window while I tried to compose myself.

"You'll have to tell Toni," I sniffed, as soon as I was able to speak. "I don't know how you can contemplate not … how can you live with yourself?" I choked, bitterly.

He turned to face me, squeezed my hand and smiled condescendingly.

"You've got it all wrong, sweetheart. Joanie's just a friend. The flowers … I was just delivering them … her fella couldn't come today." His tone was plausible but the guilt in his eyes, not to mention his reputation, belied the falsehoods that slipped from his tongue.

"And the kiss," I retorted, snatching my hand away, "I suppose you were delivering that too! Phil, I'm not a complete idiot … and

I happen to know that she's been calling the baby Philip. Answer that!"

He flinched and his colour rose. "All right, all right, I made a mistake. But the woman means nothing to me. It makes no difference anyway. She's not keeping it."

"*Makes no difference*? It makes all the difference in the world … and if you don't tell Toni, I will!" I declared passionately, my professional obligations forgotten in the heat of the moment. I was quick to realise my error but it was too late to retract my words. Maybe … yes, maybe this was the bluff that might just pull it off.

Phil drew on his cigarette, threw it out of the window and patted my thigh in a gesture that was both patronising and suggestive. I shuddered.

"Okay, you win, you little witch. I'll come clean. Now off you go and play doctors and nurses."

I scowled, got out of the car without a word, slammed the door hard and walked briskly back to the hospital.

For the next half hour, I attempted to perform my duties but my brain was in turmoil and it was impossible to focus on my work. Eventually I went and found one of the senior nurses and begged to be allowed to go home early, claiming that I was unwell. I'm generally too principled to 'throw a sickie' but I decided then and there to pack an overnight bag, get the train to Seascale and seek solace in the safety and comfort of home.

Two hours later, Dad met me at the station.

"Vicky, whatever's the matter?" he gasped, noticing my tear-stained face. "Toni's come home early in floods of tears … she's talking to her mother. Not more man trouble? Not Ray, is it?" He gave me a hug.

I shook my head. "It's all right, Dad," I mumbled into his chest. "It's not Ray, it's Toni … you see … it's all my fault … that is to say, it is and it isn't."

"Oh, you *are* a mass of contradictions," he said kindly, rubbing my back. "Come home and have a cup of tea. Nothing's that bad that can't be mended."

I wiped my eyes on my sleeve and clambered gratefully into the car.

Toni was devastated. Before I got home, she had torn the ring from her finger and consigned it to the bin. Her initial reaction was fury and righteous indignation, but by the time I walked through the door she was grief-stricken and sobbing inconsolably at the kitchen table. I ran to her and flung my arms around her trembling shoulders.

"He's not worth it," I uttered. "You can do so much better."

After dinner, she had a bath. When she came back downstairs, she was steely and reserved and refused to say how she really felt, stating that she was "all right" in an offhand manner. When Mum tried to force the issue, she stomped upstairs and shut herself in her bedroom.

At 11 p.m. I mounted the stairs and crept quietly into her room – our room, the room we had shared as children. It was dark but I knew my sister was not asleep. As I undressed, I could hear her tossing and turning restlessly under the covers and fighting back tears. I slipped on my nightdress, peeled back the bedclothes and climbed into bed next to her.

"Oh Vicky, I'm so wretched," she blurted out, her body heaving.

I kissed her head, stroked her hair and held her in my arms until she fell into a fitful slumber.

Chapter 9

The Wedding

Over the course of the next few weeks, Toni's grief was transmuted into listlessness and indifference. She slept late, paid less attention to her appearance than formerly and often complained that she felt tired. She showed little interest in life's small pleasures – a night out with friends, a trip to the movies, Sunday roast, TV sitcoms and the hit parade. She found fault with the staff and clientele at the Scawfell Hotel and thumbed disconsolately through the Situations Vacant, finding nothing to inspire her there. Mum became convinced that she was depressed and insisted on a visit to the doctor. Toni acquiesced rather reluctantly and returned from her consultation with some tiny blue pills with a very long name which remained unopened on her bedside cabinet until she no longer had need of them. Toni was never quite comfortable in her own skin, even though it did her much credit. Until she fell in love with a good man, I thought ruefully, she would probably never be truly happy.

The start of my final year of training found me back in nursing school, or 'block' as we called it. This was followed by three months in the operating theatres, where I learnt how to work in a scrupulously sterile environment, to lay out the instruments on trollies and count them back in, and ultimately to assist in the execution of highly delicate medical procedures. It was scary at first and I would approach the surgeon, who was only one step removed from God in my estimation, with a shaking hand. However, once I had overcome my fear, the opportunity to gain a more in-depth knowledge of surgical procedures, as well as the chance to work with practitioners at the highest level within the medical profession, helped me to develop the confidence I would need to embark on the next step towards becoming a qualified nurse.

Hence, I was better prepared when I finally took charge of a ward in the spring. For the first time, the onus was on me to ensure that medicines were administered and drips replaced, bloods sampled and analysed and patient reports written. I was assisted by a small team of trainees. I quickly got accustomed to issuing orders but it was hard to grasp the concept that I was effectively 'in the driving seat' and I sometimes felt bewildered by the prospect. The breezy efficiency I managed to project bore little relation to the unease that lurked just beneath the surface.

In the meantime, during one of my frequent trips home, I was checking the film listings in the local paper when I clapped eyes on an advertisement. I ran upstairs to find my sister, who was getting ready for work.

"Look, Toni!" I cried gleefully, thrusting the newspaper under her nose. "A school reunion – we absolutely *must* go!"

She read the notification with some interest but then shook her head.

"Oh, I don't think so, I might run into … well … you know who." She screwed up her face in an expression of distaste.

"I shouldn't think Phil will go," I countered. "He's far too cool. He'll think it's beneath him!"

"Well, it'll probably be rubbish anyway," she said, opening her powder compact.

"Oh please, Toni," I implored. "It'll be weird going with Chris or Michael, not that there's much chance they'll go … no, I'm sure they won't. Please … it'll be fun."

"Oh, all right, I'll think about it." She applied a liberal dose of face powder to her nose and both cheeks. "Now go away," she said good-naturedly. "You'll make me late for work."

It wasn't too hard to persuade Toni to change her mind. In her present state of mind, she was quite malleable and a few days later she announced that she 'might as well go' as she had 'nothing left to lose.' I put a lot of thought into my outfit, hair and make-up. At school, I had regarded myself as an 'ugly duckling'. Although this was no longer true, I took pains to make much of the difference, driven by the need to compensate for my former inadequacies by appearing in the guise of a 'swan'. I purchased a little red pleated skirt, a floral blouse and a new pair of platform shoes.

Then, on the day of the event, as I was styling my unruly curls into neat ringlets, Toni got cold feet.

"I'm not going," she said decisively. "You can go if you want, but I can't face all those people. They're bound to know all about Joanie's baby – she's such a blabbermouth – and I can't face the humiliation."

"I hardly think so," I argued. "It was all hushed up, if you remember. I mean, I know times have changed, but it's still a big deal, having a baby out of wedlock. She moved down to Barrow to avoid the scandal. That's why I ran into her. She's hardly going to advertise the fact."

"Well, I don't think I can be bothered," she said wearily. "You go. They'll be loads of people you know."

I sighed audibly, applied the finishing touches to my hair and went downstairs to the kitchen.

"Mum, Toni's changed her mind. She's not going. Oh, what am I going to do?" I moaned, making no attempt to conceal my frustration. "I can't go on my own."

"Oh, that's too bad," she said sympathetically. "Leave it to me. I'll see what I can do."

She hastened upstairs and returned 20 minutes later. I was ironing my blouse despondently.

"She doesn't know what's good for her, the silly girl," she tutted, "but she's going. I told her it's unkind to let you down. There's plenty more eggs in the basket. It's time she stopped hankering after the bad ones."

I laughed. "Don't you mean, 'fish in the sea'? Anyway, it amounts to the same thing. Thanks Mum." I gave her a swift kiss on the cheek and hurried upstairs to paint my nails.

Toni put on a brave face and tried her best to look cheerful. I sincerely believe she was under strict orders from Mum. She chose a stunning Biba trouser suit in emerald green which set off her tall stature and rich brown hair to a tee. I looked at my own reflection in the mirror and regarded her enviously, almost wishing she would change her mind again.

We arrived shortly after eight o'clock and bought ourselves a Cinzano at the 'bar', a collection of trestle tables manned by a small band of volunteers dressed in school uniform. Alice Cooper's 'School's Out' was blaring from a mobile disco unit at the opposite end of the hall, complete with built-in lighting effects. A large mirrorball hung from the ceiling, scattering tiny spots of moving white light over the partygoers. The hall was festooned with banners, paper chains and streamers. There were tables and chairs at the bar end so we found ourselves a seat and sat sipping our drinks. Soon we were joined by Susan and Valerie from Toni's year and the three fell into conversation.

It wasn't long before I spotted a familiar face in the crowd; it was my old school friend Sally. We had been as thick as thieves as children but had drifted apart during adolescence, as childhood friends often do. Sally was standing not far away with another girl with whom I was slightly acquainted. As I approached her gingerly, she looked across at me and beamed.

"Why Vicky, you look *amazing*. I *love* your hair!" she cried, putting both hands on my shoulders and kissing my cheek.

"Oh, it's usually a right mess," I said, deprecatingly. "I can't do a thing with it. You look great. How *are* you?"

"I'm brill, thanks. I'm married, you know." She held out her hand and brandished a broad, gold band. "He's here … somewhere."

"Oh my gosh! You didn't marry someone from school, did you?" I exclaimed, barely able to contain my curiosity. "Come on, spill the beans."

"You'll have to wait and see," she replied with a mischievous smile. "Have you seen anyone else yet?"

I shook my head. "Nah, haven't been here long. I left Toni over there, talking to a couple of girls from her year."

"How *is* your sister?" she declared emphatically, "and more importantly, how are *you*?"

We talked about this and that, about the people and places that had defined our youth.

At length, I noticed a young man whom I recognised. He was chatting to a friend at the bar. He was short in stature with dark curly hair and a pleasant face.

"Hey, isn't that that spotty kid that used to follow you around like a puppy?" I said merrily. "Over there. What was his name again? Robin … yes, that was it. Robin." I inclined my head towards the pair.

Sally burst into peals of laughter. "Oh, Vicky, you're the limit!" she giggled, catching her breath before bursting into a renewed expression of mirth.

I grinned inanely, bemused at the violence of her reaction. Then Robin smiled across at Sally, she responded with a delicate flutter of the hand and the awful truth dawned on me. If there was ever a moment when I wished the ground would open up and swallow me whole, then that moment was now. I stood rooted to the spot, tongue-tied and cringing with embarrassment.

"He's my husband!" she squealed, clapping me on the shoulder and reaching into her handbag for a tissue to dab her eyes.

"Oh Sally, I'm *so* sorry," I said earnestly, when I was finally able to speak.

"That's all right." She caught hold of my free hand. "Come and say hello to him."

During the course of the evening, I met many more of my old friends and acquaintances and danced with Robin and his friend. To my immense relief, neither Phil nor Joanie turned up. At 11 p.m., as the final strains of Donny Osmond drifted over the heads of the dancers, the lights went up and I looked around the room for my sister, conscious that I had not seen her for some considerable time. I waited on. At 11.10 my frustration started to get the better of me. The taxi was due and there was still no sign of Toni. On the way out, I spied her coat on the back of a chair near the bar and picked it up. I went out and waited just inside the main doors. The taxi duly arrived and I asked the driver to wait. Five minutes later, the doors swung open and Toni swept in, arm in arm with Jason, her face flushed and eyes shining, evidently unaware of the time. She stopped short.

"Oh, has it finished?" she said, with a note of surprise.

"It finished 20 minutes ago," I said frostily. "Here's your coat. Taxi's here. Come on, I've been waiting ages."

Jason smiled broadly. "Oh … err, hi Vicky. Sorry I kept her," he said disarmingly. "I'll see you in the week, Tone," he continued, catching up my starry-eyed sister and kissing her exuberantly.

"Glad you went?" I asked her later, as I climbed into bed.

"Mmmm …," she murmured, rolling onto her side and hugging her pillow.

After that, Toni rallied and Jason became a regular guest at Cinderdale Farm.

* * *

On the 22nd June, the family gathered to mark the occasion of Louise's first birthday. It was a fine day; the time was approaching midday. Mum and Julie were in the kitchen, preparing a cheese fondue. Dad and Chris were fixing one of the barn doors. Nan sat in a deck chair with Louise on her lap. Michael was sitting on the swing seat in the garden, reading the Daily Telegraph. A gentle breeze whispered amongst the trees and tugged at the pages of his newspaper. I was kneeling in the sandpit with Sarah, building sandcastles, when Toni emerged through the patio doors.

"Vicky, have you got a moment?" Her tone was casual. I had no inkling that she was about to drop a bombshell. Brushing the sand from my legs, I followed her indoors and upstairs to our bedroom.

She sat down on her bed and looked up at me with tears in her eyes.

I squatted at the bedside and clasped her hand.

"Toni, whatever's the matter?"

"Oh Vicky, I don't know whether to laugh or cry," she blurted out. "I'm pregnant!"

I nearly keeled over with the shock and was forced to use my spare hand to maintain my balance. I looked at her despairingly.

"Toni, Toni, how can you be so stupid?" I wailed, raising my eyes to heaven and wondering what I had done to earn my place in the front seat of the rollercoaster which appeared to be conveying my family from one catastrophe to the next.

She shrugged.

"What will you do?"

"Why, get married of course," she said airily, with a peremptory toss of the head.

I gulped. "Married? I presume you've told Jason."

"Yes, that was the easy bit. Now comes the hard bit," she said glumly.

As predicted, Dad flew into a rage when he learnt of the plight of his daughter and the two barely spoke for a week. Mum tried hard to be angry but was far too excited by the prospect of a wedding and a third grandchild to maintain a wall of silence, and they got along happily after a heated exchange lasting not more than half an hour. The preparations commenced and the date was set. They were to be married on Saturday 21st September, three months before the baby was due. Louise learnt to walk at 13 months and Toni seized upon this developmental step as a sign. She bought Louise a tiny bridesmaid's dress and insisted she followed her down the aisle alongside Sarah. With only a page boy wanting, the services of our nearest neighbour's little boy were procured and the cherubic trio was complete. James was Janice's brother, a very late addition to the Duffy clan born some five years previously, just at the point when his mother believed she was past child-bearing age. It seems you can't be too careful in our neck of the woods.

* * *

On the 21st September, I woke early, peered into the half-light to find Toni's bed already empty and directed my gaze towards the door. From the thin strip of yellow emanating from the landing, the sound of running water and the tinkle of my sister's voice as she breezed through her repertoire, I discerned that she was running a bath. I climbed out of bed, shivered and hastened to the window. The house and garden were wrapped in a clinging veil of mist which effaced the mountains but a few miles distant. A heavy drizzle hung in the chill air. Tiny droplets formed on the window pane and trickled down like tears. I felt apprehensive. Uncle Liam had crossed swords with Jason in the past and he was not the type to forgive and forget. On the other hand, eight years had elapsed since that single encounter on match day and Jason was now sporting a beard. I brushed aside my misgivings and, clutching my book, slipped back between the sheets and lost myself in the world of Miss Jean Brodie until the spell was broken by the return of my sister in high spirits.

It was evident from the mood downstairs that my family did not share my disquiet. Mum was in a state of elation. She had never quite come to terms with the sorrow wrought by the secret nature of her firstborn's marriage and relished the occasion with fervour rarely seen in sober, middle-aged folk. Nan drank wine at the breakfast table. Dad dropped his surly façade and waxed long and loud on the merits of his beautiful daughter and the amiable Jason King. Even the dour Michael managed to rattle off a couple of apposite puns.

"Look what the weather's *throne* at us!" he grinned, waving his loaded fork towards the window. "I wonder if the *reign* will last."

Toni's countenance was so full of rapture that the application of make-up could scarcely have made her look lovelier.

After breakfast, Jean arrived. Jean was Toni's oldest and dearest schoolfriend. She took her bridesmaid's duties much more seriously than I did and lost no time in ushering my sister upstairs for a makeover. Preparations ensued until noon, when Alan and Caroline arrived from Manchester and we all sat down together for tea and sandwiches.

"Mind you don't get chutney on your dresses!" cautioned Mum, handing Toni and me a handful of paper towels. "Put these on your laps."

After lunch, I ascended the stairs to apply my lipstick and scoop up a few stray hairs, then went to survey myself in the full-length mirror in Mum and Dad's room. My dress was peach-coloured with a lace bodice and full circle skirt that ended just below the knee. Mum, whose creative talents were many and varied, had crafted an abundance of tiny, raspberry red roses from an old starched table cover and stitched them onto the crocheted snood into which my hair was now bundled. So pleasing was the result that she had been inspired to forage through her collection of fabric scraps to fashion a matching corsage to adorn my dress and three large flowers to pin onto the dresses of each of the other bridesmaids. 'Colour over conformity' being the overriding principle governing my mother's creative endeavours, these charming ornaments bore little resemblance to each other. Sarah had seized upon the pink one, as might be expected of any little girl of five. Louise, who was too young to care, had been assigned the yellow because we all thought it would contrast so prettily with her dark brown hair. For Jean, Mum made a white taffeta rose.

Toni appeared in the doorway in full regalia. I moved aside and she walked over to the mirror. On her head she wore a crystal-studded tiara and short veil. Her dress was made from ivory-coloured satin. It had a scooped neckline and cap sleeves. It was tightly gathered just below the bust-line and fell to her shins in soft pleats which shimmered as she turned to check out her profile from the side.

"D'you think anyone will notice?" she said with a mixture of trepidation and levity.

"*Notice*?" I exclaimed, with less tact than the occasion demanded. "A quickie wedding and a smock generally only means one thing! It's not even white!"

"Oh, what do I care what people think!" she said with a contemptuous toss of the head. "They'll find out soon enough."

As she crossed the room, I looked at her blossoming figure with a trace of envy, wishing I shared her airy disregard for convention. Ray and I were now on intimate terms but we were so far removed from each other, both geographically and circumstantially, that it was difficult to see the way forward. Ray and his family had checked into the Scawfell Hotel late last night. I had been bitterly disappointed at this turn of events, which was the combined result of his parents' anxiety not to encroach on the wedding preparations and the prior claims of family members. Nan occupied Chris's old room. Alan and Caroline were installed in the bedroom he used to share with Michael, a second hand Pink Floyd EP being the currency with which Alan had bribed his younger brother to relinquish his bed and spend the night on the sofa.

"Help me with these." Mum's pearl necklace dangled from Toni's outstretched hand. I raised my eyebrows. "It's all right," she grinned. "Mum said I could. Something borrowed, see?" She held out her other hand. "… and here's the 'something old', look, Grandma's ring." On her middle finger gleamed an opal studded band bequeathed to her by our late paternal grandmother. "Something new …", she continued dreamily, swinging her hips and watching the light play on her dress, as I fastened the pearls around her neck. "Something blue … something blue! Cripes! Quick Vicky, think of something! Oh, I wish I'd thought of it before. I could have got myself a garter. Aren't all brides supposed to wear one?"

"Dunno." Driven by instinct rather than reason, I dived into our Mum's dressing table drawers. The first one was full of socks; the second contained tights and stockings. As I rummaged, I spied a patch of navy and gave it a tug.

"Wait, I've got an idea!" I scurried to the bathroom and returned with the haircutting scissors.

"Hold onto that end," I ordered, thrusting the foot of one leg into her hand and stepping away. I made two smart cuts across the leg and waved the small offcut triumphantly in the air. "I've made you a garter," I announced proudly.

Toni stared at me in disbelief.

"It looks awful. I can't wear that!"

"Oh, there's no pleasing some people," I huffed. "… I know, wait there". I dashed out again and returned with a bottle of silver nail polish.

"Hold this end", I commanded, pressing the offending article down on the dressing table and stretching it sideways. "Unscrew that, would you?" I loaded the brush and daubed the letters B-R-I-D-E onto the band.

Toni burst out laughing.

"It's horrible!" she squealed.

"Suit yourself." I shrugged and blew on the letters.

"No, no, Vicky, it's so tacky, it's almost cool. Of course I'll wear it! Take my end a minute."

She fetched her hairdryer and I held it taut while she applied blasts of hot air. Then she slipped it onto her right leg and gave me an affectionate hug.

A commotion downstairs signalled the arrival of Sarah and Louise, who were to travel in the bridesmaids' car chauffeured by Mum. By the time I had got downstairs, Chris had already gone. Alan, Caroline and Michael were sitting in the car with the engine running, waiting for Nan who had come back inside to fetch her hat.

"Oh, Sarah, don't you look a picture!" I cooed, bending down to give my little niece a kiss.

She giggled and spun around. "I'm a princess, I'm a princess."

"Yes, you're a princess. Now stand still while I pin this on." I fastened the pink rose to her dress.

"Can I hold Lou-Lou's hand in the church, pleeease?" she implored, looking at me with cow eyes.

"Oh course you can, lovey. Now go and use the toilet. It's nearly time to leave."

15 minutes later, we clambered into the car. The sky was heavy with cloud and intermittent puffs of wind hinted at the prospect of more rain. Jean sat in the front with Mum. I positioned myself in the back between the two girls and we set off on the short journey to St. Paul's Church.

As we neared the end of the little lane that terminated at the church, we were surprised to see the unmistakable figure of Nan tottering along the verge towards us in her conspicuous pink coat and hat. All morning, I had been suppressing the fear that something would go amiss and now a wave of panic swept over me.

"Oh dear, what *is* she doing?" exclaimed Mum, mildly. "I wonder if she's forgotten something." She pulled in and wound down the car window.

"Oh Marion," panted Nan. "Something awful's happened! The silly old man is all set to boycott the wedding and that lily-livered daughter of his is condoning it. She's taking him home … and it's all my fault! Chris is raging fit to burst!"

I glanced at Sarah, who was listening intently.

"Excuse me, darling," I said, lifting her over my lap, sliding across and climbing out of the car, while Mum did likewise.

"He's always seemed such a nice old gentleman," continued Nan, breathlessly, "so naturally I sat down next to him in the church … us old timers must stick together, you know. Well, he was staring at the groom and I asked him if he knew the chap. He couldn't remember at first and then he got a face like thunder and says, well more like growls, 'that man insulted me.' 'Whatever do you mean?' I says. Well, by this time, Chris was crimson and looked like he was about to explode. 'Now come along, Liam,' I says. 'This is Toni's wedding. Let bygones be bygones, ay?' 'Wedding or no, I'll not be civil to him,' he says. This was too much for Chris. He turns on him and says 'Just put up or get out!' quiet, between his teeth, seething like a caged animal, he was. Well, not wanting a scene, I laid my hand on the old gent's leg and says 'He's doing right by her, you know … in her condition … surely he deserves a bit of credit for that.' 'In *her* condition?' he roared. Well, it was awful … everyone was staring. Julie took him by the arm. 'Come on, Father, I'll take you home,' she says and they march off out of church. Well, Chris went marching out after them and by the time I gets out they're having a standoff. Oh, what's to be done?"

Mum looked to the heavens. "Get in," she sighed, her tone thick with exasperation. "Sarah, sit on Auntie Vicky's lap, there's a dear. We'll have to make the best of it. Oh Lord preserve us, we haven't much time. Toni'll be along in a few minutes."

We rounded the corner and parked opposite the church. While I gathered up Louise, Nan caught hold of Sarah's hand. Chris and Liam were standing on the green outside the gate, locked in combat, while Julie looked on helplessly. Liam was wagging his finger at Chris, who stood rigid with his fists clenched at his sides. Sarah's bottom lip quivered, she wrestled her hand free and ran to her mother. Louise wriggled, stretched out her arms and started to cry. "Mummy, want Mummy."

"I'll not bide with xenophobics and hussies. ''Twas a black day my Julie got mixed up with your family and no mistake."

"Oh, Father!" Julie gasped, her eyes wet with tears.

I handed her the screaming child and touched her arm gently as I retreated.

She turned to Chris. "I'm taking him home," she said, miserably. "I'd better take Lou as well. Look, the poor child's beside herself."

"Take Lou? Oh no you don't … Lou stays with me. This is a big day for her. How can you be so cavalier?"

"Rubbish, Chris! She's too young to care. She doesn't know what's going on, do you, darling?" she said, stroking her little daughter's dark curls.

"Her mother knows best," Liam cut in. "Let her be, young man. You know what your problem is? You can't say no to the little'uns. You should pay more heed to your betters."

Chris took a step towards Liam and raised his fist to strike him. I let out an involuntary yelp. He checked himself, turned around, walked away and stood by the church gate.

"Why do you and Daddy always *argue?*" sniffed Sarah.

"All mummies and daddies argue. It doesn't mean they don't love each other," Julie replied without conviction.

"Come along, Julie," said Liam briskly. "The poor mite's getting cold."

Julie looked desperately over at Chris, shrugged her shoulders and started to walk towards the car, with Sarah whimpering at her heels.

Chris strode across and positioned himself between Julie and the car.

"If the children go, I go," he said, his face red with anger. "I'm sick and tired of you and your father! He's a bully and a bigot … and you … you pander to him … all the time. You've lost the capacity to think for yourself. I didn't marry a woman, I married a puppet! "

Julie turned white and stared at her husband in disbelief.

"Oh ho! A bully and a bigot, am I? Well, at least now we know which way the land lies!"

Chris turned on Liam, his eyes blazing. "Yes, you're a bully, and just 'cause you've had a miserable life, doesn't give you the right to make everyone else's life a misery."

He looked back at Julie with contempt. "See what you've become! You *never* listen; you *never* consider my feelings; it's all about *him, him, him*. How can you be so spineless? He doesn't need you! He needs a bootlicker!" He drew in his breath. "Well I've had it with both of you! Him or me! You choose!"

He wrenched off his wedding ring, threw it down into the dirt and stomped off towards the church without a backward glance.

Julie bent down to pick up the ring.

"Leave it be. You'll not be wanting that," said her father.

By this time Sarah was wailing uncontrollably and tugging on her mother's arm.

"I want my Daddy," she choked, between her sobs.

"Let me take her," I said, feigning calmness. "Please, Uncle. She's been looking forward to it for ages. Take Louise if you must but please don't take Sarah."

He stared at me and opened his mouth to speak.

"Please Uncle," I begged. "Please don't take Sarah."

Julie let go of Sarah's hand and nudged her in my direction. "Well, Father?"

Liam frowned. "Come along, my girl," he said gruffly, addressing Julie. "I'll not stop here to be abused."

He turned and walked towards the car. Julie hesitated, then followed him mechanically, her face white and motionless.

I picked up the ring and gave it to Mum.

"You can hold my hand, Sarah," I said gently, bending down and cupping her face in my hands. "Will you, Sarah? I need looking after too, you know." I kissed her and rose quickly to divert the telltale redness in my eyes from her searching gaze.

Jean gave her a little posy of flowers to hold and her tears quickly subsided.

At that moment, the wedding car swept around the corner and glided to a halt. Dad handed Toni out of the car. I glanced uneasily over at Julie. Fortunately, she was rummaging in the boot of her car for a drink and toy to occupy Louise, an action which would not have aroused suspicion, even if my sister had been minded to notice.

Entering the church behind my sister, I glanced across and clapped eyes on Ray in the fourth pew from the front. He turned around and smiled broadly at me. It was all I could do to prevent my grief from spilling over but I fought it off valiantly and performed my duties with just enough composure to mask the turmoil in my head and sickness in my heart. The ceremony proceeded without a hitch and we all streamed out onto the green for photos, before relocating to the function room at the Scawfell Hotel for the reception. We told Toni that Louise was unwell and that Julie had taken her home.

By now, the impressionable Sarah's high spirits had returned, and she begged Chris to allow her to travel to the reception with her little playmate James in Janice's parents' car. As Julie had taken the car as well as his baby daughter, Chris squeezed into the back seat next to Sarah. Mum let me go in Ray's car and conveyed Auntie Gwen and Uncle Roger, who had come in a taxi because Roger had broken his ankle. Once in the car, with Ray's hand holding mine and our hips pressed together, the urge to cry became insurmountable and a small sob forced its way out, do what I might to suppress it.

"You sentimental old thing," teased Ray. "It's only a wedding."

"No, no, it's not that," I blurted out. "It's ... oh, perhaps I'd better start from the beginning ..." and that was how Ray became acquainted with the state of affairs between my brother and sister-in-law.

"Ruby, please don't say anything to Toni … not on her wedding day," I finished, as Uncle Bill turned off the car engine.

Ruby smiled warmly. "Of course I wouldn't. What do you take me for?"

I felt better after that.

After the meal and speeches, I gravitated back to Ray's side and we sat together exchanging news and anecdotes. Ray had graduated in the summer and had recently started a job at the Natural History Museum as a technician specialising in Geophysics. I told him proudly that they had put me in charge of a ward and spoke with trepidation about my final exams in the autumn.

"Wendy's getting married in December, you know," I prattled on, "to that junior doctor she met at the Christmas ball. Everyone's getting hitched … you know, we're at that age when …" I trailed off, suddenly feeling like a skater on thin ice. I noticed that his brown skin was tinged with red.

He fumbled in his pocket. I watched him, my heart thumping.

"Would you like another drink?"

"Oh, yes please, I'll have a glass of white wine," I said evenly, whilst inwardly chastising myself for having the stupidity to even consider that he was concealing a ring about his person.

He returned with the drinks and put them on the table in front of us.

"Dutch courage," he grinned, taking hold of my hand. "Hell, I'm not good at this sort of thing." He took a deep breath. "This isn't a proposal, right? It's just something to think about. I'm … well … I'm not ready to get married, but I guess when I am, I'll let you know, right? I just don't *feel* ready …so you'll have to be patient. I don't want to feel pressurised. That doesn't mean I don't love you but please don't assume that I'm going to propose to you any time soon, because I'm not, okay?"

I bit my lip and gulped my wine. I felt vaguely disappointed without fully comprehending why.

"Ah, Vicky, come here." He patted his knees. "Come on, sit here on my lap." I did as he bid and he clasped me in his arms and kissed my ear. "Don't be like that, sweetheart. It *is* a proposal of sorts, just not an official one. I thought you'd be pleased." He squeezed me tightly.

"Of course I'm pleased," I said, feeling somewhat reassured. "I don't mind waiting," I added, injecting as much casual indifference into my voice as I could muster.

Meanwhile, across the room, Sarah and James sat at Janice's feet playing 'paper, scissors, stone'. Chris sat next to Janice. They were having a serious conversation, if the expressions on their faces were anything to go by.

"Oh look at those two love birds." I pointed towards the children.

"What, the adults or the kids?" chuckled Ray.

"Oh, give over!" I giggled, unable to resist the wicked impulse to laugh at the irony of the scene before my eyes.

Later, there was dancing and a buffet. Just before eight o'clock, Chris put Sarah to bed in Auntie Gwen's room and returned with his jacket on. I was standing in the food queue with Mum.

"Oh, are you going already, dear?" said Mum with a note of surprise.

"Look, would you be an angel and take Sarah home with you tonight? I've got some things to sort out. It's awkward; I'll explain later. She can sleep with Vicky."

He turned to address me. "She can sleep in Toni's bed, can't she? Toni won't need it," he added impishly.

"All right, son. Mind how you go," said Mum, giving Chris a cursory hug. "You patched things up with Julie?"

He shrugged.

"Bye Mum, bye Vicks." He hesitated. "Vicks ... would you look after Sarah for me?" There was something peculiar in the request and in the manner in which it was delivered. In point of fact, his mood seemed rather buoyant for a man in the midst of a domestic crisis.

"Don't say it like that, Chris. You're freaking me out."

"Don't be silly … I'll see you tomorrow," he said, his voice barely audible above the alarm bells that were ringing in my head.

After waving off the bride and groom amid the customary rattle of tin cans, we went back indoors and danced some more. Ray pressed me close, my head against his shoulder. As the dying notes of "Your Song" trickled from the PA, he put his face close to my ear. "Would you like to see my room?" I nodded. To speak would have been to break the spell. "I'll go first; I'll see you in five; first floor, door number 8." He loosened his hold on me, kissed me peremptorily and sauntered out of the function room. I waited, sipping my drink, for a decent interval, before making my exit alone. Half an hour later, I returned with a spring in my step and a guilty smile on my face. Whether anybody actually noticed, or merely chose not to, is a question which remains unanswered to this day.

At 11 o'clock, the lights went up and we gathered up our coats, hats and children. I parted from Ray with a mixture of regret and relief. The day had been long and emotionally draining and I craved the safety and solitude of my bed.

Early on Sunday morning, I was startled out of my slumber by the sound of frantic banging on the front door. I rolled over and looked at the clock: 7.43 … 7.44 and still it continued unabated. Dad must be milking the herd. Mum was probably in the shower with the radio on. I muttered a curse, stumbled out of bed, threw on my dressing gown, ran downstairs and flung the door open.

"Vicky, thank God! Can I speak to Chris? Is he still asleep?" Julie stood before me, her hair in a mess and her face pale and drawn.

"Chris? He's not here. I thought he was with you."

"No. He's not with me. He didn't come home last night. I thought he was here … oh my God, where's Sarah? He's taken Sarah!" The words tumbled from her lips in a breathless torrent.

"It's all right, Sarah's here. She's sleeping in my room."

"Oh, thank God! Where's Chris? I want to talk to him."

I took her gently by the arm and conducted her along the passage into the kitchen.

"I don't know, Julie. Now sit down and stop panicking," I said firmly. "I'll make some tea."

"Are you absolutely certain he's not here?" She looked round the room wildly, as if expecting him to materialise before her eyes.

"Wait there, I'll check." I put the kettle on, went out into the hall and peered into the front room. It was empty. Softly, I opened the lounge door. The sole occupant was Michael, who was snoring on the sofa. I returned to the kitchen.

"He's definitely not here," I said with an air of resignation which might have been mistaken for nonchalance, when glimpsing the flicker of impatience that was eclipsed on the face of my sister-in-law by a renewed cloud of despair.

She sat down at the table and buried her head in her hands.

"Oh, where *is* he? I wish my mother was here. She would know what to do," she said forlornly.

I started. "Your mother? You've found your mother? You know where she is?" I cried out impetuously, hardly knowing what I was saying and reacting in a manner that ill-befitted the occasion.

She threw me a hostile glance.

"No … and I haven't the faintest idea," she sighed, with an effort to conceal her vexation which was almost tangible.

"Oh … sorry, only I thought she was … at least, I didn't know if …"

"I told you, Vicky," she cut in defensively. "I haven't the faintest idea."

"Sorry …" I mumbled, wincing at the sting of her response.

She brought her fist down hard on the table.

"Everyone deserts me. Why does everyone hate me so?" she burst out vehemently. Her bottom lip trembled.

"Oh no, Julie, nobody hates you." I wrapped my arm round her shoulders and pressed her head against my bosom.

Soon after, to my immense relief, Mum came in and made tea.

Chapter 10

Farewell Cumberland

When I had finished my tea, I went back up to my room. Sarah was sitting up in bed.

"Now, Jemima," she said earnestly, holding her ragdoll at arm's length. "Stop crying. You can't sing Happy Birthday to Daddy. He's not well."

I drew in my breath. "Sarah …"

"Oh, hello Auntie Vicky," she said brightly.

Taking control of the impulse to satisfy my curiosity for fear of alarming my little niece, I walked casually over to her bedside, sat down and gave her a kiss.

"Morning, sweetie. Did you sleep well?"

"Oh yes, this bed is soooo comfy." She yawned, stretched both arms above her head and pressed her back into the pillows behind her. "When's Daddy coming back?" she continued, in a matter-of-fact tone. "Is the doctor going to make him better?"

"Oh, I'm not sure …" I paused to steady my voice. "Doctor? What did he say to you last night, Sarah?"

"He said he was poorly," she replied simply. "He said he's going away and he's going to come back when he's better. Is he in hospital?"

"Yes, perhaps he's gone to hospital. Yes, I expect that's it," I said, clutching eagerly at the lifeline springing from this innocent remark.

She chortled. "Has he gone to *your* hospital? Are you going to look after him, Auntie?"

I forced a smile. "Yes, of course. Don't worry, I'll take care of him." I got up swiftly, walked over to the window and opened the curtains, as a means of hiding from her the pain expressed in my features. "Sarah, Mummy's downstairs. Why don't I go down and tell her you're awake? You put some clothes on and come down in a minute." I sidestepped to the wardrobe with my back turned, pulled out a green knitted tunic and threw it behind me. "Here, wear this," I said, my voice taut and constrained. "It'll swamp you, but at least you won't get cold," whereupon, I hastened out to the sanctuary of the landing to regain mastery over my inclination to give vent to the conflicting emotions which I had been compelled to rein in since the arrival of my sister-in-law in a state of extreme distress.

"Julie," I said softly, re-entering the kitchen, closing the door quietly and pulling out a chair. "Chris has told Sarah he's ill and he's going away for bit. You need to be strong … for her sake. She doesn't seem at all distressed, she just said he's coming back … she didn't say when."

"Oh, thank goodness," she breathed, "only I thought … well you know what I thought. Wait though, he only *said* that. What if …?"

"He's not the quitting kind," I countered, "… and he wouldn't lie to Sarah." *No, he wouldn't lie to Sarah*, I reflected, harkening to the voice of my own common sense. "He'll be all right," I added, squeezing her hand.

Shortly after, Sarah came shuffling in, clutching Jemima against her chest through the sleeve of my tunic. The hem of the garment brushed the floor and the other sleeve flapped around her knees.

"Look Mummy! Look at my floppy arms," she giggled, raising them, shaking the half-empty sleeves and watching them dance wildly from side to side.

"Oh, Sarah, you do look funny!" I laughed.

Even the stricken Julie was unable to resist a smile. She scooped up her daughter, took her on her knee and gave her a hug.

"Now Sarah, how about some bacon and eggs before we go?" she said breezily, cleverly disguising the tremor in her voice with a light cough.

"Yes please, I'm starving. Can Jemima have some too? … and Mummy, is Lou-Lou better?" babbled the irrepressible girl, clambering down to retrieve her doll, whom she had let fall in her enthusiasm to show off her 'floppy arms'.

"Yes, Lou-Lou's much better now," Julie said reassuringly. "Now go and wash your hands and Granny will fry you an egg. Nothing for me, thank you, Marion. I couldn't eat a scrap."

Sarah was polishing the egg off her plate using her toast, a habit she had picked up from her father, much to the consternation of her more refined mother. Although presently too distraught to attend to her daughter's table manners, Julie was nonetheless quick to perceive the sprightly old dame in the doorway, wearing full make-up and wrapped in an elegant pink robe. As their eyes met, the confusion and embarrassment on both sides was palpable.

Nan was first to speak. "Oh, Julie dear, I'm so very sorry. It's all my fault. When will I learn to keep my big mouth shut?"

"No, no, of course it's not. You weren't to know … and Father … well, he's so *very* old fashioned." Julie smiled apologetically, rose unsteadily and held out her hand deferentially.

"Yes, I see it all now," said Nan in a kindly tone. "Caught between a rock and a hard place; parents can be *so* difficult."

Sarah looked up, frowned and nodded vigorously.

"Oh yes, Mummy and Daddy are *always* arguing. They're so *difficult*. Can I make a birthday card for Daddy? Please, Mummy?"

"Oh gosh, it's that boy's birthday today, isn't it?" exclaimed Nan, stepping towards Mum. "I'd clean forgotten, what with the wedding an' all. Oh Lor', I've *such* a pounding headache, Marion. Got any aspirin? Now how old would he be?"

"26 … but …"

"Well where *is* he? I simply *must* give my grandson a hug; such a fine young man!"

"Daddy's in hospital," chirruped Sarah. "He's …"

"*Hospital?*" Julie shrieked and spun around in alarm, gaping wildly first at her daughter and then at me.

"Now Sarah," I cut in. "*I* never said Daddy was in hospital. That was all *your* idea, remember?"

The little girl's face fell and my heart went out to her.

"Would someone mind telling me what's going on?" interjected Nan.

I caught Sarah up and hustled her out of the kitchen.

"Go and wash your hands and then you can make a birthday card for Daddy." I gave her a gentle nudge. "I'll get the crayons out. Now, run along."

Back in the kitchen, Mum was conferring with Nan in hushed tones.

"As a matter of fact, Mother, we were hoping he might have said something to you … about his intentions."

"Me? Good gracious me, no! Why would he choose to confide in an old bird like me! I doubt if I'd have remembered, even if he did. Now where have you put the aspirins?"

"If you drank less, you'd remember more!" retorted Mum, testily.

"Tush, Marion. A girl's got to live a little."

"*Girl?* Mother, you're 72!"

"All the more reason, since I haven't much time left. Don't be such a stick in the mud, child! I'll have a nice strong coffee too, if you're making one. My head feels like a lead balloon."

"What's that you've drawn?" asked Julie, peering across the table.

Sarah pushed the paper towards her mother and leant forward.

"That's Daddy," she said, pointing to a stick figure recumbent in bed. "And that's Auntie Vicky, there." A stick figure in a lop-sided blue dress stood next to the bed. "Look, she's wearing her nurse's uniform. There's me, and there's Lou-Lou."

"What are all those dots on Daddy?"

"They're his chicken pops."

"And where's Mummy?"

"At home with Grandpa, of course."

Julie bit her lip and set her pale face.

"And that's where we must be going ... back home to Grandpa and Lou-Lou," she replied, her voice wavering. "Maybe Daddy will be at home too, and you can give him your picture."

"It's not a picture, it's a card, look it's got writing inside, and anyway, Daddy *definitely won't* be home 'cause he said he was going away, so can I stay a bit longer ... pleeease?"

"No Sarah, not today, some other time, now tidy up the crayons, darling."

Sarah pouted and started picking up the crayons one at a time in a slow, deliberate manner clearly designed to antagonise her mother, who surveyed her wearily.

"Auntie Vicky, will *you* give Daddy his birthday card?" cried the little girl, brandishing the sheet of folded paper in the air. Julie shrugged and signalled acquiescence with a desultory wave of her hand. I received the missive from the clutch of my niece with not a little guilt.

"All right, Sarah. Now hurry up and pack away. Mummy's waiting."

At the door, I kissed my sister-in-law a fond goodbye.

"You *will* let me know straight away if you hear from him, won't you?" she said anxiously.

"Yes, of course I will …likewise."

Julie turned and trudged dejectedly across the yard, her daughter skipping along behind.

I mounted the stairs with a heavy heart to fetch my books, determined not to waste another minute fretting about issues that were out of my control. The final exams would be upon me in a matter of days, and the time and energy I had devoted to the preparations for Toni's wedding had left precious little space for study. I could have done more, but shopping and planning exerted much more appeal than the pressing need to secure my future career. I had deluded myself into believing that neglecting my pivotal role in the run-up to my sister's big day in favour of my books would be tantamount to treachery. Now I found myself paying the price for procrastination. I felt ill-prepared, especially for the written element, which had never been my forte. The task that lay ahead was like a millstone around my neck, the course content being incalculably huge and my mental state far from serene.

I settled myself at the kitchen table with my books and notes before me and tried to steady my mind. Alas, the words swam before my eyes, an endless stream of meaningless facts and figures. The harder I tried, the more I began to panic. My courage faltered; my head swarmed with nightmarish images of Chris; broken and bloodied at the base of Broad Stand; lying unconscious in a ditch at the roadside; washed up on the beach at Seascale.

After an indefinite period of time, I was mercifully jolted from my ruminations by the clamour of footsteps on the stairs and the rumbustious demands of my brother Alan, who swept into the kitchen, flushed and out of breath.

"Can't stop, Mum," he panted. "Got any bacon?"

"I've kept some hot for you, in the pan there. Aren't you staying for breakfast?"

"Nah, sorry, got tons of marking to do and Caroline has a lesson to plan. Overslept. Hangover. We'll grab a sarnie and hit the road, if you don't mind."

He snatched the Alka-Seltzer powder from the cupboard next to the sink, filled a beaker, threw in a liberal dose and downed it in one draught. Then he rummaged in the bread bin and yanked out four slices of bread, which he slapped carelessly on the worktop. Next came the bacon, which he dumped on the bread with all the finesse of a bear in boxing gloves.

"Ketchup?" he demanded, throwing out his spare arm. Mum placed the bottle in his outstretched hand with a sigh. "Ta."

He turned it upside down, gave it a shake, smeared the sauce over the bacon, plonked the spare bread on top, piled one sandwich upon the other, pressed them down hard and cut them in half in a single swipe of the breadknife. The whole operation took less than two minutes.

Caroline looked in from the doorway, wearing her coat and clutching a small, brown suitcase.

"Here, Carrie, have a bacon sarnie."

"Urgh … that looks disgusting, I *hate* squashed bread," I observed, looking with disdain at the sandwich.

"Lucky you don't have to eat it then, ha ha!" he laughed, as he handed one to his girlfriend and dug his teeth into another. "Where's Dad?"

"Oh, I don't know, try the hay barn, love."

He bolted out of the back door, disappeared across the garden and returned moments later.

"Did you find him, dear?"

"Sure. Bye Mum, bye Vicks." He ruffled my head, deposited a hurried kiss on Mum's cheek, slung his coat over his arm and snatched up the remaining two halves.

Caroline's voice was heard from the hall. "Thanks, Mrs. Kelly. Thanks for having me. Bye, Vicky."

"Bye," we called out together.

"Come and see us again soon," added Mum. "Aren't you going to say goodbye to Nan, Alan?"

"She's out for the count, sleeping off the booze. I guess that's where I get it from, ha ha!" He stuffed his mouth full of bread and made a hasty exit.

I listened to the slamming of the car doors, the purr of the engine and the crunch of the tyres on the gravel. Harry Nilsson's 'Without You' was playing on the radio, dragging me back to my own private purgatory.

Soon after, Michael emerged from the lounge, bleary-eyed and grumpy.

"That stupid brother of mine woke me up," he grumbled, putting on the kettle and disappearing again.

"Good morning would be nice," called out Mum, addressing his back.

10 minutes later he returned fully dressed and filled the teapot.

"Sorry, Mum. Awful night on the sofa. Hey, what was all that banging about?"

"Oh, Michael," Mum burst out. "We had an early morning visit from Julie. Chris has gone AWOL. Nobody knows where he is."

"Chris?" said Michael, casually. "He'll turn up. Probably needs a break. God … that woman … she's such a cow. I don't know how he puts up with her!"

"Michael, I won't have you talking about Julie like that! She's a sweet girl."

"Huh! Sweet? She's about as sweet as a dose of hydrochloric acid! He should have stuck to Janice. She was fun."

I started. An image formed in my mind, the image of Chris and Janice seated side by side on the opposite wall at the wedding reception, deep in conversation; an image of Chris slipping off early in a state of animation; an image of … I dared not imagine what. I slammed my book shut.

"I'm going out," I declared. "I'm going to talk to Janice."

"Janice? Oh … I see …" Mum said slowly. "Vicky, don't meddle where you're not wanted. It'll be your undoing, you know."

"I can't help that!" I cried petulantly. "I can't stand by and watch Chris throw away his future!"

"The future he could have had with Janice," muttered Michael, under his breath.

"Oh shut up, Michael!" I hissed. I tossed my head, marched out of the kitchen, tugged on my coat and slammed the front door shut behind me.

The cool September air caressed my face like an angel's wing. Birds twittered and trees rustled in the autumn breeze. The sounds of nature filtered into my ears, chasing into the recesses of my mind snatches of conversation that repeated like echoes in my head. I hastened across the yard and out of the front gate and bent my steps towards the neighbouring farmstead. The damp earth gave off its own unique redolence. A bright patch amongst the clouds overhead indicated the position of the sun in the heavens. As I tramped up the lane, I became acutely aware of the green and living world of which I was a minute part and found relief in silent tears. It felt good to be outdoors.

I rang on the bell and Mrs. Duffy came to the door.

"Hello Vicky." She peered at me closely. "Why, child, your eyes are all red. Are you all right?"

"Yes, yes I'm fine, it's the wind," I mumbled, rubbing my eyes. "Is Janice in?"

"She's out the back, mucking out the horses. Come through."

In the stable yard behind the house, Janice was sweeping up. She leant on her broom and beamed at me.

"Hiya, Vick. What can I do you for?"

In a striped polo-neck sweater, jeans and mud-spattered wellingtons, her blonde hair dishevelled and a total absence of make-up, she looked every bit the wholesome country girl. One look at her open countenance was all I needed to convince me of her innocence. I wondered how I could ever have thought otherwise and began to wish I'd curbed my impetuosity and listened to my mum's advice. Still, I was here now and had to make the best of it.

"Er … Janice," I faltered. "We've lost Chris. I wondered if … well nobody's seen him since last night; that is, nobody knows where he is. I thought maybe …"

"He was with me?" She smiled benevolently. "Oh Vicky, I gave him up long ago. I could never compete with that gorgeous creature he married; and now he's got two lovely daughters, I wouldn't dream of coming between them."

Well, I thought, *at least she's not offended.*

"No, I know that," I said, injecting some much needed conviction into my voice, "only … he didn't say anything to you yesterday, did he? Anything?"

"Well yes, he did say he couldn't go on with things the way they are, but he didn't elaborate. He doesn't have a very high opinion of himself, does he?"

"I don't know, I never really thought about it."

"A poor excuse for a father; that's how he described himself. It's awfully sad."

"Sad? It's tragic! Janice, I confess I'm terrified."

"Terrified?" Janice seemed genuinely surprised. "What of?"

"Oh Janice, I keep thinking … thinking the worst," I spluttered, suppressing a sob.

The kind-hearted girl dropped her broom, hurried across the yard and clasped me to her.

"Come now, Vicky. I expect he just needs some time out. Perhaps he's staying with a friend." She stroked my hair and patted my back reassuringly.

"Surely he would have *told* me," I whined, helplessly.

"No he wouldn't," she replied firmly. "I know Chris better than you think I do, and I'll tell you something, Vicky. When he's made up his mind about something you won't like, you're the last person he's likely to tell. He'd run away rather than go against your wishes. Why do you think he married the girl on the sly?"

"Oh, I don't know. I *hate* how he's become so secretive," I said vehemently.

"Hush Vicky and try to understand this. Chris has lots of fine qualities, but courage isn't one of them. You're strong and persuasive, but he doesn't want persuading right now. He needs some space to make up his own mind, so he's lying low. See?"

"Yeah, maybe," I conceded.

"Don't take it so hard, Vicky. Why the cover-up if he didn't care for your opinion? What would be the point? His problem is, he cares too much. Looked at that way, it's a compliment."

Janice loosened her hold on me and planted her hands on my shoulders.

"Now please be sensible. He's keeping a low profile, that's all."

With my rational self once more in control, I turned home with renewed resolve to bury my head in my books.

Sunday lunch was a sober affair. Nan sat opposite me in the seat next to Michael vacated by Toni. As I listened idly to their conversation about the devastating effects of Hurricane Fi-Fi, which was currently wreaking havoc on the opposite side of the Atlantic, I was struck with the notion that nothing would ever be the same again. One by one, my brothers and sister had left the homestead and forged their own path, leaving behind a series of chasms brimming with memories of happier times, times when the epitome of misery had been grappling with the laws of algebra, trigonometry and Pythagoras. Mum picked at her food absent-mindedly. Dad was dour and taciturn and spent no longer than was absolutely necessary at the dinner table, evidently preferring the company of his herd. Such a dismal affair rendered the prospect of an afternoon of study with Dr. W. Gordon Sears, MD, MRCP, quite agreeable by comparison.

At bedtime, there was still no word from Chris. I drifted upstairs, my head in a mess, climbed into bed and attempted to find solace in sleep. I must have lain there for several hours before my brain finally gave way, numbed by sheer mental exhaustion. Just after 9 a.m. I fought myself awake in the throes of a nightmare. I dreamt I was dragging myself through a field of poppies like the one in The Wizard of Oz, except that this one was dotted in every direction with large pools. The ground beneath my feet was waterlogged. I was ankle-deep in mud, my legs and eyelids as heavy as lead. Chris was standing at the opposite end of the field, his face white and expressionless. As I stepped forward, I began to sink into the mire. A hand reached out towards me. It was the hand of Julie's father. I made a grab at the hand and then hesitated, fearing that the hand would push me further into the mire. In that fatal moment, I was sucked out of reach.

I was munching half-heartedly on my Cornflakes when the telephone rang. I started. Mum scurried out into the hall.

"Chris! Chris, oh thank God! Where are you?" … … "At Simon's? No he didn't tell us." … … "Well, that really is the limit! We've all been worried sick. Wait till I get my hands on that boy!" … … "You've done what?" … …

I hurtled out of the back door and made straight for the dairy, almost tripping over the hem of my dressing gown in the process.

"Dad! Dad!" I panted. "He's all right. Chris is all right!"

Dad smiled a smile that was in part indulgent and in part amused.

"I never doubted it for a minute. Come here, cherub." He gave me a hug. "Now go and put the kettle on and we all can celebrate the return of normality. Your mother's been driving me to distraction, moping around like the boy was dead in a ditch."

"Chris will be along later," said Mum, in response to the barrage of questions pouring from my lips.

"I won't be here later," I moaned. "I've got to go back to work."

"Well then, in a nutshell, he's handed in his notice and he's moving to Manchester."

"*What*?" I replied incredulously.

"He's going down to live near to Alan, who incidentally knew where he was all along, the stupid boy! He was *supposed* to tell us," added Mum, grimly.

"What, you mean Alan *knew* he was at this what's-his-name's house … Simon, wasn't it?"

"Simon … yes … he's a colleague apparently. He's going to stay with Simon while he works out his notice. I think he's hoping Alan will put him up till he finds a place to live in Manchester. At least he's all right. That's the most important thing."

"But … *Manchester*. Oh Mum, I don't know whether to laugh or cry, and there's Julie and the girls. What will happen to them?"

"What always happens. Julie will keep the children and they'll come to some arrangement. I never thought I'd live to see a son of mine getting divorced, but it's a changing world and it doesn't carry the stigma it used to. I suppose that marriage was doomed to failure from the start."

"I thought you liked Julie," I said tersely.

"Well I do, but it was all so underhand. Of course, it's her father that's the problem, but that doesn't alter the outcome … families are funny things," she added, half to herself, before lapsing into a thoughtful silence.

"On a practical note," Mum said, as we sat sipping tea at the kitchen table with Dad 10 minutes later, "I'll need you to drive up to the Head before lunch and pick up his things, Robert. Will that give you enough time, Vicky. You'll need to go too."

"Me? What's it got to do with me?" I rejoined, baulking at the presumptuous nature of her request.

"It's going to be tricky. You always got along particularly well with Liam. I think it will sound better coming from you."

"Oh Mum, do I *have* to," I complained, filled with dread at the likelihood of an unpleasant scene.

"Yes you do. Go and get dressed. I'll call Julie and let her know the boy's okay. Let's hope she's not working today."

Mum deemed it unwise to share with Julie Chris's intended plan to move out permanently, preferring to relay a diluted version of events, to the effect that her husband was staying with a friend in Whitehaven for the time being. Consequently, when I arrived at Lingmell Old Stead with Dad and a couple of suitcases, Julie was subdued, apologetic and keen to assist, acknowledging her part in the catastrophe and anxious to make amends. To my unutterable relief, Liam was out walking Shirley, *probably on purpose* I thought cynically. As we gathered up Chris's belongings, Julie started to cry.

"It's all my fault," she said abjectly. "I should have stood up to Father, but I'm trapped because he lost my mother and sister. If he loses me too, he loses everything. That's why he can't let me go."

"It's no-one's fault, especially not yours. Please don't think it is," I said tenderly.

"I'm just not brave enough to take the risk, Vicky; to move out and leave him alone and friendless. To inflict a wound of such magnitude on a tortured soul would be akin to murder. I have to choose between them; that's the bottom line. Besides, who's going to look after Father when he can't look after himself anymore?"

"I'm so sorry, Julie."

"It's all right. At least I still have the children," she sniffed, drying her eyes.

We piled the cases into the boot of the car and exchanged an emotional goodbye. Dad injected his farewell with uncharacteristic warmth, showing genuine concern for Julie's plight and offering to help in any way he could. I climbed into the passenger seat and we trundled home. I was acutely aware that a chapter in my life had ended.

* * *

Less than a week later, I boarded a train with Wendy bound for Lancaster, which was the location of our final exams. I'm not sure which of us was the most nervous. As the train rattled along, we took turns in asking and answering questions to test our knowledge. However, this quickly dissolved into a farce, when Wendy asked me in a plummy accent why a 'long weight' might be useful in the traction process. The exam consisted of three parts; oral, written and practical. It wasn't as bad as I had anticipated and I returned home feeling relatively confident, lighter of heart and ready for some serious drinking. With only 12 weeks left to go and the guarantee of a job in the service once we had qualified, we all had good reason to celebrate.

All this time, I had been quietly wondering whether my parents had completely forgotten my 21st birthday. Recollecting my sister's elaborate party, I considered it rather unfair that all the evidence pointed to a big, fat nothing. This seemed a particularly cruel blow, especially coming hot on the heels of my final exams. I'd even booked annual leave for the weekend before my birthday, on the assumption that the family would be doing something ... anything. *It's probably been swallowed up by the wedding*, I thought ruefully, whereupon I resolved to throw my own little party at 19 Sutherland Street, the small two-up, two-down which I shared with Wendy and another coursemate called Gina. It's in the nature of the job that 'Saturday night' often isn't 'alright for fighting', partying, or any other social diversion for those unfortunate enough to do shift work. For this reason, I decided to throw mine the actual day I turned 21, which was a Tuesday. It was lucky that I did.

With only a week left to go, I called Mum (from the public

call box down the street as we couldn't afford a telephone) for my customary chat.

"You *will* be home Friday night, won't you?" she enquired.

"Yeah … I guess I might as well. Wendy and Gina are both working. I'd rather not sit indoors on my own like Billy No-Mates."

"Good. I'll ask Chris over. He'd love to see you."

I brightened. Every cloud …

"Michael will be here but Toni and Jason are busy, I'm afraid. You'll have to manage without Julie and the girls too, for obvious reasons. Maybe you could pop over and see them on Sunday morning … but don't arrange anything till I've spoken to Chris. Let's find out how the land lies before we make any plans. What would you like me to cook on Friday. You decide."

"Can you make lasagne?" I asked cheekily, anticipating the reply which ricocheted down the line exactly as I had expected.

"Lasagne? Whatever's that?"

"It's pasta; it's flat sheets with mince and cheese in-between. I'm sure you'll be able to find it in a recipe book. It's Italian … absolutely gorgeous. I had it in a restaurant."

"Well, I'll do my best but I can't promise it'll be as good as the real thing."

I laughed. "Oh, it'll be the real thing, all right. A lasagne's a lasagne, as long as you follow the recipe."

"Then I thought we could make an early start on Saturday, drive to Carlisle and amble round the Lanes," Mum continued. "The shops there are very quaint; you used to love going as a child. Then we can go to Nan's for lunch and have a meal out in the town later. You can choose the restaurant."

Oh, great! I thought. *I'm not a child anymore.* I felt a pang of resentment and squashed it. Mum was doing her best and the timing of Toni's wedding was just … well … unfortunate.

"Yeah, Mum, that sounds cool," I said casually, doing my best to conceal my disappointment but evidently not succeeding.

"I'm sorry, Vicky, but the truth is I'm exhausted after the wedding. I know it's not much but perhaps we can make up for it some other time. Would you like goose on Sunday?"

"Yeah … goose. It'll be like Christmas," I said good-humouredly, guessing at her embarrassment. "Seriously, Mum, it's fine."

When I got home on Friday evening, the table was set complete with white tablecloth, place mats and coasters, wine glasses and *two* sets of cutlery.

"Goodness, are we expecting royalty?" I joked, as I slung my coat over the back of a chair.

"Pick up your coat, girl, and don't make a mess," said Dad, in mock vexation. "Her Majesty will be along shortly."

We had prawn cocktail for starters. Mum's lasagne was pretty good for a first attempt. We had lemon snow with sprinkles in wine glasses for dessert, rounded off by cheese and biscuits, which was a particular favourite of Dad's.

"Can I have a coffee?" I chirped, passing my empty plate to Mum.

"Coffee? You can't have coffee *after* the meal. You have to have tea."

"Oh, Mum, you're *so* 1920s! I *always* have a coffee after a slap-up meal."

We retired to the comfy chairs in the lounge, Mum arrived bearing the tea tray and we played rummy until 10 o'clock.

It transpired that Chris had made no attempt to contact Julie during the three weeks since the breakup. I thought this was rather mean and irresponsible of him but refrained from letting my feelings be known for fear of alienating him. I was beginning to learn when to speak and when to hold my tongue. He had already been to two interviews and his job prospects looked promising.

Just before bedtime, I let Rufus out of the back door for his customary 'comfort break'. Mum came into the kitchen with the tray of empty cups.

"Toni will be joining us tomorrow," she said. "She's decided she'd like to come to Carlisle with us."

"Oh, brilliant, actually that's great!" I answered cheerfully, visualising an afternoon wandering around the department stores and boutiques of Carlisle with my sister, an infinitely more appealing scenario than tea and scones at Nan's.

"We'll need to make an early start. We're leaving at nine."

I groaned. "That's *so* early."

"It's further than you think, and I've promised Mother we'll be there in time for lunch. We won't have time to browse, otherwise."

"All right, I'll be ready," I said reluctantly. "Come, Rufus, in your bed." I patted my thighs loudly and the good-natured beast bounced indoors, tail wagging, jumped in his basket and laid his head on his front paws.

"Oh, and wear something smart," she added. "You know what these restaurants can be like."

The next morning, Toni breezed into the bedroom as I was applying my mascara.

"Hi sis," she grinned. "Here, let me do something with your hair. Shall I do a French plait for you?"

"Why all this fuss about my hair? Mum's just as bad, telling me I have to 'wear something smart'. Oh all right, then, do what you want. I can't do a thing with it."

"It's your birthday treat," she said, picking up my hairbrush. "You have to look nice."

Just after the appointed hour, I got into the back of the car with my sister. Mum was loading a large, canvas bag into the boot.

"That's a big bag, Mum," I commented. "Anyone would think we were staying a week."

"Oh, it's just some things for Nan," she said, in an offhand manner, climbing into the passenger seat and shutting the car door.

15 minutes later, we hit the coast road. I noticed a signpost towards Ravenglass.

"Ravenglass, that's south. Are you sure you're going the right way?"

"Oh yes, I'm going the right way," chuckled Dad.

Toni exploded into laughter.

"What's going on?"

"Um … we've had a change of plan," said Mum.

"Oh … where are we going?"

"South," said Dad, with a note of finality in his voice.

Toni started to sing softly … "Roll up, roll up for the Mystery Tour …"

I expect we're going to Manchester instead, I thought smugly, pleased at my deductive powers. Caroline had enthused about the fabulous new Salford Shopping Centre. No doubt my brother and his girlfriend were 'in on it' and meeting us later in the day. In the meantime, I'd forgotten all about the big bag in the boot.

Nearly two hours later, we pulled in at Charnock Richard Services.

"We'll stop here for the toilet and get some snacks," said Dad.

"Aren't we nearly there?" I said, with a note of surprise in my voice.

"Oh no," we've got *ages* to go yet," said Toni, tapping the side of her nose and winking at Mum.

As we proceeded down the M6, my astonishment turned to utter disbelief and I began to question whether I was awake or dreaming. We stopped for lunch at Corley Services, which suggested that we still had some way to go. When we finally filtered onto the M1, the penny dropped.

"Oh my God! We're going to London!" I squealed.

"We're going to a show, we're going to a show," chanted Toni with glee.

It took seven hours to reach our destination. I couldn't help but feel enormous admiration for Dad. To drive the 300 miles to London and back in a weekend was to go above and beyond the call of duty. We parked in a side street close to Covent Garden and hopped on the Central Line to Oxford Circus.

We whiled away a delightful hour amongst the retail outlets in Oxford Street and Carnaby Street. Then Dad ushered us through the doorway of a brand new eatery in Wardour Street called the St. Moritz, which claimed to serve 'genuine traditional Swiss cuisine.' The name of the restaurant alone speaks volumes. As my eyes adjusted to the light and I gazed around the smart interior, my heart leapt in my chest. Sitting at a large table with his family was Ray, his hair slicked back, wearing a black suit and white bow tie, looking more like Jay Gatsby than Robert Redford did. He caught my eye and smiled broadly. Then he rose and came across to me, took my hand and escorted me to my seat. I felt like a million dollars. For our starter, we had cheese fondue. I thought I had never tasted anything so exquisite before. For the main course, I chose a dish called Pork Eintopf and for dessert I had Geneva pear flan. After the meal, we walked 15 minutes to the Theatre Royal, Drury Lane.

To my wondering eyes, the beautiful Georgian building with its elegant façade complete with pillared portico looked like a palace. The inside was more fabulous still. I had never before seen anything so spectacular. The main auditorium was encircled by three tiers made up of boxes and balconies, all with highly ornate plasterwork fronts decorated in red, white and gold. Immense bowls of light hung from a vast, opulent and many-faceted ceiling. The carpet beneath my feet was a deep, lush pink. Spellbound, I glided to my seat and waited for the curtain to rise.

'Billy' is a musical based on the 1959 novel 'Billy Liar' by Keith Waterhouse about a hapless young dreamer with a propensity to lie his way out of the numerous scrapes he gets himself into. Billy is caught between two very different women; his fiancée, straight-laced Barbara, and sassy Rita to whom he has promised Barbara's ring. When his chickens come home to roost, he plans to escape to London by train with free-spirited Liz, his former girlfriend and the only one capable of saving him from himself. At the last moment he bottles out and the train pulls away with Liz on board, leaving him behind on the station platform. Michael 'Frank Spencer' Crawford, who played the lead, received a standing ovation.

After the show, we checked into the Charing Cross Hotel. It was very grand, richly furnished with a broad, sweeping staircase and long, wide, vaulted corridors lit by chandeliers. Although our accommodation was very splendid, I would have quite liked to have gone back to Ray's house for the night. However, this would have added an extra 45 minutes to our journey home and Dad was keen to make an early start. The following morning, we had a full English breakfast and hit the road at 10 a.m.

* * *

As 1974 drew to a close, I found myself playing the role of bridesmaid again. This time, the lucky bride was Wendy, who was to wed the young doctor she had met at the staff ball two Christmases ago. The ceremony took place at St. Mary Magdalene Parish Church in Broughton-in-Furness. The reception was held at the Victory Hall. At the reception, I fell into conversation with my old friend Linda, one of the first girls who had befriended me when I signed up more than four years ago as a cadet nurse.

"I don't know, Linda … I should be feeling happy. I've finished the course, I've got lots of friends, a lovely family, a wonderful boyfriend and I live in a beautiful part of the country … but I'm not. I just feel empty, like there's nothing left to look forward to."

Coming back down to earth after the euphoria of three big events – my 21st birthday celebrations; passing my final exams and playing a key role in two weddings within the space of three months – was proving to be a bigger challenge than even I had anticipated.

"Why don't you come down to Manchester with me?"

"Come to Manchester?"

"You obviously miss your brothers; well so do I and mine's in Stockport. I've applied to St. Mary's. It's massive, spanking brand new, all mod cons. We could rent a place and have a laugh. Go on, Vicky, take the plunge."

"We-ell, all right, I'll think about it. I guess it won't be quite as far from London … and Ray," I added with a mischievous smile.

The alternatives did seem pretty bleak. Gina was moving back to her parents. To remain in Barrow would mean finding some new housemates, and fast. If I went home, I would be saddled with a long, difficult commute even if I secured a position at the closest hospital to where I lived. As I didn't possess a car, or even the ability to drive one, that was out of the question. Besides, I had no wish to take what I regarded as a step backwards. One by one, Chris, Alan and Toni had fled the nest and I'd grown accustomed to independent living. I had begun to appreciate my parents and ceased to malign them as nags and bores. I had finally recognised the value of their love and support and I didn't want that to change. Indecision had led to lethargy; hence, I hadn't bothered to apply for any local jobs. I was lonely and jealous; jealous of my sister and jealous of Wendy. All things considered, Manchester looked inviting.

Two days before Christmas, Toni gave birth to a baby boy. She called him Scott.

"That's *such* a *posey* name," I said to Mum later over tea and cake, pulling a face.

"No it's not," said Mum. "What about Scott of the Antarctic?"

"That's his surname, Mum! He was called Captain Robert Scott, which is precisely my point. Scott's a surname. Only film stars and hippies are called Scott."

"Well, why shouldn't he have a glamorous name like his Dad? Dear me, Victoria, you're turning into a bigger grouch than your father. What's got into you lately?"

I had a sinking feeling she was right. Envy can do that to a person.

"I think I'll take Rufus out," I announced, standing up and brushing the crumbs from my jeans. "Here boy, walkies." I pulled on my coat and sauntered outdoors with my faithful old friend at my heels.

It was already dark but there was a full moon and the sky was studded with stars. The night air was cold, crisp and still. I strolled the short distance to the little bridge at the crossroads a few yards from our front gate; Cinderdale Bridge. The only sound was the murmer and splash of the shallow stream wending its way to the open sea, seven miles distant. I stopped on the bridge and gazed down into the sparkling water, coursing effortlessly towards its final destination.

"Oh Rufus, what am I to do?" I said out loud to my canine companion.

Everything had changed. Aside from my own personal circumstances, I had witnessed many changes in our immediate neighbourhood, in the farming community and in the wider world.

Britain's entry into the Common Market two years ago and the introduction of the Common Agricultural Policy was already causing wide scale over-production, especially in the dairy sector. Technical innovation had given rise to larger, more efficient farms. Dad had been forced to invest heavily in new machinery to reduce his running costs and keep his prices competitive, only to watch the value of his produce drop like a stone. The abolition of the Farm Improvement Grant in favour of the new European subsidies had not worked entirely in his favour either. Consequently, he had seen a sharp fall in his income.

The pressure to join the technological revolution had been too great even for Dad to resist. In the last few years, the acquisition of a colour television, automatic washing machine and freezer had burnt a series of holes in his pocket. *Let's hope the miners don't call another strike*, I thought cynically, recalling the Three-Day Week and interminable power cuts last winter. There's not much point investing in anything with a plug on it when the electricity goes down.

A Government Act had resulted in the reorganisation of our region's boundaries, which meant that, effective from April,

Cumberland and Westmorland had ceased to exist and had been replaced by a shiny new county called 'Cumbria'. Yet another bureaucratic decision had already found our local village, formerly Strands, stripped of its name and rebranded 'Nether Wasdale'. This was a move presumably intended to place it on the map in the minds of the endless stream of tourists who poured into our valley in ever increasing numbers during the high season, with the surge in car ownership.

In a figurative as well as in a literal sense, I was standing at the crossroads. In my mind's eye I saw Billy, standing on the station platform, watching the train pull away and taking with it his hopes and dreams. *When Linda gets on board that train to Manchester*, I concluded, *I'm getting on it with her*.

Part Two

Seesaw

Chapter 11

A Happy Accident

"Have some Maltesers." Linda grinned at me from the opposite side of the railway compartment of which we were the sole occupants. She reached across the aisle and shook the upturned packet into my outstretched palm.

"Thanks … not too many," I added, recollecting Christmas as I eyed the chocolate-coated balls with a mixture of relish and guilt and felt my belt pinching at my waist. I lent back and sucked at my Maltesers in silence, gazing distractedly out at the frost-encrusted fields of North Lancashire flashing past. Shafts of sunshine flickered in my face like a strobe light and threw the white-green landscape into shadow.

"Penny for your thoughts."

"I was thinking about Mum," I said wistfully. "She's been so touchy lately, it's almost a relief to get away, though I hate myself for saying it. I can't do a thing right. Every time I open my mouth, she either snaps or makes like she's the victim. I wish I knew what's bothering her. I used to love going home on my days off but nowadays it's more trouble than it's worth."

"Probably the change," replied Linda casually.

"It can't be that," I countered. "She's been like it for ages. I only told her I was moving out last week."

"I don't mean that sort of change, I mean the other sort! Honestly, Vicky, for someone in the medical profession, you've got a lot to learn! How old is your Mum?"

"Er … 48, I think."

"Well, it's obviously her hormones. My sister-in-law's just the same. She was the Devil incarnate till they put her on Valium. I don't know how my brother put up with her."

"Oh … I never thought of that."

"They told her to get a job and take up evening classes. To be fair, she's having a tough time; two teenagers and she's losing her looks, poor mare. She used to be a stunner. It never rains but it pours." Linda shrugged. "Our turn will come."

"Gosh, you make it sound awful. Poor Mum … and me, Toni and Chris all moving miles away in the space of three months. Well, Toni's not gone that far, only Torver, but they're starting their own business so she doesn't have any spare time, what with the new baby. She's only been over twice since they got married. Mum complains about it all the time. She started crying when I told her I was moving down to Manchester. It was *so* embarrassing."

"She needs a purpose; at least, that's what they told our Margaret. What does she like doing in her spare time?"

"Spare time? Huh! I don't think she has any."

"Margaret's doing pottery. Her pots are absolutely terrible but it gets her out of the house. Kids can leave an awful big hole behind when they leave home … not that I'd know. Margaret told me. She read it in a self-help book. She's a lot better now."

Linda rummaged in her handbag and pulled out a small mirror and lipstick, which she applied with the dexterity of an experienced practitioner, before she resumed talking.

"So what's your sister up to? Has she left the Scawfell at last? She's been there *forever*."

"Jason's dad's lent them the deposit on a smallholding. They're opening a tea room to start with but Jason's got grand ideas. He wants to start his own farm shop and café and grow and sell his own stuff. He's been assistant manager in his dad's greengrocer's shop for a long time now and Toni's worked in the hotel trade for seven years, so they're both quite experienced."

"Hmmm … maybe your Mum could launch her own range of jams and they could sell it in the café," said Linda, half earnestly and half in jest.

"… and chutneys, and cakes and biscuits, even bread," I continued eagerly.

"She wouldn't need a hobby then," said Linda brightly.

"They could sell your sister-in-law's pots," I giggled.

Linda exploded into laughter. "Oh … give over!"

Although it would be many years before 'Kelly's Kitchen' featured amongst the local produce on the shelves of King's of Torver, Linda's throwaway remark that morning on the train turned out to be a prophetic one.

Linda's brother Clive met us off the train at Manchester Piccadilly. He was a lot older than I had imagined, until I recalled that he had a son just three years younger than we were.

"I've arranged for the landlord to meet us at the house at two o'clock," he explained. Clive had found us a ground floor flat in a large Victorian property on Mayfield Road in the southern quarter. The location was ideal, being less than two miles on foot from St. Mary's Hospital and roughly equidistant from Stockport and Droylsden, the respective homes of Clive and Alan. It meant sharing a bedroom, but the rent was cheap.

"Margaret's looked out some things for you; some pots and pans, cooking utensils, cutlery and crockery that belonged to her mother. It's rather old fashioned but it'll do the job. I'll send her over with it later. Now, how about a spot of early lunch?"

The flat had a large front room containing some shabby, free-standing bedroom furniture, two single beds and a gas fire. The carpet was brown and rather worn-looking and the walls were painted tangerine. At the far end of the passage was a bathroom which seemed to be emitting an eerie glow until we peered in and discovered that the suite, tiles and walls were all yellow.

"Blimey, I'm going to need to wear sunglasses every time I take a bath," quipped Linda.

A door to the left revealed a kitchen-diner with French windows to the garden. Bold, blue flowers bedecked the walls. Two slipper chairs made an incongruous intrusion into a room intended for cooking and eating. The sun streamed in, lending much-needed warmth to a room whose only heat source appeared to be the gas rings on the cooker hob. The décor was quite dated but the flat was roomy, clean and comfortable.

Because St. Mary's Hospital specialised in gynaecology, obstetrics and paediatrics, I ought to have been well placed to take a step closer towards my dream of a career in midwifery. However, Murphy's Law had other plans for me and we were both assigned to the Paediatric department until a position came up in my preferred field of medicine several months later.

On Monday morning, we donned our uniforms and presented ourselves at St. Mary's at the appointed time. During our long years of training, we had grown accustomed to being harangued by sour-faced superiors, so we could not have been more surprised when a senior nurse breezed into the large, modern reception area, where we waited in a state of agitation, and greeted us warmly.

"I'm Sister Sparks." She grinned broadly and held out her hand.

"I'm Linda … Linda Loughborough," replied my friend, who was never backward in coming forward.

"I'm Vicky Kelly," I said tentatively, my bag sliding off my shoulder into the crook of my outstretched arm with a bump. I grabbed at the strap with my free hand and felt my colour rise.

Sister Sparks smiled indulgently. "There's really no need to be nervous. Now, come along and I'll introduce you to Matron. Don't worry; her bark is much worse than her bite," she added with a wink.

Matron was a large woman in her 50s with a florid complexion, a dour countenance and a commanding manner. She resembled the archetype spoofed in the 'Carry On' films, I thought, suppressing a smirk.

"So you're new, are you?" she boomed, peering over the top of her glasses with a disparaging glance before continuing her perusal of a hefty official-looking document.

We waited in silence for what seemed like an hour, but what was in fact only a few minutes.

Eventually, she turned her beady eyes upon us.

"Now, don't go making any mischief," she said sternly. "You youngsters may think you know it all but you don't. Let's get one thing clear. You're here to do a job of work and there will be no fraternising with the patients and no idle chit-chat, is that understood? I won't tolerate time-wasters."

As she droned on, I found it increasingly difficult to keep a straight face. Images of Hattie Jacques thrusting herself mercilessly upon a confounded Kenneth Williams filled my head, making it impossible to take in the barrage of dos and don'ts firing from the lips of the indomitable old battleaxe.

By contrast, Sister Sparks seemed exceptionally friendly and easy-going. Our relief, when we learnt that we would be reporting directly to her, was inexpressible, and a better acquaintance with the venerable lady bore out our first impressions. She was a woman with formidable talents. She was roughly my mother's age but looked considerably younger. She was exceedingly attractive with large, round eyes and a brilliant smile which she lavished freely on staff and patients alike. She had a plenitude of coiffed blonde curls sustained on a diet of peroxide and hair lacquer. She had a trim figure which, by her own admission, she worked hard to maintain. She was the sort likely to ignite the passions of men and the envy of woman, except that it was impossible to feel antipathy towards someone with such a sunny disposition. Linda was gifted with the same capacity to captivate the opposite sex and the similarities between the two were striking, although Linda lacked the tact and finesse of the older woman.

From a professional prospective, Sister Sparks was brisk, capable, kind and good-natured. From a social standpoint, she was vivacious and gregarious. She cheered the staff and charmed the patients. She was known amongst the children on the ward as 'Sister Sparkles' and revelled in her moniker, which suited her well. She would turn a blind eye if she caught us chatting to the children or their parents, being frequently guilty of the same crime herself. On rare occasions when we let our timekeeping slip, she would merely look at her watch and remark, "Don't let Matron catch you being late!" Her tolerance paid dividends. Everyone who worked under her never hesitated to go the extra mile when called upon to do so. She was admired and appreciated by all who had the good fortune to cross paths with her, with the possible exception of Matron who almost certainly considered her too lax and liberal. In summary, Rose Sparks was a woman once met, never forgotten.

She was especially magnanimous towards those who earned her respect through the energy, diligence and commitment they brought to the job and, if I possessed one outstanding quality, it was an excellent work ethic. I had been told this time and again during my training. She soon perceived this and took a personal interest in my welfare. I found myself revealing details about my family, about Ray and about the precarious state of my finances. One Friday morning in March, as I was preparing to leave at the end of my shift, I told her how much I was looking forward to going over to Alan's the next day. Mum was bringing Sarah down to spend the weekend with her father and I missed my little niece.

Chris had been sleeping (rather badly) on the sofa at his brother's flat for six months and, I'm sorry to say, was looking rather the worse for it. He seemed resigned to living in a state of limbo and showed no inclination to move out, having neither the energy nor drive to shave or get a haircut, let alone go flat-hunting at the end of the working day or at weekends. His current favourite pastime was staying in drinking beer and watching TV. He was still not on speaking terms with Julie, despite several attempts at reconciliation on her part, and all communication was directed through our long-suffering mum. I didn't think Chris had it in him to be so petty but he seemed to be in no mood to listen to reason.

Towards Louise, his attitude was indifferent and this frustrated and distressed me. He had only made the effort to see her once since he had parted company with her mother on the day of the wedding last September. It had been on the eve of her second Christmas, when she had been full of cold, and the experience had not been a helpful one. Louise was fretful, and Chris tired and irritable after the long drive back to the farm. Perhaps she was conscious of this, because nothing he could muster from his limited resources of patience could pacify her and he had spent most of the night pacing the floor with his daughter in his arms. Julie was summoned on Christmas morning to take her home. I watched them through the open kitchen door. She was standing on the front step with an apologetic smile, which Chris had returned with a cursory nod before handing over the crying child. As her sobs subsided and she nestled into her mother's shoulder, I saw his face fall as he turned and hurried upstairs without a word, his head bowed, and shut himself in his room. After that, he became even more convinced that he was a bad parent and gave up trying to be a good one, at least as far as his youngest was concerned. "She's better off without me," he would argue, whenever Mum chastised him for his neglect of her. "She's too young to care," he would persist "and besides the journey would unsettle her." If my suspicions were correct and Louise was conceived in the hope of salvaging a marriage which was already falling apart, then clearly their gamble had not paid off.

Six year old Sarah was not easily daunted by her father's dark moods and continued to make regular visits to Manchester, being possessed with enough naïvety not to notice the change in him. Her exuberance lifted his spirits and gave us a glimpse of the inner light flickering through the cracks in the dull veneer. Perhaps Chris was harbouring a grudge against the innocent creature whose arrival had been instrumental in causing his relationship with his wife to break down completely. One thing was certain; there would be little love left for Louise all the time Chris was intent on building walls, not bridges.

I liked living with Linda; she was frivolous, fun and the perfect antidote when family worries got the better of me. We quickly settled into our new life in the metropolis, which had a lot to offer to a girl accustomed to rural life. I confess I had had reservations about my new flatmate to start with. She had gained a reputation as a girl with a loose tongue and loose morals. Granted, she had a flirtatious nature but in truth the rumours were merely supposition based on her propensity to fall in and out of love on a weekly basis and wear her heart on her sleeve. On the plus side, because she was confident, sociable and a crowd-puller, I got a lot of exposure, especially amongst the local boys. Linda could get free drinks with a flutter of her long, mascara-laden lashes, which was a very useful ploy for two young women living on a shoestring. Things sometimes got a bit complicated. After half a bottle of Cinzano, I would sometimes forget my pledge to Ray and succumb to temptation in the heat of the moment. True love had not sufficient power to blind me to the attractions of the opposite sex. However my midnight ride with Kawasaki Keith back in '73 had taught me my limitations. Consequently, my dalliances rarely amounted to more than a kiss and I always stopped myself just in time.

* * *

Easter was early that year, falling on the last weekend in March. I was not scheduled to work on Saturday and had arranged to meet Alan, Caroline and Chris in town for lunch. It was a pleasant, spring day marred only by a stiff breeze that came in fits and starts, whipping my hair across my face. I boarded the bus, relieved to be out of the wind, found a seat next to the window and lapped up the warmth of the early spring sun as we trundled through the sprawling suburbs towards the city centre. I got off at Church Street and merged into the throng of shoppers; ordinary people like me with their own extraordinary tales to tell. The city felt fresh, vibrant and exciting to one accustomed to the stillness of the countryside. The wind buffeted my face and body as I weaved down Tib Street, passing shop fronts crammed with Easter bargains. A dishevelled youth sat huddled in a doorway, begging plaintively for the price of a cup of tea. On an impulse, I reached into my purse and pressed a 10p coin into his grubby, outstretched palm. Then I noticed an empty bottle lying at his side and wondered if this small act of humanity would merely fuel his addiction.

I met Caroline outside C&A. She was easy to pick out from the crowd, with her flame-coloured hair and sunflower yellow trapeze coat. We crossed the street to the Blackbird Café, where my two brothers had managed to secure a table after a short wait. We lunched on pie and chips, washed down with a mug of tea. Then Caroline and I trawled around C&A and Littlewoods while the boys headed off to Virgin Records in Lever Street. We met up at half past three outside Lewis's department store and then made our way to the underground market where Caroline bought a cheap pair of jeans.

"Let's get a drink here and then walk along the canal to the Pev," suggested Caroline. "There's someone I want you to meet, Vicky."

"So who's this friend of yours?" I said, sipping my tea.

"His name's Gary. He's a good mate. He works behind the bar. Whenever I'm down in the dumps, I call him up and pour my heart out. He's my sounding board too," she grinned. "Everyone needs a Gary".

"You've known him a while, then."

"Yeah, ages; it would be … let me see, yes … eight years. We met in '67 when we were both working at the chippy, you know the one, in Garston where I first clapped eyes on your brother."

"No … what? Where's Garston? I'm confused."

"Oh, *surely* you've heard *that* old story!"

"Sorry Caroline, I have absolutely no idea what you're talking about," I said with mock affectation, leaning forward and fixing her with an inquisitive gaze.

"You haven't? Well, remember that swimming competition in Liverpool? Alan would have been …" she hesitated; "17, I think. You all came down and had fish and chips the night before … you and your family. Well, I was waitressing at the time. I served you your dinner! Small world, isn't it?"

I cast my mind back. "Oh my gosh! I remember now. Alan couldn't take his eyes off you!" I took a swig of tea. "But I thought you met at college."

"We did. We didn't discover the connection until we'd been dating for a couple of weeks. Alan was talking about his swimming, well boasting actually, and then as you can imagine the penny dropped. Mind you, he'd been telling me for months that he thought I looked familiar; that was before he plucked up the courage to ask me out. I can't say I recognised him," she added confidentially.

"Well, he's no oil painting," I said, with a mischievous grin.

We finished our tea and ambled down Market Street to Piccadilly Gardens. I looked up at the gathering clouds and cursed the rising wind which pounded at the side of my face, making my eyes water. Shortly we arrived at Canal Street and turned right. Back in the 1970s, this celebrated hotspot was not the liberal, lively and cosmopolitan meeting place we know today, where Mancunians and tourists of every colour, creed and sexual orientation can enjoy the pleasures of food, drink and conversation. Back then, it was a rather shabby backstreet with offices and warehouses on one side and a low wall on the other, from which an unsuspecting drunk could topple into the canal with little more than a misplaced step.

On my face and hands, and on the pavement at my feet, intermittent splashes of water announced the arrival of a shower. A minute later, we found ourselves being pelted mercilessly with a battery of hailstones.

"Share my umbrella," Caroline called above the din. I hastened to her side and she tilted the umbrella forward into the path of the maelstrom, but our progress along the street was slow and effortful due to the force of the wind against the surface of the umbrella.

"Can we stop here a minute?" she shouted, tugging at the back of Alan's jacket. "I'm getting nowhere fast."

We halted next to a lock and stood with our backs to the wind. A narrowboat was chugging into the chamber. A middle-aged man watched its progress from the towpath below us. He looked up at us, grinned, and motioned towards the sky with a look of cheerful resignation. Then he put his shoulder to the balance beam, the gates closed and the water level inside the chamber began to recede slowly. I watched the procedure with interest, while Alan explained to me the science behind this simple mechanism which enables boats to go up and down aquatic stairs. Presently the hail stopped and the wind became tolerable again.

As we started westwards along Canal Street, a girl of about my own age emerged from the shelter of a doorway ahead of us with a small dog at her heels. She was wrapped in a camel-coloured coat which looked oversized on her diminutive frame. Her boots were tan. The wind tugged at her hair, which was light brown and fell just past her shoulders. As she drew closer, I noticed that her facial features were very well proportioned, if a little too chiselled, and I thought her unconventionally pretty. I glanced across at Chris. If the intensity of his expression at that moment was anything to go by, he evidently thought so too.

All of a sudden, a gust of wind caught hold of the pages of a discarded newspaper and sent it spinning across the pavement a few feet in front of the girl. The dog dashed forward yapping wildly, careered sideways in pursuit of its flying quarry, bounced over the wall and tumbled headlong into the canal. The girl screamed and ran to the wall. The narrowboat had by now almost cleared the gate and its bow was aiming directly for the bewildered animal. The dog paddled frantically towards the moving vessel, its little body bobbing up and down in the swell.

"Oh my God! My puppy! My puppy!" she cried out hysterically, a look of abject terror on her face.

Without a word, Alan flung off his jacket and pumps, dived into the path of the boat, narrowly missing the bow, made a grab for the puppy with one hand and pushed hard against the hull with his free arm just in time to dodge a potentially fatal blow to the fragile beast. As the boat continued forward, he plunged beneath the surface to avoid hitting his head on the side. We waited breathlessly for what felt like an eternity but what was, in fact, about half a minute. Alan emerged clutching the puppy and propelled himself back to the towpath, red-faced and panting.

Chris strode over to the stricken girl. "You stupid woman!" he yelled. "Where's the lead?" She fumbled in her bag. "Why aren't you using it, you idiot?" he continued remorselessly.

She turned white and looked at him blankly.

I walked up to the pair. "Leave her alone, Chris. Can't you see she's upset." I touched her gently on the arm. She was shaking. "Don't mind my brother," I said gently. "He's got rather a hot temper."

Chris coloured, turned away and looked absent-mindedly at the narrowboat, which had glided to a halt alongside us.

"It's all right," she sniffed. "It's my fault … only she's such a good dog."

In the meantime, Caroline had clambered down onto the towpath and retrieved the shivering puppy, which was spluttering and choking. She pulled off her scarf, wrapped it around the little animal and handed the bundle up into the outstretched arms of its grateful owner.

"Oh, he's alive, he's alive, thank God." The girl hugged the whimpering animal and started to cry.

The skipper heralded us from the deck. "Ahoy there, are you all right?"

"We're all right," I called back, "but my brother's a bit wet."

"Hold up, I'll reverse."

With not a little skill, he manoeuvred the vessel in a backward direction so that it was possible for Alan to climb aboard from the end of the towpath. He disappeared into the cabin and reappeared a few minutes later wearing an old green windcheater and a pair of faded brown cords. He thanked the skipper heartily and came ashore.

Caroline looked him up and down and laughed out loud.

"You're not going to the pub dressed like that, are you?"

"Have you got a better idea?" he replied with a careless shrug, holding up a carrier bag full of wet clothes.

The girl smiled. "I think you look just fine," she said shyly. "I don't know who you are or how I can ever repay you. You saved my dog's life. You could have drowned."

"Not me," said Alan with a twinkle. "Alan Kelly, North West Region Youth Championships 1967 … runner-up. Delighted to make your acquaintance." He held out his hand.

"Amanda Browne … Mandy." She extended her forearm cautiously and clutched at his fingers, whilst maintaining a firm hold on the puppy to prevent it from wriggling from her grasp.

"You can buy me drink, for a start," he grinned. "I'm gasping."

Chris turned round with a pained expression on his face.

"I'll buy them," he said gruffly. "Sorry, Amanda. I shouldn't have sounded off at you like that. It was wrong of me. Forgive me. Let me get you a drink."

The girl blushed and nodded her assent. "Thank you, that would be lovely," she said nervously. "Will you help me with Bella's lead, please? I think she's ready to walk now. It's in my bag, there.

Look, tucked down the side. Would you get it out for me please, only I don't want to risk putting her down." She inclined her head towards a black leather shoulder bag which hung at her side.

He reached into the bag and felt awkwardly for the lead, keeping his face averted, evidently embarrassed at finding himself in such close personal contact with a virtual stranger, especially such an attractive one.

"Can you put it on, please?" she continued. "I'm sorry, but I don't think I can do it while I'm holding on to her."

He turned a deeper shade of crimson, grappled with the clasp and eventually managed to attach it to the collar with trembling fingers. He stepped back with his eyes fixed on the floor.

However, the young lady was not done with him yet.

"So … what's your name then?" she said gingerly.

"I'm Chris."

There was an uncomfortable silence.

"Oh yes, I remember now." Her reply baffled me, until I figured that I must have used his name when I reprimanded him for his attack on her. After an awfully long pause, during which I vainly hoped that Chris might make a little more effort, she resumed talking. "And your friends …?"

"They're not my friends. Alan's my brother. Caroline … the one with the red hair … that's his girlfriend. The short one's my sister, Vicky."

I managed to resist the temptation to thump him, but only just.

"Do you live round here?"

"We do now but we've moved down from Cumberland, apart from Caroline. She's from Liverpool."

"Oh, what part of Cumberland?"

The girl's persistence paid off and it was not long before the tension between them evaporated and they relaxed into easy conversation.

We entered the Peveril of the Peak and found a table without difficulty, as it was still quite early. Chris bought a round, while

Caroline enquired of the landlady if Gary could be spared from the kitchen for a couple of minutes so that we could be introduced. She assented 'with the greatest of pleasure' and Gary duly emerged through a door at the side of the bar, strolled across to our table and shook me by the hand. He was a gangly fellow with a mop of black, curly hair, a matching beard, a cheerful demeanour and charming manners. Caroline was keen to recount the afternoon's events, lest he should think that her boyfriend's attire was of his own choosing.

"That's a very sweet dog," Gary said, when Caroline had finished describing its brush with death. "What kind is it?"

"It's a Shih Tzu Yorkie cross," Mandy replied. "Her name's Bella. Would you like to stroke her?" She picked up the puppy and placed it in her lap.

"It's funny," said Alan, after Gary had returned to the kitchen. "That boy Richard … the one that pipped me at the post all those years ago in that momentous backstroke race; I remember he said I'd do something amazing one day, and now … well … I have."

Chris put down his beer. "Who wants to play table football? Mandy, d'you want a game?"

"Oh, yes please. I'd love a game," she said eagerly, her eyes shining. "Would you mind looking after Bella, please Vicky?" she said, handing me the puppy.

I shot a knowing glance at Caroline. As soon as the pair were out of earshot, I wasted no time in giving my opinion.

"That boy's looking better already," I said with a chuckle. "Next thing we know, he'll be shaving."

"With any luck, he'll move out," added Caroline with a sigh. "We get no privacy. Every time I go round, there he is, slobbing on the sofa, beer in hand."

Presently the pair returned, their faces glowing.

"You only won 'cause I let you," laughed Chris. "I could have thrashed you but I'm too much of a gentleman."

"That's not true," she countered. "You're just not as good as me."

"Fancy a game, Carrie?" said Alan.

"Sure. Come on, Vicks. You can play with me."

I shook my head. "Nah … I'm rubbish. I think I'll just sit here and drink."

Mandy sat down and picked up her glass. "I couldn't help noticing your T-shirt. Did you see Queen, Chris?"

"Yeah … saw 'em last year at Blackpool … with my ex." He pulled a face.

"I absolutely *love* the Eagles? D'you like the Eagles?"

"They're all right."

"Don't you think 'Desperado' is just the greatest song ever made? Every time I hear it, I want to cry. To be honest, I sometimes do."

"Well you would, you're a girl," he said flippantly. "I still reckon I could have beaten you at the football. Must be having an off day."

"I like Elton John too. D'you like him?"

"Gosh, Mand. I'll tell you what you *do* like. Asking questions!"

I began to feel like a third wheel so I made my excuses, handed back the dog and wandered over to the football table. Caroline moved over, I seized the handles with both hands and gave it my best shot. The result was two own goals and a third in our favour, a wild strike that was entirely down to luck and bore no relation to the skill I possessed, which amounted to zero. My embarrassment at my ineptitude was marginally less than the discomfiture engendered by playing chaperone to the happy couple.

"I'm hungry," I said at the end of the game. "I can't afford to eat out. Do you think we should make a move?"

"Yes, I think we probably should," agreed Caroline. "We weren't planning on eating out either."

We returned to the table.

"Come on, drink up. We're making tracks," announced Alan, knocking back his pint.

While Chris disappeared off to the gents, Mandy sidled up to me.

"Your brother's rather dishy. Is he single?" she enquired, in hushed tones.

"I assume so. He's only seen his wife once in the last six months, and when he did they barely spoke. He's got children you know ... two girls, six and nearly two."

"Don't you think he looks like Don Henley, that one in the Eagles that sings and plays the drums?" she giggled, clearly undeterred by this new revelation.

"Oh, I don't know. Well, actually, I don't know what Don Henley looks like."

"Well, you see, Chris doesn't have that big mass of curly hair, but apart from that, they're very similar." She hesitated; then added almost as an afterthought, "Which is a good thing ... I mean, the resemblance *and* the hair. Chris has much nicer hair."

"Shh ... he's coming," I cautioned. "By the way, you're welcome to him. He's badly in need of a woman's touch."

We spilled out onto the pavement and walked briskly back up Portland Street towards the car park.

"So, Mandy, where's home, and more importantly, how are you getting back?" asked Chris, who was by now surpassing himself in his bid to create a favourable impression.

"I live in Stockport, in Derby Street ... it's in Edgeley. Do you know Edgeley?"

"Can't say I do," he replied.

"It's one stop from Piccadilly," she said, "and it's quite close to the station at the other end ... an easy walk, so I'll be all right from here."

"Do you live on your own? Or with ... *someone,*" he said, placing emphasis on the key part of the question.

"I live with my mum."

"Oh ... may I call you?"

They exchanged numbers and parted company at the top of Piccadilly. She gave him her hand and he kissed it gallantly with a flourish. She turned scarlet and scurried off down the street, looking back coyly before she was lost to view.

As we completed the short walk to Dale Street, I lapsed into thought. Once before, a fluke meeting involving a dog had been instrumental in altering the course of many lives. I still remembered the vehemence with which Liam had attacked me when Rufus had made a lunge at Shirley at the lake; that his apology had marked the beginning of a solid and lasting friendship between us. It was my belief that the love, respect and empathy which bound us together had played a key part in sustaining, for almost seven years, a marriage bound to fail. Many were the times that I had counselled Chris to exercise patience and restraint out of sympathy for the old man. Many were the times that I had tacitly begged Liam, with a significant glance or subtle touch of my hand, to offer a kind word to my brother, if only to please me. What of Louise, who owed her existence to the longevity of her parents' marriage? What also of Sarah? Would anyone, other than a brother of mine, have been allowed even a fighting chance after denying a father the right to give his only daughter away at the altar?

How ironic, I reflected, that Chris had reacted in the selfsame way to a chance encounter so uncannily alike. How distressing, that he had mirrored the behaviour that he despised in his father-in-law. How auspicious, that his apology had produced such a promising outcome.

And so ended a day brimming with coincidences; a day that had started as little more than a lunch date; a day that had evolved into an adventure; a day that had culminated in the birth of a partnership with life-changing potential.

Chapter 12

The Benefactress

A few weeks later, when I saw Chris again, the change in him was remarkable. He was clean-shaven, his hair was an inch or two shorter and he had on a new pair of jeans. Mum had brought Sarah down for the weekend and I arrived at Alan's flat during the morning. I found Chris in the kitchen making sandwiches. I greeted him with an appreciative smile.

"So what's all this in aid of?" I said, looking him up and down. "I mean, the hair … the beard, or should I say the lack of it … you look so smart! Are we having lunch with the Queen?"

"Er, no … not the Queen, but I have invited a *friend*," he said significantly.

"Ah, I see. That wouldn't be the lovely Amanda, by any chance?" I said impishly.

"Ye-es," he replied cautiously.

I raised my eyebrows. "Have you told Sarah?" I asked, lowering my voice.

"Well … not exactly, but Mum's told her."

"You coward!" I exclaimed, half in jest. "What's Sarah's take on it, or don't you know?"

"She's cool with it," he said casually, slapping a slice of buttered bread down upon another loaded with cheese and picking up the bread knife.

"So where are we going? Oh, you *are* making *me* a sarnie, aren't you? I'm skint and I've run out of bread." I reached into my bag and brandished an apple. "Look, my lunch. I can't last all afternoon on this!"

"Yeah, sure," he mumbled, reaching into the breadbin. "Hold on, what am I doing? Do it yourself, you lazy cow!"

Some things never change.

It was one of those delightful May mornings. The sun was warm and a mild spring breeze kissed our faces with the lightest of touches. Our destination was Gorton Reservoir in the Manchester suburb of Debdale two miles distant, a picturesque beauty spot with a water sports centre, lakeshore walks and a children's play area in the adjoining park. A pleasant 40 minute stroll brought us to the waterside cafeteria where we met Mandy. She was evidently nervous from the manner in which she twisted the strap of her handbag between her fingers and glanced down at Bella every few seconds. Mum did her best to put her at her ease by applying the tried and tested method of asking a dog lover about their dog, but it was Sarah's clumsy overtures that finally instilled some much needed confidence into her father's fair companion. Mandy turned her attention to the little girl sitting next to her, while Mum went across to help Caroline bring the teas to the table.

"You must be Sarah. Do you have a dog?" she asked, knowing the answer.

"Yes, she's called Shirley. She's a border collie, she's black and white and she's very, very old," Sarah replied sagely.

"Mine's just a baby," said Mandy. "Would you like to stroke her? Her name's Bella. It means 'beautiful' in Italian."

Sarah smirked, clambered off her chair and disappeared under the table. She emerged a minute later, giggling, hopped back onto her chair and put her face close to Mandy's ear.

"My boyfriend's Italian. He's called Carlo. He's in my class. We're going to get married when we're 16," she said confidentially. "Don't tell Daddy though. He thinks I'm too young to have a boyfriend."

"Do you like school?"

"Hmmm ... sometimes. I like it when Miss Simpson reads us stories. She's pretty, like you."

"Oh, thank you Sarah, only I don't think I'm all that pretty."

"Well, you're *quite* pretty. Only you've got a rather long face, like Mildred Hubble."

"Goodness, is that a good thing, then? Having a long face like ... what was her name?" said Mandy, laughing.

"Mildred Hubble. *Everyone's* heard of Mildred Hubble. She's a witch."

"I thought witches were old and ugly."

"Oh, no. Mildred's very pretty but she's not a very good witch. In fact," she said emphatically, "she's the Worst Witch.

"Oh dear, is she very bad?" Mandy asked in a voice loaded with concern.

"No, she's not *that* sort of bad. She's a good witch but her spells keep going wrong. Would you like to borrow my book when I've finished it? Mummy's reading it to me."

"Oh yes please, Sarah, that would be lovely," said Mandy indulgently. "Now why don't you tell me some more about Mildred Hubble."

Sarah prattled on while Mandy listened intently and sipped her tea. By the time we left the cafeteria, Sarah was making a bid for Mandy's hand. *That's a relief*, I thought to myself. I rarely got the opportunity to chat uninterrupted to Mum as Sarah would insist on claiming my attention and I found it very hard to say no for fear of hurting her feelings.

We ambled along the edge of the lake, then turned inwards and found a sward on which to picnic. The water twinkled between the trunks of the ash trees that dotted the shoreline. The lush green grass at our feet was spangled with spring flowers; daisies, buttercups and forget-me-nots. I munched on my sandwich in silence, feasting my eyes on the verdant pastoral scene which seemed such a far cry from the grim spectacle of post-industrial 1970s Manchester in a decade characterised by disused factories, dusty construction sites and homogenous high-rise developments. Here the air was fresh and clean and the trees whispered a welcome. A squirrel foraged amongst the roots of a weeping willow and a robin perched on the branch of a nearby shrub was ticking a warning. An image formed in my mind's eye, a picture of Wasdale at its loveliest and most benign, and I questioned, just for a minute or two, if the road I was on was the right one.

I was woken from my reverie by Sarah's shrill voice at my elbow.

"Auntie Vicky, can we feed the ducks?"

A few yards along the shore, a small group of mallards had gathered and were gobbling noisily at the contents of a Tupperware box which two young children were emptying into the shallows. Chris dived into his rucksack, pulled out a plastic bag containing half a dozen slices of bread and tossed it to Sarah. She tugged me to my feet and trotted over to the bank, dragging me along behind. I watched ruefully as a goodly amount of decent bread disappeared into the rotund bellies of the feathered flock, wondering forlornly what miracle I could rustle up for lunch tomorrow from the few remaining morsels in my kitchen cupboard at home. After Sarah had accosted the two small children and introduced them to Bella, we packed up and continued our circuit of the reservoir, stopping frequently to admire the view, contemplate the flora and fauna we chanced upon and befriend the canine contingent we met along the way. Back at the cafeteria, Mum bought ice creams and we made our way to the children's play area. For the next hour, Sarah amused herself on the swings, seesaw, slide, roundabout and rocking horse on springs, assisted by Mandy who had been working hard all day to make a good impression. Relieved of my childminding duties, I lay back on the grass, closed my eyes and enjoyed the heat of the sun on my face, the sounds of nature and the happy chatter of the children playing nearby. I was going to like this girl.

* * *

One morning in early June, on a trip to the local minimarket, I came face to face with Sister Sparks in the frozen food aisle. She greeted me with a broad smile.

"Why, Vicky, this *is* a pleasant surprise, although perhaps not so very *much* of a surprise. You're local, aren't you?"

"Yes, Mayfield Road. I didn't know you were from round this way ... well, that is, are you?"

"Goodness me, yes. I live about a mile off, in Lindsay Avenue."

"I'm afraid I don't know where that is. You see, I've only been living here for a few months ... but of course you know that. Would you mind passing me those fish fingers, there?" I said, pointing towards the freezer cabinet she was standing in front of.

"Ooh, look!" she exclaimed. "They've got Arctic Roll. I simply *must* get some for Deborah. She *will* be pleased. Deborah's my daughter, you know."

"I didn't know you had a daughter," I said, genuinely surprised. She had never mentioned her daughter before.

"Oh yes. Deborah's eight. I had her rather late in life. She's rather partial to Arctic Roll. It *is* rather good. Have you tried it?"

"No, I don't believe I have. I was brought up on a farm. Mum wouldn't have dreamt of serving up a frozen pudding. I honestly think my Dad would have divorced her on the spot if she did. I can see him now. 'What do you want to go serving up that rubbish for? We've got cows can deliver us a good, cheap junket?'" I gave a wry laugh and was rewarded with a hearty one.

"Go on, treat yourself," she urged, thrusting the box into my hand. "You won't regret it."

I looked wistfully at the ticket on the side. "I'm afraid it's a little out of my price range," I said with a sigh.

"Nonsense!" she rejoined. "It's cheap as chips."

"Well, unfortunately it's not quite cheap enough for me. Maybe another time …" I handed it back reluctantly.

"Oh dear, is it really that bad?" she asked, in a tone of sympathy.

I shrugged. "I get by."

"Oh, you poor dear. Here, let me buy it for you. You're a good, hardworking girl. You deserve a treat."

"Oh, Sister, I couldn't possibly!"

"Don't be silly. Of course you could." She reached into the freezer and pulled out a second Arctic Roll. "I'll get two. You can have one. Oh … let me get you those fish fingers. Bless me, I nearly forgot. Now is that all you need?"

We made our way to the checkout together, paid for our shopping and went outside. She pressed the carton into my hand.

"Thank you, it's awfully kind of you," I said bashfully.

Sister Sparks paused, a thoughtful expression on her face.

"How would you like to earn a little bit of extra money, Vicky?"

"We-ell, maybe. What would I need to do?"

"Just look after Deborah for me. Me and my hubby like a night out every once in a while. The neighbour's girl's been doing it for me for the last few years but she's sitting her 'O' levels at the moment and she'll be starting work in a matter of weeks. She's told me already that she doesn't want to do it anymore and … well, I've seen how you are with the children on the ward. You have a lovely way with them. Come on, Vicky. What do you say?"

"We-ell, if you think I'd be all right," I said diffidently.

"All right? You'll be just perfect! Deborah will love you! Now, when would you like to come over and meet her? How about later on today?"

"Well … I guess I could," I replied in a state of bemusement, hardly realising what I was saying.

"That's settled then," she said briskly. She rummaged in her handbag and wrote down her address on a piece of paper. "Shall we say four o'clock?" She shook my hand vigorously and we parted company.

Deborah stepped in through the French windows, her cheeks pink and glowing and her breath shallow. She pulled off her plimsolls and dropped her skipping rope on the floor. She was an attractive girl of above average height, whose face resembled her mother's. She had the same large eyes but her lips were fuller and her nose was sprinkled with freckles. She walked up to me with a confident, self-possessed manner that belied her young years and bobbed a pretty curtsy.

"Hello, I'm Deborah," she said, between gulps of air.

"I'm Vicky. I'm very pleased to meet you. My, you sound exhausted."

"I did 185 skips, that's my second best ever!" she panted. "I'm practising for the sponsored skip at school next week. If I can get to 200, Mummy's going to give an extra five pounds. I'm *soooo* thirsty. Mummy, can I have some Lilt … pleeease?"

"All right, poppet," said her mother. "And pick up that skipping rope! Someone's going to fall over it. Would you like a cup of tea, Vicky?"

I nodded my assent. Deborah shuffled across the lounge, threw her skipping rope into a large plastic crate, dropped onto the sofa and looked up at me.

"What are you going to do with the money … from the sponsored skip?" I asked.

"We're going to give it to Clare's Daddy. Clare's in my class. Her Daddy had an accident. He's going to give it to the policemen and firemen and doctors and nurses … and the people in the shop."

"Oh dear, did he have an accident in a shop?"

"Yes, in Lewis's, but he's all right now. It wasn't a *bad* accident."

Sister Sparks reappeared bearing a tray containing two cups of tea, a plate of Jaffa Cakes and a tall glass of pale yellow cloudy liquid.

"Do sit down and make yourself comfortable, Vicky," she said, motioning towards the sofa. "Deborah, go and put your slippers on and then perhaps Vicky will help you with your jigsaw when she's finished her tea."

Deborah scurried upstairs and we sat down on the sofa together.

"The father of one of the children in Deborah's class got caught up in the IRA bombing at Lewis's department store in January," she said in hushed tones. "They're raising money to thank the emergency services and the staff in the shop. They were fantastic. Luckily his injuries were fairly minor. I'm not sure how much Deborah knows, or understands. The school don't want the children unduly alarmed so they're keeping it very low key. Would you like a Jaffa Cake?" she continued. "I do hope you won't object to helping Deborah with her jigsaw when she comes down. She's a bit stuck on the sky. It'll be an opportunity for you to get to know one another. Now, you must call me Rose. I insist on it."

Anybody with recollections of the strict hierarchical axiom which governed the NHS back in the 1970s will appreciate the discomfiture engendered by her generous concession, that of permitting me to address a superior by her Christian name, as well as the awkwardness I experienced over the succeeding weeks when compelled to do it. It took several months and a number of arch reminders before it flowed naturally off my tongue. By that time, Deborah and I had become firm friends and the babysitting, into which I felt I had been coerced by my well-intentioned but rather overbearing employer, proved to be a huge success as well as a welcome supplement to my modest income.

On one such occasion in early September, Rose put me onto a vacancy, as yet unannounced, in the Obstetrics department.

“I don’t want to lose you,” she said. “You’re a real asset to the ward, but I can’t stand by and watch you throw up the chance to take your career to the next level. I can help you get the position. I’ll put a good word in for you. All you need do is apply once the job is advertised.”

She was as good as her word and five weeks later, on the eve of my 22nd birthday, I took up my new post, one which brought me into daily contact with expectant mothers and allowed me to share the magical experience of childbirth at first hand, assist in the care of the tiny infants who passed through my hands and move a step closer to my dream.

* * *

On Saturday 29th November, Rose held a party in her home to mark her 50th birthday. She had quickly come to regard me as a friend and was unerring in her quest to break the habit formed by convention and treat me as her equal outside working hours. However, all the time I was working under her, this required considerable mental agility on both sides and it was not until I left the ward that the social barriers bred in a culture of rigour and restraint were completely dispelled, on her part at least. On mine, it took much longer; I was young, prone to self-doubt and humbled by the partiality shown me by my benefactress. Consequently I was pleasantly surprised, not to mention embarrassed, when she handed me a party invitation.

“I’m not sure I even want to go,” I said to Linda later that day, tossing the invitation onto the dining room table. “I’ll be the youngest one there and no-one’ll talk to me. Goodness knows what bigwigs might turn up. It’s all too terrifying.”

“Rubbish, don’t be such a drama queen! You’ll be fine,” retorted Linda in the no-nonsense tone she habitually used, which left no room for debate. “I’d give my eyeteeth for an opportunity like that. Now stop complaining; you should regard it as an honour, not a trial!"

She was right, of course. Nevertheless, it was with a great deal of trepidation that I donned a borrowed suit, walked the familiar route to Lindsay Avenue with a beating heart and approached the front door. The sounds of music, laughter and clinking glasses met my ears. I summoned my courage, rang the bell and was admitted by Deborah's father. Leslie Sparks was tall, exceptionally handsome and considerably younger than Rose. Although I knew him to be a Liverpudlian man, his accent was flavoured with a slight drawl and his speech was peppered with Americanisms. He walked with a pronounced limp. He greeted me warmly, helped me off with my coat and handed it to Deborah who, on hearing my voice, had come to the door. Then he showed me into the kitchen and poured me a Martini.

"I'm guessing you've not met my folks," he said, inclining his head towards the doorway. "Come through, I'll introduce you."

I began to suspect that Rose, recognising the inequality in age and social standing between her protégée and her guests, had briefed Leslie to take care of me. Whatever the reason, I was extremely grateful for his attentiveness.

Leslie's parents were a friendly couple who were getting on in years. His father was American; his mother English. That explained the idiosyncrasies in his diction, I concluded. We fell into easy conversation, Leslie taking the lead.

"I was born in New Jersey. I don't remember my real Mom. She died in childbirth. Pop was a GI in World War II, a fighter pilot," he continued, surveying his father with pride. "He was stationed in Warrington … never went back to the homeland. When I was a kid, I lived in the States with my grandma. Pop got remarried and I came over after the War, when I was … er … how old was I, Pop?"

"Let me see … 1947 … you would have been … eight, I think. Yeah, that's it, eight. After the war, we ran a training programme at the base so I stayed put. Later I got a job at Speke Aerodrome with the Ministry of Aviation. There was no getting Gracie off her home turf; she's an Anglophile through and through," he said, winking at the elderly lady beside him. "He's an ex-pilot too, you know," he continued, motioning towards his son. "Good job we settled here, what with Vietnam 'n' all. He'd 've been dead meat for sure, either that or a victim of a different sort … demonised by the backlash of the American people against a futile war," he concluded bitterly.

"Come, Pop. I was barely out of training school, before … *this*," Leslie said emphatically, giving his left leg an impatient jerk.

"Well, better a cripple than a corpse," rejoined his father, picking up his beer and taking a long draught.

"Your leg?" I said, addressing Leslie, anxious to move the conversation on. "Was that a flying accident, then?"

"Actually … no. That's the irony of it. I suppose you're too young to remember Coppenhall, the train crash?"

I shook my head.

"It was on Boxing Day 1962 at the start of the big freeze; worst winter in living memory. I was on my way down to Birmingham to visit a pal from Flying School. It was dark and bitterly cold; we were caught in a blizzard. We were waiting at a red signal at Crewe when the London-bound train ploughed into us from behind and wrecked the last two carriages. 18 dead and loads more injured. I thought I'd got off lightly … until this happened."

Leslie pulled up his trouser leg and revealed a prosthetic leg, joined at the knee.

"Oh my gosh, I had no idea!" I exclaimed. "Was it crushed, then?"

"No; that's the sickening part. I was whisked off to hospital for some minor surgery but it turned gangrenous and … well … that put paid to a career in the RAF." He shook his head mournfully. "I'm no Douglas Bader, you know."

"There ain't no shame in that, son," his father cut in, "and you've a fine wife."

“There’s many a patient falls for their nurse, but few have the good fortune to marry them,” he grinned, smoothing down the left leg of his trousers. “We got hitched two years later and moved here. By that time I’d retrained as an air traffic controller and got a job at Manchester Airport. I love my job but I miss the thrill of flying. Still, every cloud … eh?”

“I’ve always had a liking for a man in uniform,” quipped Rose, who happened to be passing with a bottle in her hand, “especially when he’s on his back!”

The music was especially good that night, 1975 being the year which gave us the likes of ‘Bohemian Rhapsody‘, ‘I’m Not in Love’ and ‘Space Oddity’, which was enjoying its second stint in the UK singles chart. Even Barry Manilow excelled himself that year, with a decent ballad entitled ‘Mandy’ which was conspicuous by dint of the name of its central character. I dined on vol-au-vents, quiche, cocktail stick savouries, salmon and cucumber sandwiches and sherry trifle, washed down with Tequila Sunrise, wobbled home in the early hours of the morning and woke up with a pounding head.

* * *

The summer of ’76 was the hottest since records began. For six weeks the sun shone unremittingly, and while we enjoyed picnics in the park, trips to Blackpool beach on days off and long, balmy evenings at the flat sipping Blue Nun on the shabby veranda, Dad worked from dawn till dusk and beyond, attempting to rescue his crops from the catastrophic effects of the prolonged drought. At the beginning of August, Alan and Caroline got married in the suburb of Liverpool called Allerton. Chris had received his marching orders and had found himself a ground floor flat on Edgeley Road in Stockport, a short walk from Mandy’s house. Three weeks before the wedding, Mandy moved in with Chris, much to the consternation of our parents, who complained to me unrelentingly that Chris was still married to Julie and ought to make his mind up where his allegiance lay. They had a point.

Around that time, I happened to converse with Rose about the difficulty I was having finding somewhere affordable to stop overnight after the wedding.

"Mum and Dad are staying at the Stalbridge but it's prohibitively expensive. Besides, Ray's coming up from London and ... well ... we may as well share," I said, blushing. "My parents don't really approve of that sort of thing, so I'd rather not do it right under their noses. You don't happen to know of anywhere cheaper, do you, with your local connections?"

"Of course! Why didn't I think of it before? My Les's parents live at Halewood; that's just down the road from Allerton. You can stay with them. They've got plenty of space and I'm sure they would love to have you. They're very open-minded," she added, with a twinkle.

The elder Sparks were duly contacted and arrangements made.

Linda very obligingly volunteered to stay at her brother's house on the Friday night preceding the wedding on Saturday, and Ray drove up from London in his battered old Mini Clubman, a 21st birthday gift from his parents which was not in great shape when he acquired it nearly four years ago yet somehow kept on going. We dined at the Rice Bowl in Cross Street. I had never tasted Chinese food before and thought it divine. As we sat facing one another, waiting for the bill, Ray reached forward and took hold of my hand. I felt my heart flutter and my body tremble.

"Vicky, have you ever thought about moving to London?"

"I ... I don't know," I stammered. "I guess I have, you being there, but ..."

"But what?" he coaxed, gently.

"It's such a long way from home, and where would I live? It's so expensive."

"You can live with us."

"Us? What, you mean ... with your family?" I said incredulously.

"That's exactly what I mean. Ruby's getting married next spring. I've talked to Mum and Dad. You can have her room."

"Oh … I thought …" I stopped short. "Well, I don't know what I thought," I resumed in a murmur, attempting to conceal my disappointment, which was all too apparent.

"You thought it was marriage proposal? Look, I'm sorry, darling, I just don't *feel* ready, but it's a step in the right direction. We could live together first and see how we get on."

"*Get on*?" I echoed, incredulously. "We've been getting on for *nine years*!"

"Give me time," he replied softly, giving my hand a squeeze. "You know I love you. Please come to London. I want you to."

"All right, I'll think about it. That is, I'll ask Rose … and Mum," I replied, inwardly quashing my doubts and heeding my rational self. After all, his proposition was the next best thing to matrimony.

Ray stood up, leant across the table, cupped my face in his hands and kissed me on the lips.

"Don't do that, they'll throw us out," I scolded merrily, buoyed by his little display of affection like so many before, which had never failed to charm me.

He paid for the meal and we walked home hand in hand, as it was too lovely a night to be cooped up in the car. At the end of a beautiful evening, we pushed the beds together, mine and Linda's, lay down side by side and strengthened the invisible threads that bound us together in a union that was intensely sweet after many a long month of separation and abstinence.

The following day, Alan married Caroline at All Souls Church, Springwood. Louise, who had recently turned four, stood proudly behind her Uncle and Aunt at the altar with the two other bridesmaids, Caroline's cousin and best friend. After an initial protest, seven year old Sarah had been persuaded to relinquish her customary starring role. It was only fair, her mother reasoned, since Louise had been denied the opportunity to walk down the aisle with her sister on that fateful day two years ago when Toni had married Jason; the day that had marked the end of an era. We spilled out of the cool, dimly-lit church onto the hot, bright pavement and waved off the newlyweds. Then we made our way on foot to the reception at a modern, purpose-built Conservative Club venue in Heath Road a short distance from the church. Julie walked near the front of the wedding party with Toni and Jason and the children, Chris at the back with Mandy.

On arrival, we were greeted by the bride and groom and gathered in the hall. Toni had taken Sarah and Scott outside to let off steam in the car park. Jason was standing at the bar with Dad, Michael and Nan, who had polished off her welcome drink in less than three minutes. Julie stood on her own with Louise. She wore a chiffon dress of cornflower blue with a broad band about the waist, surmounting a loosely pleated skirt which floated to her knees with the weightlessness of gossamer. Chris left Mandy in conversation with Mum and sidled up to me. He had not set eyes on his wife or youngest daughter for more than 18 months and seemed genuinely surprised at how much Louise had grown.

"She's beautiful, absolutely beautiful," he mused, sipping his drink and gazing at the pretty, dark-haired girl clutching her mother's hand. "Do you think she knows who I am?"

"Why don't you ask her?" I replied frostily. Although I loved my brother dearly, I found it very difficult to turn a blind eye to his partiality for Sarah and total neglect of Louise.

"Vicky, I can't. Look, she's with her mother."

"And …? Chris, you're 27 years old and you're acting like a child. Talk to her! She's your wife!"

"What shall I say to her?"

"I don't know. How about asking her to explain Stephen Hawking's theory on black holes?" I retorted irritably, "or just ask her how she is."

"Come with me, Vicks," he implored, evincing genuine fear at the prospect of coming face to face with Julie.

"All right, I will this time," I sighed. "Honestly Chris, you're such a baby!" I recalled the numerous occasions when he had chastised me in the selfsame manner and wondered at the incongruous reversal in our respective roles. "I'm sorry, Ray. Would you mind excusing us for a minute?"

Chris walked casually across to Julie, with me in tow. He opened his mouth to speak but no sound came. She smiled at him and looked down at Louise, who was gazing up at us with an inquisitive look.

"Lou, this is your daddy," said Julie in the tone one adopts when talking to a small child.

"I know," replied the little girl. "Sarah told me."

Chris squatted down so that his face was level with his daughter's.

"Hello Louise," he began hesitantly. "My, you've grown. What a pretty dress that is."

Louise tugged at Julie's hand. "Can I have a drink, please Mummy?" she said, ignoring her father's friendly overtures and peering up at her mother.

"Why don't you stay here with Daddy and Auntie Vicky, there's a good girl, and I'll get you some squash. Daddy's come a long way. He wants to see you," she added, making a move to go.

Louise stuck out her bottom lip in a gesture of protest and tightened her grip on her mother's hand.

"Come along, Louise, remember what I told you. Where are your manners, child?"

With an elegant little twist, Julie extricated herself from her daughter's grasp and hastened away. Louise looked hard into her father's face. Chris smiled awkwardly.

"How do you like school, sweetheart?"

"It's all right."

There was a long pause.

"What do you do … at school, I mean?

"Read, write, do sums. Sometimes we sing and go on the apparatus. I like the apparatus best."

"What's that then?" asked Chris, seizing upon the conversational line with evident relief.

"There's climbing frames, bars we balance on and different ones we swing on and ropes and things," she said, all in one breath.

"It's PE then," said her father bluntly, for want of a more interesting rejoinder.

Fortunately, by now Louise was getting into her comfort zone and didn't need too much prompting.

"Sometimes we do PE out of doors. That's nearly as fun. We play with hoops and balls. We had Sports Day, it was brilliant," she continued, becoming animated. "I won the egg and spoon race."

"Oh, that's terrific. Did you win a prize?"

"Yes, I won some Spangles but Mummy made me share them with Sarah. Why can't I come and stay with you like Sarah does? It's not fair. What's wrong with me?"

Chris's face fell. It was the question his subconscious mind had been dreading and it had come sooner than he had expected. He had been endeavouring, over the last few weeks, to hide his head in the sand. This was evident since Mum had hit a wall every time she had pressed him on the appalling way in which he constantly neglected Louise. Now, confronted by his iniquity, he had nothing to say. An uneasy silence ensued.

"Daddy hasn't been well," I ventured, drawing on the stock reply which was beginning to sound uncomfortably like a cliché. If his underlying mental state was in some measure responsible for his failings as a father, my assertion was probably not too far wide of the mark.

Julie reappeared then, carrying a drink which she handed down to Louise.

"Mummy, can I visit Daddy when he's better," cried the little girl, looking from one parent to the other. An expression of momentary confusion was effaced from Julie's countenance by an intuitive smile which she bestowed upon Chris with all the warmth of a compassionate lover. His colour rose.

"I'm sure Daddy would love to have you down as soon as he's well enough," she said, looking at him searchingly.

There was another embarrassing pause.

"You will invite her down, won't you, Chris?" I put in, eventually.

"Yeah, sure," he mumbled almost incoherently, staring past Julie at the opposite wall.

Julie was a woman not easily deterred.

"How do you like your new flat?" she asked amicably, keeping her eyes fixed on him.

"It's all right."

"Do you have further to travel, to get to work?" she persisted.

"'Bout the same."

I was standing behind and slightly to the left of Chris. With mounting vexation, I raised my left hand as if to straighten my hair, knocked my handbag off the opposite shoulder, propelled the strap down my arm with a subtle shake and caught it up in my outstretched fingers. Then I took aim and swung it smartly into the back of his leg. I saw him wince and instantly regretted the force with which I had delivered the blow. It did, however, produce the desired outcome.

"You all right, Julie?" said my brother, shifting his weight onto his right leg.

"Yes, I'm well, thank you."

"And your father?"

"He's well too. It's sweet of you to ask."

"How did you find the journey?" he continued, getting into his stride.

I left them exchanging pleasantries and slunk back to Ray to await the wrath of my brother on account of my attack on his person. 10 minutes later he marched over to me with renewed vigour.

"You vicious creature!" he spat, with genuine venom. "What the hell did you do that for?"

"I'm sorry, I didn't mean to hit you that hard," I replied honestly, but unable to resist a giggle at his expense.

"You'll be sorry you hit me at all!" he scowled.

"It did the trick though," I said audaciously, ducking behind Ray.

Presently we took up our allotted places on circular tables of eight, then drifted to the buffet to fill our plates. I sat between Ray and Chris. Julie sat next to Michael with Jason on the other side, on a table in the opposite corner of the room. During the meal and speeches, Chris was distant and preoccupied. He punctuated the conversation with comments which were non-committal and vague, and barely spoke to Mandy. His eyes constantly wandered in the direction of Julie's table and as soon as he could decently accomplish the mission, he excused himself, sauntered over and sat down in the place vacated by Jason, who had gone to the bar.

Mandy bristled. "I wish I'd never come," she said disconsolately. "I might as well be invisible. Look at him! He's all over her! I thought they didn't get on."

"Yes, well we all did," I concurred. "Don't worry, Mandy. He's probably making an effort for the sake of the children. He hasn't seen Louise for more than a year and I expect Mum's warned him to be on his best behaviour. I'm to blame. I made him go and talk to her."

"If only that were true. Did you see the way he was looking at her?"

It was useless to refute it.

"Would you like me to hit him with my handbag again?" I volunteered, with a wicked grin. "I sure would like to."

During the early evening, there was entertainment. A friend of the best man performed some card tricks and Michael played a few songs on his guitar culminating with a quaint rendition of 'Sweet Caroline'. Then Sarah took centre stage with a display of her considerable talent on the violin.

"She wanted to be a bridesmaid like her sister so they let her play instead," I explained to Ray. "She's good, mind you."

Soon after, there was a disco and finger foods. It goes without saying that Status Quo's 'Caroline' featured on the playlist; and more than once.

After a short absence, the bride and groom reappeared at nine o'clock wearing their day clothes in readiness to depart.

"I almost forgot," Caroline remarked as she bade me goodbye. "Paul McCartney grew up a few streets away. I know you're a massive fan. You should take a walk up to his house while you're here. It would be a shame to miss out when you're so close. Let me write the details down for you."

I fetched my handbag and pulled out a scrap of paper and a pen. She wrote down the directions and kissed me affectionately on the cheek.

Towards the end of the evening, I took my leave with Ray. Chris had recovered his temper but his offhand attitude towards Mandy had been painful to witness.

"I can't believe it. She's not angry with me," he said, his eyes shining and his face flushed.

"She jolly well is."

"No, no … I meant Julie, not Mand."

"It's taken you two years to work that out?" I replied scornfully. "Go and talk to Mandy, you oaf. You've been behaving like an absolute beast. Shame on you!"

"Oh, give over, Vicky," he growled. The message hit the spot however, as he immediately returned to his girlfriend's side as soon as he thought I wasn't looking.

Outdoors, it was a glorious evening, still and serene. A short walk brought us to the childhood home of my hero.

"It's amazing," I mused, "that such extraordinary talent evolved in such an ordinary place." I stood in wonder, awestruck by the streetscape, the stars and the solitude. It was one of those rare moments in time that crystallises in the mind like a snapshot and retains its vividness throughout life.

Our late night stroll back to Leslie's parents' house in Halewood took longer than we had anticipated but I didn't care. I was walking on air and wished heartily that it would never end. We arrived just before midnight, retrieved the front door key from under the mat, tiptoed upstairs and crept into bed together. The following morning, we dined on bacon pancakes drenched in maple syrup and drove back to Manchester with full stomachs and full hearts.

* * *

On Christmas Eve, back at the farm, Chris dropped a bombshell.

"By the way, Mandy's expecting," he said carelessly over tea, as soon as she was out of earshot in the bath.

Mum gasped and dropped her cup, which shattered in pieces on the floor.

"What's the problem, Mum?" he enquired, with leisurely indifference.

"You know full well what the problem is," she said severely. "You two aren't married."

"Toni wasn't married," countered Chris resentfully.

"Well, she is now," Mum snapped back, exasperated by his nonchalance in the face of such a grave situation. "How can you be so cavalier, Christopher, when you have a wife and children already?"

"Mum, it's 1976," he huffed.

"Be that as it may. Have you stopped to consider how young she is?"

"She's 22, for heaven's sake. If I remember rightly, you had me when you were 21."

"Things were different then. Besides, we were married," she argued.

"Precisely! Things were different then," he said triumphantly. "That makes it all right now." He banged his mug down on the table, stood up and stomped out of the kitchen, slamming the door behind him.

"Oh, what a mess," wailed Mum, burying her head in her hands.

"It'll work out," I said tenderly, with as much conviction as I could muster. "You'll see. I'll get you a fresh cup."

Chapter 13

Capital Letters

81 South Park Road,
South Wimbledon,
London. SW19 8RU

10th September 1977

Dear Mum,
Thank you so much for the brownies, which survived the 300 mile journey by Royal Mail intact and tasted every bit as fresh and good as they always do. I must confess I shed a little tear when they arrived on the doorstep this morning. You would have thought my two-and-a-half year stint in Manchester would have cured me of homesickness but London is so far away and there isn't a field or farm within miles.

Battersea Park is very pretty. I went there on Sunday with Ray but it's a poor substitute for lovely Wasdale, or indeed anywhere in our beautiful county where boundless airy summits, unfettered plantlife and the minds of poets are scintillated by the patter, trickle, rush and swell of moving water. London is like a desert by comparison. It NEVER rains here!

My first week as a student midwife has flown by. We have been issued with our uniforms, which are white – not a great colour when you're delivering a baby! Thankfully they've done away with those dreadful caps. I got my rota yesterday. I've been assigned to the Antenatal ward first. I'm told that the ward sister is a fearsome specimen of womankind, not unlike Nurse Ratched out of 'One Flew Over the Cuckoo's Nest' only older. I will have to watch my 'p's and q's'.

They have read us the riot act. Woe betide the student midwife who has the impertinence to perform a simple medical procedure without asking a senior nurse for permission first. It will be hard relearning the art of being subservient when I start on the wards at the end of next week. As a qualified nurse, I got accustomed to using my initiative, making decisions, getting things done and giving orders to the student nurses. I'm afraid Rose spoiled me rather in that regard, when she gave me more freedom and responsibility than is the usual premise of a staff nurse. As you will no doubt remember, it was the cause of a few run-ins with Sister Traynor in Obstetrics when I joined the team. It's lucky I had Rose to vouch for me until I'd earned the respect of the old boot (ha ha!) who, incidentally, gave me a fabulous bouquet and a book token when I left St. Mary's last month. I do miss Rose, and the adorable Deborah who started secondary school last week and is almost my height already!

I've struck up a friendship with a student midwife called Nicky, who went to the Lakes last year on holiday, although not to our part. She stayed in Keswick. I felt such a fool, never having actually been there! She says Skiddaw is a magnificent mountain, like a great, benevolent dinosaur, beautiful and omnipotent, watching over the inhabitants of the town in an attitude of easy repose. There is poetry in the soul of this woman and I'm minded to go there.

I'm sleeping in Ruby's old room, which is the large one at the front. Ray's room is next door to mine and half the size. I feel terribly guilty but Ray says he can't be bothered to move all his stuff into the big bedroom and anyway girls have more clutter!

Aunt Anji is a fantastic cook (although not in your league!) Last night we had curry which she told me was not all that hot. If that was mild, I hate to imagine what one of her hot ones is like; it would probably kill me! Talking of food, supper is nearly ready. We're having cannelloni tonight. I'm not sure what it is but it's got pasta in it.

Send my love to Dad, Michael and dear old Rufus of course.

Love,
Vicky xxx

* * *

Cinderdale Farm,
Nether Wasdale,
Seascale,
Cumbria.

16th September 1977

Dear Vicky,
I'm glad you liked the brownies.

A spell of your fine, dry weather would be welcome indeed! We've had more than our fair share of rain in the last fortnight but we've managed to get the fruit and veg into storage before the wet did any real damage. It was a damp and dreary affair and Dad has been rather grumpy. We all pitched in, even Michael at the weekend and on a couple of weeknights, though not without a battle. That young man really does have the most infuriating habit of making himself scarce every time there's work to be done on the farm.

Thankfully, the harvest has been declared a success and all is well. The beetroot has done exceptionally well although the beans were a little disappointing. The overall yield is a lot larger this year than last – Dad thinks about 40% more. Of course, it could hardly have been worse since we lost almost half of our cash crops in that interminable drought last summer. We've found a new customer for the cooking apples after Hampson's closed down last year and Dad is pleased he's found someone to take them off our hands. Toni is taking some too, along with some of our courgettes and beans, to sell outside her tea shop. I do hope she does well.

The blackberries in the east field are very prolific this year and it's a job keeping on top of them. In the last three days, I've picked three bucketfuls; they just keep on coming. Yesterday I made eight jars of bramble jelly for your Dad – you know how he hates the pips. I should have enough for another three batches as long as I leave in the seeds next time, especially if I throw in the windfalls, which of course we won't be able to sell. Toni claims her latest craving is blackberry and apple jam with pips (although it may be a ruse just to get her hands on some cheap produce for the shop). Let's hope her customers share her enthusiasm, as she has threatened to commandeer my entire stock this year but may lose her passion for jam once the baby arrives and end up with more jam than she can eat!

Louise started school last Monday and loves it, by all accounts, although I've been too busy to have a proper chat with Julie. She's got the same teacher that Sarah had last year, which is a bit of luck as I gather she's such a nice lady and Sarah did very well under her.

I managed to escape the harvest for long enough to pop down with Sarah to visit Chris, Mandy and baby Julia last weekend. Mandy seemed rather subdued and I'm getting concerned about her. I hope it's just exhaustion, as she hasn't had a decent night's sleep for the last seven weeks since the baby came along. Louise missed out again, thanks to my obdurate son. It's a crying shame as she so wanted to meet her new little half-sister. Chris can be exasperating! He bats away Louise with any number of excuses, poor child. This time he argued that she's just started school, so I couldn't really object, especially as Julie agreed with him for once. No doubt it'll be something else next time. There's always an obstacle and she gets short shrift from him. It's downright cruelty and I've a good mind to take her with me next time, even if it means getting the rough edge of his tongue. I do wish I knew what lay at the root of it but I never could get him to open up; even as a child he was a sulky boy.

Michael has been out a few times lately with a young lady called Donna who was apparently a friend of yours back in your training days. She's quite pretty but rather 'gothic', has a nose stud and wears an awful lot of make-up. She's actually quite a nice girl (despite my initial reservations) but I fear his heart belongs to Polly. They still write to each other, chat on the phone occasionally and go to the odd festival together. He's adamant he'll never get married (unless it's to her). Poor Donna! Michael actually had the audacity to admit to me that he's only dating her because she was so insistent, because it meant he could avoid picking the beans and because he's beginning to tire of his new Pink Floyd album (which he leaves on the turntable in-between plays, such is his obsession). The sleeve has been propped up against the hi-fi on the floor for months, which is a thing I rather like, since Michael pointed out to me that it depicts Battersea Power Station and I find myself thinking of you – fancy that! I've told your father to stop asking Michael to put it away and leave it just where it is!

Dad still has that irritating cough of his. Sometimes it gets so bad it keeps him awake at nights. I've told him time and again to get it checked out but he says it's probably just a virus, or pollen, or the chemicals they use, anything to avoid a visit to the GP. You know your Dad; he's as stubborn as a mule and never takes advice.

The sun is just peeping through the clouds so I think I ought to walk Rufus now, before it starts to rain again! Do write soon and let me know how you're getting on in your placement.

Love to you both,
Mum x

* * *

21 Stanley Street,
Ulverston,
Cumbria.
LA12 7BS

17th September 1977

Dear Vicky,
Heaven will have a new star tonight, for today we mourn the tragic and sudden loss of the beautiful and talented Marc Bolan. Although I hate to admit it, I've cried bucketloads since I heard about the accident on the news this morning and even put on a black dress today. You must think me a sentimental fool; it's not as if I even know the man. Funny that – I can cope with no problem at all with death on the

wards, but go to pieces at the demise of a complete stranger. Fortunately it's my day off today, as I'm not at all sure how I would have explained the precarious state of my emotions to Sister Mason. As you will recall, she's really quite nice but no doubt would have considered me incredibly silly indeed, as does my long suffering husband who thinks I've taken temporary leave of my senses! Ah well, I will have to make do with David Essex from now on.

You'll never guess what! Remember Donna? Well, she left last year and moved up the coast to Whitehaven. Rumour has it (correct me if I'm wrong) that she's been seen painting the town with your brother Michael! Apparently she ran into him at a party a few weeks ago and got straight to work on him. Well, you know Donna, she always had a thing about Michael and she's certainly not backward in coming forward. If truth be told, he was probably too afraid to say no! You won't have seen her for years, but she got into punk and she actually looks quite scary when she dons her leather jacket, stilettos and make-up! She used to terrify him back in the old days – ha ha! Maybe he likes a dominatrix!

The house is coming along nicely. We did most of the walls in woodchip to keep the cost down, then got some ideas from 'Ideal Home' magazine to jazz things up a bit. Most of the lounge is in buttermilk but to add interest we have what is called a 'feature' wall which is chocolate brown. Then we splashed out on a gorgeous gold shag-pile rug. It was rather pricey but it makes all the difference and we're thrilled with the result! We don't have enough money left for a three-piece suite but Mum's promised we can have her old one soon so we bought a couple of second-hand beanbag chairs from the small ads; they're orange and really comfy. We're having a new bathroom suite fitted next week. It's avocado – so much more modern than the boring old white one we currently have. We're getting it done 'on the cheap' as we were lucky enough to befriend a neighbour at our Jubilee street party in June who does plumbing. We're going to do the kitchen in turquoise – when we can afford the paint, and I've fallen in love with some fab yellow floral wallpaper which I want in our bedroom, although I fear it might be out of our price range so we might just resort to woodchipping it along with the rest.

Do let me know all about Toni's baby as and when he or she arrives. I wonder what she'll have this time. Talking of babies, what was your brother thinking of when they decided on 'Julia' for a name? I do hope Mandy's all right with it, but if I was her, there's no way I'd agree on one that's virtually the same as my partner's ex! Well, you'd worry, wouldn't you? – having that constant reminder. Maybe she likes the name, perhaps it was her idea, but between you and me I thought it was rather an unfortunate choice.

Work is so-so. I nearly went for a position that came up in Casualty as I fancied a change but, while we're on the subject of babies, I have other plans in mind so I held off applying. No luck yet but we live in hope.

I do hope the Midwifery course is going well and, of course, that life with Ray is moving in the right direction.

Lots of love,

Wendy xxx

* * *

81 South Park Road,
South Wimbledon,
London. SW19 8RU

29th September 1977

Dear Wendy,

Breaking news! This morning at 4.10, Toni gave birth to

a baby boy – Ryan Robert. It was a very straightforward affair and she should be home in three days. Scott is very excited and Toni seems happy enough with another boy. She says it evens things out a bit – Chris having three girls – and he'll be good company for Scott in the future, as there will only be two-and-a-half years between them. Call me old fashioned but Ryan is (or always used to be) a surname – Scott too; however it's quite the thing now. Toni would have us believe she's broken the mould twice over but surely the nation that gave us Ryan O'Neal and Scott Walker must take the credit! As for Kelly, you wouldn't believe how popular that has got – I reckon I must share my surname with practically every other baby girl born in the last year!

'Julia' – now there's a story. Chris is adamant it's got nothing to do with his wife (I hesitate to use the term 'ex' since technically they're still married) but I beg to differ. He claims he's always liked the name because he heard it in a Beatles song of the same name, which John Lennon wrote about his mother. Well, we all know how obsessed he is with John Lennon (almost as obsessed as I am about Paul McCartney – ha ha!) It didn't wash with me. I'm not too sure it washed with Mandy either but, as you said, maybe she likes the name anyway – let's hope so and she wasn't coerced.

Michael – that's another story. According to Mum, he's only going out with Donna because he prefers it to harvesting the beans! Poor Donna, for goodness sake don't tell her if you happen to run into her, she'd be mortified. Back in '72 when she had a massive crush on him, do you remember he eventually managed to fob her off with some story about meeting the girl of his dreams at a peace festival? To be fair, that was true to a point, only he 'ramped up' the girl's part in the 'affair' and gave Donna to understand that this girl (Polly) reciprocated his feelings. Well personally, I don't think Polly's affection for Michael has ever extended beyond the lukewarm, but they still write to each other and meet up very occasionally. As a matter of fact, they went to Reading Festival together on August bank holiday and Knebworth has evolved into an annual pilgrimage. She's heavily into 'causes' such as Greenpeace, CND and Friends of the Earth, and they both like their rock music. It should be a match made in heaven but it's never really got off the starting block. Anyway, he's evidently not 'getting his oats' on a regular basis and men have needs – ha ha! (that's where Donna comes in).

So do girls, for that matter, and I've spent far too long living with Linda to pussyfoot around. Besides, it's 1978! Suffice to say, Ray sleeps in the room next door to mine, which is tantamount to torture. His parents go out about once a week and we never miss an opportunity. I expect they know all about our shenanigans but are wise enough to realise that there's not a lot they can do about it. My wedding day can't come soon enough – it will be sheer bliss not to have to 'dodge the parents' every time we fancy a quickie but at 'Ray-speed', I expect I'll be drawing my pension before I'm spliced!

The Maternity department is presided over by three nursing officers. Two are harridans but the other one is very sweet and gives us Bourbons at the end of our shifts. The ward sister is a dragon. The consultant obstetricians – we have three of those too – are quite jolly but rather overbearing. I'm on the Antenatal ward currently, where they look after expectant mothers with complications. As part of our training, we have to accompany the consultants on their ward rounds. They pounce on us at random (metaphorically speaking, of course!) and ask us impossible questions. Sometimes we have to do an examination, usually on a woman with a breech baby or twins whom they pick on purpose so that they can enjoy watching us flounder. I pity the poor inmates, who lie there looking horrified while the consultant describes the worst case scenario in all its gory detail! Fortunately, things are rarely as bad as they make out.

Yes it was incredibly sad about Marc Bolan and I felt for you when I heard the shocking news. The infamous tree which his car hit is actually less than five miles from our house. We drove past it last week. It's covered with photos and tributes and there are literally hundreds of bouquets. I said a little prayer for him as we passed the spot. I can't quite make up my mind whether I believe in God or not, so I thought 'Why not? No harm in it'.

Your house sounds very nice – can't wait for a guided tour next time I'm up your way. Are you charging an entrance fee? Ha ha! Write soon.

Love and kisses,

Vicky xxx

* * *

81 South Park Road,
South Wimbledon,
London. SW19 8RU

19th January 1978

Dear Mum,

My first week in the Labour ward has been amazing, although I've yet to deliver a baby. My role so far has been strictly in the capacity of an observer. We have to be present at 20 births before we're allowed to take an active part, and then we get a few practice runs whereby the midwife's hands are poised over ours, before they throw us in at the deep end! There's so much more to the birthing process than I ever imagined possible that I don't know how I'll remember it all.

First there are the 'preliminaries'; the less said about them, the better! Once labour is in full swing, you have to say when to push and when to breathe (as it can make all the difference), and get the baby into position. Catching the baby is the most exciting part! As soon as it's born, we have to check its breathing and heartbeat. I hate that part as I can't help fearing the worst and find myself thinking … 'what if?' They always go in the cot for a minute or two and we give them oxygen before we hand them to mum – just to be on the safe side. I can't wait to do my first delivery, although I expect it will be quite overwhelming and I'm sure I'll cry. To 'earn our stripes', we have to deliver 40 babies – that's an awful lot and about 10 times the number required if you're a trainee doctor – it's so unfair!

Anyway, I can't complain. It's heaps better than working in the Special Care Baby Unit which, as you will remember from the state I was in during the run-up to Christmas, I was far from enamoured with! Of course it's a vital part of the job, but the sight of all those poor, helpless little mites broke my heart and it was hard to know what to say to the parents, especially when the news was not good. There were moments of joy, such as when the babies pulled through and got well enough to go home, but the procedures were so exacting and the stress so enormous that there were times I would have gladly exchanged it for a grilling from the nursing officers, which is saying something! Honestly, Mum, I was so scared of making a mistake that I barely slept for weeks.

We've had a visit from the Manchester contingent. They came down overnight last weekend for Alan's birthday. Chris and Mandy stayed with her sister, who has a flat in Balham, and Alan and Caroline slept upstairs in the attic here. We all went to see the much acclaimed new movie 'Star Wars' which has just come over from the States. The special effects were literally out of this world (did you like my pun?) and the leading man (Luke Skywalker) was quite dishy. Mandy was rather quiet and seemed troubled. She did mention that her Mum hasn't been well lately and is having some tests, but between you and me I thought Chris was rather cold towards her. I noticed it at Christmas too but assumed they'd had a row, but having seen them both again, I'm rather worried. Ray is adamant that it's none of my business and I shouldn't get involved but it's hard to turn a blind eye when Mandy is evidently unhappy.

I worry about Rufus too. That lethargy is most probably old age but I hate to think of him in pain and perhaps it's not his age at all and just some arthritis or something that we could treat with painkillers. Did the vet have any idea what it was?

Talking of dogs, I've finally finished reading 'The Plague Dogs' – that was the book I bought with my book token. I did enjoy 'Watership Down', and never give up on a book, but this one (by the same author) is a lot weirder, very long-winded and political, and positively disturbing in places – definitely not for the faint-hearted. On the plus side, the descriptions of the wild Lakeland scenery are magnificent and transported me home. The plot concerns two dogs who escape from an animal research centre in the Lake District where they conduct the most horrific and unnecessary experiments on every creature from mice to monkeys. The experiments described by the author (Richard Adams) are apparently founded on fact and enough to turn one into an animal rights activist on the spot. Perhaps we should get Michael to start a campaign! Anyway these two dogs are pursued all around Cumberland; even Wast Water gets a mention. Whether the ending is happy or not I will leave you to guess, in case you should want to read it one day.

Ah … I do so miss home, even when the weather is foul. Ray tells me that today is technically the coldest day of the year, according to scientific calculations based on the distance of the sun from the earth and the average sea temperature. That's so typically Ray – absolutely brimming with useless facts but can't boil an egg! It's actually very mild down here today, so he's wrong and I shall tell him! Of course, he will argue that theoretical surmises and reality are very rarely the same but I'll tease him all the same. Anyhow, it's nice to think we've reached the turning point at last and the nights are drawing out. The snowdrops in the front garden are such a cheery sight.

Do write again soon and send me some photos of the farm that I can show to the girls at work.

Love,
Vicky xxx

* * *

Cinderdale Farm,
Nether Wasdale,
Seascale,
Cumbria.

16th April 1978

Dear Vicky,
Congratulations on hitting your target 40 deliveries. We both have every confidence that you will sail through the rest of the course and we are very proud of your achievements so far.

Your phone call brought us both some much needed good cheer at what I can only describe as a devastating time. They say things happen in threes and that would certainly seem to be the case.

I'm afraid that Rufus is no better, if anything he has gone a little downhill. He has become rather unsteady on his feet lately. The vet says he is medically fine but he is a very old dog and probably doesn't have long to go.

That's not the worst of it though. You must brace yourself for a shock, for what I am about to impart to you is such grave news that I felt unable to convey it over the telephone for fear of breaking down completely. Your father was finally persuaded to seek medical advice after he found himself so short of breath that he was forced to take frequent breaks. On one occasion he passed out. It was during the calving season, which is always physically demanding, so he shrugged it off at first. I wish to God he'd done it sooner but he's a tough nut to crack and it was Walter who finally convinced him to refer himself to the GP. Walter is the type who takes everything in his stride and isn't easily alarmed, and for that reason Robert holds his opinion in high regard. It would appear that he's suffering from farmer's lung, which is a form of lung damage caused by long-term exposure to antigens found in crops, hay, animal feed and chemicals. Sadly there's no cure so we must manage as best we can.

As if that wasn't enough, Chris and Mandy have had the most awful row, and all over Louise! They came up to visit us over the Easter weekend and had arranged to take Louise back with them to Manchester for a few days. On the day they arrived, Julie rang and told me that there had been an outbreak of chicken pox at school. "Well, that's it!" announces Chris. "We can't put the baby at risk." Mandy told him that was plain silly but he dug his heels in. We both pointed out to him how unreasonable he was being but he just got angry and defensive and refused to discuss it. Then he accused poor Mandy of spending all her free time at her Mum's and naturally that infuriated her (because I understand her mother is genuinely ill). It was a very difficult weekend and Louise was so disappointed not to go.

Fortunately it's not quite all doom and gloom and I do have one piece of good news for you. Sarah passed her grade two exam on the violin with distinction. She's a promising little musician like her mother, who is thrilled that she is so keen to develop her very obvious talent.

Michael is still dating Donna, which has rather surprised us as we didn't expect it to last very long. Perhaps he'll settle down now and stop hankering after this mysterious girl 'Polly' who has never shown more than a casual interest in him. Last week he went with Donna to see 'Close Encounters of the Third Kind' at the cinema, which sounds rather like 'Star Wars', not that I've seen either! Science fiction is all the rage, it seems, although personally I prefer a good period drama. We thoroughly enjoyed the 'Pennies from Heaven' mini-series on TV over the last few weeks and I will miss my Tuesday night treat now it's all over.

I really must walk Rufus before it gets dark. We don't take him far nowadays, but he can manage a short walk and is due a 'comfort break'! Write back soon.

With much love to you all.

Mum x

* * *

81 South Park Road,
South Wimbledon,
London. SW19 8RU

27th April 1978

Dear Wendy,
It never rains but it pours! I'm in a terrible state. I've cried

every day for the last fortnight and I could use a hug right now. To give him his due, Ray does try to understand but he can't get inside my head and will stop at nothing to pursue his precious ambition – there, it's said.

Last night, my wedding day receded further into the future when Ray announced his intention to study for a Master's degree in Archaeology. He's not prepared to give up his job so he's expecting it'll take at least three years to qualify – THREE YEARS! I'll be 28 in three years and still a spinster living with my boyfriend's parents. I'm not sure how much more of this I can take. Sometimes I wish I'd fallen in love with a local farmhand!

Perhaps I'm being rather selfish after all, as my own personal gripes are nothing compared to the catastrophic news concerning my Dad, who has been diagnosed with an irreversible respiratory condition called farmer's lung which is badly affecting him. Mum has skirted round the longer-term implications but there's no escaping the inevitable and we must face it eventually.

Dear old Rufus is on his last legs. We got him as a pup in 1965, so he's 13 and a good age for a labrador, but it will be terribly hard when he goes – like losing a member of the family.

Sadly, Mandy's Mum has got pancreatic cancer – she found out last week. She's not expected to get any better, rather the reverse, and Mandy is determined to do all the caring herself, which I foresee could have disastrous consequences as Chris will claim she's neglecting him (which may or may not be true).

Thank goodness I have my work to distract me. I'm due to start my next placement in the Postnatal ward next Monday and can't wait! Just imagine – all those babies to feed, change and bath. The night shifts will be fun (as long as I can stay awake) as we have the little ones all to ourselves in the nursery and won't be obliged to share them with their mums! It'll make a pleasant change from the Antenatal clinic, where I spent the last few weeks. I didn't enjoy it all that much as at times it felt more like a production line than a healthcare service. The only clients I formed any kind of relationship with were the ones assigned to my antenatal class. It was quite nerve-racking 'teaching' expectant mothers how to cope with labour and, to be honest, I felt a bit of a fraud, never having been through it myself!

The weekend after next, Ray and I are off to Chichester as a friend from his university days is getting married. Maybe he'll jump on the bandwagon and make me an offer. I suppose an engagement ring would be better than nothing.

Please write soon and send me some good news. I'm in desperate need of a pick-me-up.

Love and hugs,

Vicky xxx

* * *

21 Stanley Street,
Ulverston,
Cumbria.
LA12 7BS

12th May 1978

Dear Vicky,

You wrote me that you wanted some good news – well here's some. I'm expecting a baby, and you're to be Godmother! I don't care if you're an atheist, agnostic or devout. No-one else is even in the running! It's been hard keeping it a secret these last few weeks, but now I'm three months in, I can tell you that sometime in early November, we will be celebrating the arrival of our first child.

That said, I am very much aware that you're having a really tough time right now and it might be the last thing on earth you want to hear, but I can't pretend I'm not over the moon and I'm sure that you'll be pleased too, if only for my sake, because you have such a warm and wonderful nature.

Ideally I would prefer to give up work once the baby arrives but the mortgage rate is creeping back up and looks likely to rise even more. Unemployment is at an all-time high too, which could make it difficult to get another job if I change my mind later. Perhaps things would be better under the Conservatives, but David is adamant that there will never be a woman Prime Minister and perhaps they'd stand a better chance with Willie Whitelaw at the helm.

I'm truly sorry that you're having such an awful time. Your dad's illness must be an immense blow. I asked David whether he had heard of farmer's lung and he said that he had and to prepare yourself for the worst, as it's only a matter of time. If you should need a shoulder to cry on, now or when the time comes, I'm here for you, any time of the day or night. Just pick up the telephone or knock on my door if need be.

I've enclosed two books which you might like to read, as I know how much you enjoy romantic fiction, especially the classics. They're both by Thomas Hardy, so perhaps you'd be best advised to save them until you're in a better place, as he's not renowned for happy endings!

How was the dirty weekend in Chichester? Did he put an engagement ring on your finger, or is that too much to ask?

Lots of love,
Wendy xxx

* * *

81 South Park Road,
South Wimbledon,
London. SW19 8RU

2nd June 1978

Dear Mum,
I do hope that Dad and Rufus are both bearing up.

I recently finished my placement in the Postnatal ward. I did enjoy it but it was much more 'regimented' than I had expected, with everything done by the clock and the babies all fed simultaneously at four-hourly intervals, so that the mums could get a decent rest between feeds. Fathers are only allowed to visit twice a day for one hour. I'm not sure if I liked the regime; I wonder if it makes it harder for mother and baby to bond but who am I to question long-established practice?

Since the beginning of the week, I've been doing home visits with the district midwife. She's a nice old stick with a wicked sense of humour and we have lots of laughs as we go about our daily business, providing pre- and post-natal care, physical and emotional support and advice, and attending home births. Sometimes we work in the clinic at the GP practice which she is attached to. Because her role encompasses the entire process from early pregnancy to aftercare, she can develop meaningful relationships with the families in her remit, which makes a refreshing change as most of the women we meet on the wards come and go in less than a week and, like so many items on a conveyer belt, it can be hard to get to know them as individuals. One of the wealthy mums on her caseload has just acquired a birthing pool from France and had it installed in her home. She must be loaded! I do hope I get to see it in use.

They've given us a rundown on what to expect in the final exams, which includes a 15 minute oral test at the Royal

College of Midwives in North London. That's the part I'm dreading the most. I'm convinced I'll forget everything I've learnt and most likely lose the power of speech altogether, which will be a first!

Assuming I pass, practising midwifery might well be the closest I ever get to experiencing childbirth now that Ray has applied for his postgraduate qualification, which looks like taking at least three years because he wants to do it alongside his job. I would have preferred it if we'd got married before he embarked on his studies and I can't help feeling disappointed, bitter even, but I wouldn't dream of standing in his way as it would do more harm than good and can only lead to resentment on his part. It's what his parents want for him, which rules out any hope I have of arguing my point. I always planned to have children before 30. He knows that but seems to have forgotten in his quest to advance his career.

Life is so unfair! Toni's got two children, Chris has three; even my best friend is expecting a baby! I've been to countless weddings, two in the last year, and I'm not even engaged yet!

Thank goodness at least I have the summer holidays to look forward to. Ray's family are taking me to France. We'll be spending the first week in the French Alps near Geneva and the second week in Paris – a little piece of heaven! Perhaps he's planning to propose to me at the top of the Eiffel Tower or at a quaint little café in the Latin Quarter (not that I'm holding out much hope).

How awful that Mandy's mum is so poorly. Chris should be more understanding. Granted, his head's in a mess over Julie. Is it possible for someone to love two women at the same time? I believe it must be. I think he does love Mandy and hates the amount of time she spends at her mum's, but evidently loves Julie too because he won't get divorced, has a daughter he named Julia and spurns Louise, probably because he wants to distance himself from a past he's unable to let go of.

I've still got just enough time to do a bit of revision before dinner. Send my love to Dad, Michael and say hi to Donna if you get the chance.

Love,

Vicky xxx

* * *

Cinderdale Farm,
Nether Wasdale,
Seascale,
Cumbria.

1st August 1978

Dear Vicky,

I do hope this letter reaches you before you depart for France, which is this Friday I believe.

Regrettably, dear old Rufus passed away quietly yesterday. He's been struggling to keep his food down in the last week and stopped eating altogether at the weekend. To some extent, it's a relief. Walter is digging a pit for him at the bottom of the garden this afternoon, where we will lay him to rest. Your father is quite beside himself with grief and hasn't left the house since last night.

The change in him over the last few weeks is very worrying. He seems to have lost his motivation, struggles to get up in the mornings and will nap in his chair most afternoons for an hour or two. He constantly complains of aches and pains and his cough is getting worse. He finds it hard to concentrate and is struggling even to manage the business side of things. He's even made a few mistakes lately – so unlike him – so we've invested in an electronic calculator. It was shockingly expensive – almost £50 for such a small piece of equipment!

I never found the opportunity to send your regards to Donna unfortunately, as she ended her relationship with Michael last month. It seems they fell out over Polly, whom he met up with at the Knebworth festival at the end of June. Donna was rather jealous, not because she wanted to go (she hates Genesis, by all accounts) but because of his friendship with that elusive 'other woman' of his. Perhaps it's not such a bad thing, as now that he has lots more time on his hands, he's stepped up his efforts and has shown remarkable initiative and tenacity in terms of keeping the farm ticking over.

I'm not sure how you'll receive this news – your situation being what it is, but were you aware that Caroline is expecting a baby next February? You might like to give them a call sometime, which I understand will be difficult for you but undoubtedly the honourable thing to do.

I do hope you remembered Julia's birthday yesterday. It's hard to believe she's already a year old. They held a little party for her on Saturday and I went down to Manchester on the train with Mother (who got rather drunk, I'm afraid). I took Louise along with me, which pleased Sarah immensely as she has been asking lately why her sister never goes down with her – well, after all she's nine years old and no fool. You can imagine your brother's surprise when confronted with both daughters! It was rather awkward at first but thankfully there were a number of other friends and relatives present to alleviate the tension, which is what I had hoped. Louise was all over the baby, which is encouraging, and all in all I think it was the right decision and will pay dividends. Unfortunately, we had to travel back the same day as I didn't feel comfortable about leaving your Dad overnight (or Rufus, for that matter), even though Michael insisted that it would be all right. It's a shame you had to work, but it is rather a long way for you both to come.

Sarah played a beautiful piece on the violin at the end of term school concert a few weeks ago. Julie says if she keeps it up, she will go far. Being a music teacher, she ought to know.

Have a wonderful time in France!

Much love,

Mum x

* * *

81 South Park Road,
South Wimbledon,
London. SW19 8RU

25th August 1978

Dear Mum,

It's hard to feel genuine joy at the prospect of welcoming yet another baby Kelly into the family, and although I've tried to pretend to Ray, to my colleagues at work and to the world at large that I'm all right, I'm falling to pieces inside. All I've ever wanted is a home and family of my own. Instead I'm stuck in limbo with no job, no privacy and no prospect of either in the foreseeable future. I miss my home, my family, the fells and fields, lanes and lakes – I even miss the rain!

True I passed the course, but what chance do I have when there's 10, 20, 50 applicants all fighting for one position? Perhaps I should be thankful for small mercies. At least being out of work means that I can escape from the interminable hordes of doting mothers and squealing tots. If anyone as much as mentions babies to me, I swear I'll scream! Whatever possessed me to consider such a stupid career move? In Manchester I had family, friends, a flat and a job. In London I have nothing!

At least I got to go to France, which was amazing! We went up the Aiguille du Midi by cable car and from the summit we looked across to Mont Blanc, which is the highest mountain in Europe! The glaciers were awesome. We went to Lake Geneva and stood under the tallest fountain in the world! We visited the spectacular Cathedral Saint-Pierre. We had freshly-baked croissants for breakfast every morning and wine with our dinner. In Paris, we climbed up the Eiffel Tower, visited the Louvre, Notre-Dame and the Arc de Triomphe and took a riverboat cruise along the Seine. The only thing missing was the marriage proposal; well what did you expect?

I had lunch with Rose on Wednesday. She brought Deborah down to London on her birthday to see the West End musical 'Annie' and we met up the following day. It's hard to believe Deborah is only 12. She looks more like 16 and is developing a 'tweenage' passion for clothes, hair, make-up and boys, probably fuelled by her current obsession with 'Grease' (especially John Travolta – who does absolutely nothing for me!) That girl will break a few hearts and no mistake. Anyway, Rose gave me some useful interview tips and suggested I should write to all the hospitals in the area, rather than waiting for a position to come up in the paper. I don't hold out much hope, but I've got nothing to lose.

I tried to speak to Chris yesterday on the phone but he was at the pub. I did have a longish conversation with Mandy though, and she's obviously extremely worried about him. She says he's not taking good care of himself. He stays up late and then oversleeps, won't shave unless she nags him and can't be bothered to iron his shirts. He eats junk for lunch and drinks too much. He's moody and preoccupied, and sulks when she goes to her mum's. He won't tell her what's wrong – just says he's fine. She's terrified he'll get sacked for persistent lateness and then what will they live on?

Oh, I almost forgot to tell you, I'm learning to drive. My first lesson is next week and I'm really excited – a bit scared too! The car I'm learning in is a Vauxhall Chevette. If I'm any good, Ray says I can practise in his, although he might change his mind after a spin round the block with me!

Ah well, time to go. Dinner is on the plate. We've got tandoori chicken tikka tonight, which is gorgeous!

Love,

Vicky xxx

* * *

78 Edgeley Road,
Stockport,
Cheshire.
SK3 9NQ

14th October 1978

Dear Vicks,

Happy birthday, little sis! Mum told me you wanted the Billy Joel LP so I've sent you a record token instead as I was too embarrassed to be seen with it in my hand – ha ha, only joking!

Congrats on the new job, by the way – about time too, what took you so long? At least one of us has something to be happy about. I thought you hated babies.

Oh my God, you're learning to drive! How many cars have you smashed up?

Seriously though, sweetheart, life's a bit rubbish at the moment. Work's boring and Mandy practically lives at her mum's. Louise has been down twice recently but it's hard to know what to say to a five year old. She's not much of a talker; sometimes I think she'd be happier back home with her mother and grandad. Sarah's different, of course. I've known her all her life; she's a right chatterbox. It's quite astonishing how well she's turned out, considering she's got me for a father. Call me weird but I get jittery around Louise. I guess she reminds me of her mother. Oh my, Julie is a beautiful woman but I was never good enough for her. Mandy's a diamond and I love her to bits, so why the hell am I obsessing about my ex? I usually know when I'm being a pig (which is most of the time) but it's like I've got this kamikaze streak and I can't stop myself. She will keep quizzing me – trying to get inside my head. There's no point telling her; she wouldn't understand. I wouldn't blame her in the least if she walked out on me – serve me right. I love her, Vicky, but every time I try to tell her, the words get stuck.

Julia is walking now. She's a little treasure, probably the only thing that's keeping me sane, but not a great sleeper so I'm knackered half the time and the dark mornings are doing my head in. It doesn't help when you've had a tankful the night before, but I'm not very good at saying no to booze. I like the taste and it helps me to forget.

Dad was in pretty good shape when I went up last month on my birthday. I could have done without the trek up north, but Mum had gone overboard as usual, baked a cake and suchlike, and I didn't like to let the old girl down. She thinks I need cheering up – she's right, of course, but she might have more luck if she hired a Swedish masseuse! Apparently, Dad was having a 'good' day, but you know how she frets. Maybe he's not as bad as all that.

Keep smiling – someone's got to.

Chris x

* * *

TELEGRAM: 21 Feb 1979
DAD HOSPITALISED – (STOP) – COME HOME DON'T DELAY . . .

Chapter 14

The Funeral

A shaft of sunlight pierced the dim interior of the hospital ward and cast a pale streak across the bed where my father lay sleeping. I sat at the bedside next to Toni, trying to think of something to say, gazing languidly at the tiny particles of airborne dust dancing in the beam to the regular beep of the cardiac monitor and listening to the monotonous ticking of the clock on the wall above the door. The room was hot and smelt of disinfectant. I pulled nervously at a lock of stray hair and held it to my face, inhaling the scent of my sister's perfume. It called to mind our clinging embrace at the railway turnstile and I reached for her hand and clutched on to it. It is only in times of extreme sorrow that we feel the full force of familial love.

Mum sat opposite, her eyes red and her face pallid. Presently she spoke.

"Have you had lunch, Vicky?" she asked me, making an effort to sound normal. Dear old Mum; even when her heart was breaking, she still maintained her habitual concern for the bodily comforts of her little brood.

"Yes thanks, I got a sandwich on the train," I replied flatly, with a feeble attempt at a smile. "I expect Alan will want something when he arrives later," I added after pause, for want of some substance with which to bolster the conversation. "I don't think he was planning to stop off at Caroline's."

Caroline was a fortnight past her due date and had already had a couple of false alarms. Therefore, with wisdom that could be described as prophetic, she had decided to go and stay with her parents in Allerton, a small town south east of Liverpool. The prospect of the main event, whilst sitting in the front seat of Alan's Morris Marina, was just too big a risk, even with a qualified midwife on hand at the end of the journey.

"I do wish Chris was here," I sighed, before lapsing into silence. My mind began to wander. I imagined myself a little girl again, wrapped in the strong, protective arms of my older brother, in whose infallibility I used to possess unshakeable faith.

"He'll come at the weekend; it's only three days," said Toni soothingly, giving my hand a squeeze.

"Three days," I lamented. "Three days might be too late!"

"Hush, don't say such things," interjected Mum, throwing an anxious glance at my father's inert form.

"Besides," continued Toni, reasonably. "We don't know what's keeping him. It might be something really important."

"And this isn't?" I cried bitterly.

"Look Vicky, he's lucky to have a job at all," countered Toni, with a faint note of irritation in her voice. "You of all people should know that. From what I hear, he's on his last warning."

At length, a hospital physician wearing a white coat came in carrying a clipboard. He was very tall, middle-aged and had a kindly face.

"Good afternoon ladies," he beamed. "I'm Dr. Harris-Wright. How's the patient?"

"I don't think he's any better," replied Mum, with an air of resignation.

The doctor peered at the cardiac monitor on a stand next to the bed, to which my father was attached by a series of wires which disappeared beneath the bedclothes. He knitted his brows, then smiled benevolently down at Mum.

"Hmmm … well, he's lucky to be alive, Mrs. Kelly. If you hadn't acted so promptly when the chest pain came on, it might have been too late to bring him back. Technically he was dead for a few minutes. It's hard to say whether there's been any damage to the brain but I have to forewarn you that any physical exertion is apt to trigger another attack and he may not be so fortunate next time. In my opinion, it's only a matter of time. I'm very sorry."

Tears pricked my eyes and Mum stifled a sob.

He bent down and placed a gentle hand on her shoulder.

"You must be brave, Mrs. Kelly. We can't have him seeing you like this when he wakes up."

He took two plastic bags from a kidney dish, removed a syringe from one and a needle from the other, and attached the two together.

"We have to check the composition of his blood," he explained as he folded back the bedcovers, rolled up the sleeve of my father's striped pyjamas and drew a tourniquet from his pocket. "It's apt to go haywire after episodes of this nature."

As he applied the tourniquet, Dad stirred and opened his eyes.

"All right, Mr. Kelly, just a little pinprick," he said, dabbing the inside of my father's elbow with a piece of gauze.

Dad, being only partially awake, paid no heed at all, until he was drawn out of his slumber by the sound of my mother's voice. He opened his eyes and looked blearily around the room, slowly taking in his surroundings.

"Hello, love. What's the time? How did I get here?" he asked Mum finally.

Dad had been brought in by ambulance during the small hours after he had been gripped with chest pains and collapsed whilst assisting the vet with abdominal surgery on a cow with an advanced case of peritonitis.

"It's half past three… in the afternoon."

"Good gracious. Dear, oh dear …" he paused, gulping in a large mouthful of air, "… and such a glorious day outdoors. How's my heifer?"

"Vet says she'll pull through. Don't you go worrying about her."

"Same can't be said for me, eh Marion?" he smiled, wryly.

"Don't talk so!"

"Don't soft-soap me, woman," he said playfully. "You know as well as I do, I'll be leaving here in a box. It was only ever a matter of time." He stopped abruptly, gasped, and there followed a prolonged bout of coughing.

Mum was trying hard not to cry, fortified, no doubt, by the doctor's stern but kindly eye, as he stood at the end of the bed making notes. I felt Toni's hand tighten around mine.

"Take it easy, Mr. Kelly," cautioned Dr. Harris-Wright. "Not too much chit-chat, now." He put down his clipboard, swept around the back of my chair, signalled to Mum and together they propped up Dad's recumbent form.

"You might need this," continued the physician, handing my father an oxygen mask which he attached at the other end to an outlet in the wall behind the bed. "I'll send nurse along to change the drip. Would you like some tea?"

"Yes please", croaked Dad, nodding feebly.

"Righto!" He smiled broadly and made his exit.

It was all too much for Mum. Released from the imperative gaze of Dr. Harris-Wright, the tears came fast and freely.

"Don't fret, Marion," importuned Dad. "I'm resigned to my fate. It's not such a bad one at that," whereupon he was seized by another round of coughing. He cast aside the oxygen mask with a look of disdain.

"I still have my pride," he rasped, catching Mum's hand as she reached down to retrieve it. "Leave it, there's a good girl."

"Oh … Robert … don't throw your life away!"

"Don't be a fool, Marion. I'm spent, love. Look at me? I can't work on the land. I can't even manage the business." He raised his hand, indicating that he had more to say, and we waited while he regained his breath. "I'm all in, and when I shuffle off this mortal coil, which is likely to be very soon now, I want my dignity intact." He stopped, his hand aloft marking time, inhaled deeply and continued with an effort. "My work here is done … we've a fine, big family." He winked at Mum and she smiled in spite of herself. "There'll be Kellys at Cinderdale yet, you mark my words, Marion."

He smiled indulgently at my sister and me.

"Ah … my girls. Toni … you're a wild one. Not so wild now, eh?" he chuckled.

"And little Vicky, so earnest, so compassionate. That fella of yours takes you for granted. Someone should take him in hand. Where are my boys?" he continued breathlessly, addressing Mum.

"Michael and Alan will be in to see you this evening, dearest."

"Ah yes, Michael. He's a visionary, a chip off the old block despite his silly notions about saving the planet. A Kelly through and through," he uttered, his voice disintegrating as gave himself over to another spate of coughing. "I was wrong about Alan," he continued hoarsely. "He's not farming material, too bookish. Good thing he paid no heed to me … a fine teacher. Where's our Chris?"

"I told him to come but he's stubborn as a mule. He's working … I'm sorry," said Mum apologetically.

"Quite right too," proceeded Dad, in fractured sentences punctuated by gaps in which he attempted to regain mastery over his insurgent lungs. "It's high time that boy stopped moping around and faced up to his responsibilities … He's a 30 year old man with a wife and three little ones … three, mind," he said emphatically. "You be sure to remind him of that when I'm gone; ... he's apt to overlook his second-born. The way I see it is this; ... why waste time on a dying man when your job's at stake?... a most commendable choice," he finished, choking hard and waving his hand towards a glass of water placed on the bedside cabinet earlier by a solicitous nurse.

Mum placed the glass in his hand and threw me a helpless glance, which was not lost on Dad.

"I know your mind, Marion," resumed Dad, between sips. "You think his duty lies here ... Look, it's my belief he's a frightened man ... too frightened, I imagine, to look death in the face. ... There's no shame in human frailty ... He must be made to see that he's right ... I want him to know he has my blessing."

Presently, the nurse arrived with a cup of tea. She was about my age, short, plump and comely.

"Five more minutes, ladies; then you must let the gentleman rest," she said briskly, as she set about renewing the drip. "Dinner is at six, Mr. Kelly."

We made our goodbyes and headed back to the farm with heavy hearts.

Alan greeted us at the door. He was in a buoyant mood, given the circumstances.

"Hey, how's the invalid?"

Mum bit her lip and shook her head.

"Ah, poor show." He gave Mum a hug and we traipsed up the hall, a sorry bunch of individuals. "There's tea in the pot," came my brother's voice from behind us. "Hey, you'll never guess what?"

Mum sat down heavily at the kitchen table. "I don't know," she sighed. "What?"

"Carrie's only gone into labour," he prattled, unable to conceal his pleasure despite the gravity of the situation.

"Ah, that's nice," she said vaguely.

There was an awkward pause.

"How's she coming along?" I asked diplomatically.

"Pretty quickly, by all accounts."

Suddenly, without warning, I was consumed by insurmountable waves of panic. Lights flashed before my eyes; my head swam; my heart began to race; my temperature rose; my legs gave way; I was gripped by nausea.

"Excuse me … my coat … I …"

Hastening out of the kitchen, I half ran and half stumbled up the stairs into my room and threw myself face down on the bed. Images forced themselves into my head. In my mind's eye I saw my father; strong, steadfast and passionate; his body battered and his spirit broken. I saw Sarah, Louise, Scott, Ryan, Julia and the tiny infant waiting at the threshold. I saw countless mothers nursing countless babies, none of them mine. I felt an emptiness deep in the pit of my stomach, stared hopelessly through the gloom at my naked left hand and cursed my misfortune at falling in love with Ray. I wanted to cry but no tears came. After a few minutes, I heard Toni calling my name. I opened my mouth and shut it again, lest my voice should fail me and I should give myself away. I listened tremulously to the sound of her approaching footsteps. She opened the door softly and peeped in.

"Vicky, oh Vicky … darling, what's the matter?" she cried, rushing to the bedside.

I burst into tears, rolled over and flung myself into her outstretched arms. Some time later, we came downstairs together. Our tea was cold and my brothers had eaten all the fruitcake but now I felt calm, composed, unburdened. With my sister at my side, I felt prepared for what I knew must come.

After supper, Mum returned to the hospital with Alan and Michael. Just before eight o'clock, as I sat watching 'Morecambe and Wise at the BBC' with Toni, who had delayed her departure on account of my fragile mental state, the telephone rang.

"Mrs. Kelly?" said a woman's voice at other end of the line.

"No, this is her daughter. Mrs. Kelly is out," I replied. "Can I take a message?"

"Er … it was actually Alan I wanted to speak to," said the voice. "Is he there?"

"Oh … no, sorry, he's gone out with Mum."

"That's all right. It's Joy Lambert, Caroline's Mum."

"Oh yes … Caroline's Mum. It's Vicky. We met at the wedding. Is everything all right?" I asked hesitantly, my heart in my mouth.

"Why yes, absolutely!" she trilled. "Caroline is resting but she wanted me to pass on the happy news. Your brother has a baby daughter."

"A girl, how delightful!" I exclaimed.

"She's eight pounds, has her mother's red hair, an excellent pair of lungs, and her name is Leonie," she gushed.

"Ah … she sounds gorgeous. I'll tell Alan as soon as he gets home. He'll be thrilled!"

"Look, it's been lovely talking to you again Vicky, but I have 101 calls to make," she said hurriedly.

"No problem. Thank you, Mrs. Lambert. He shouldn't be too long now. Shall I get him to ring?"

"You'd better give it an hour or two. Caroline is very tired right now."

"Okay. Bye now."

I put down the receiver and turned to my sister, who was standing at the living room door.

"Another girl," I said, with an ironic smirk.

The following afternoon, we went to visit Dad again. He was sitting up in bed, listening to a portable cassette recorder which Michael had lent him. The rhythmic lilt of Benny Goodman's jazz clarinet emitted a pleasant backdrop that was in stark contrast to the incessant, monotone beep of the cardiac monitor, which had thankfully now been removed. This time I was accompanied by Mum and Alan, who was in excellent humour and talked expansively about his baby daughter, his job and his new Morris Marina. Dad seemed less inclined to dwell on his mortality and made light of his precarious health under the cheering influence of a dram of his favourite single malt whisky smuggled in by Alan in a hip flask, much to the consternation of Mum, who was terrified that we would all get thrown out. They made a merry pair.

As I looked on in amusement, my mind began to wander. Perhaps it was talk of Leonie; suffice to say that, fight as I might, I found myself dwelling on my childless state, the blank canvas staring at me from a directionless future and a gnawing resentment towards anyone blessed with joy of progeny. Eventually I lost the thread of the conversation altogether.

"Vicky … Vicky?" I started. Dad was calling me softly. He beckoned to me, raised himself up on one elbow, leaned sideways, took hold of my hand and addressed me in slow, deliberate speech between swigs from the hip flask.

"Don't worry, child. Your turn will come … You must count your blessings while you have a chance … You'll be counting sheep soon enough, when the bairns come, what with all the worrying … How old are you? Goodness me, I've forgotten."

"I'm 25, Dad."

"Ah … a mere chit. You have plenty of time left. … Why, I recall Ellie was over 40 when she had young Jamie."

George and Ellie Duffy were our nearest neighbours, farmers like us and parents of Janice and James.

"40! I can't wait till I'm 40!"

"Well, don't go wishing your life away, my girl. Now Marion," he said, releasing my hand and rolling over to address Mum. "These are hard times. …The economy's a mess and we must bumble along as best we can. … You must talk to George. He will help you when I'm gone."

"Robert, please don't say such things," she pleaded, the colour draining from her face.

"Nonsense, old girl. If the malady doesn't kill me, the whisky will, ha ha!" He exploded into a guffaw which brought on a coughing fit, so alarming in its severity that it precipitated the arrival of the nurse, whose footsteps could be heard running down the corridor. Dad shoved the hip flask into Alan's hand and he stuffed it under his jacket just in the nick of time. "Now you must all run along," spluttered Dad, peering up sheepishly at the nurse from under his eyebrows with the air of a naughty schoolboy. "This young lady can be a little Hitler, can't you sweetheart?"

We put on our coats. As I was about to leave the room, I was seized by a presentiment. I had seen patients rally as the moment of their death approached. I ran back to the bedside, clutched hold of Dad's hand and pressed my lips to his knuckles.

"I love you, Daddy," I murmured.

"I know," he replied, stroking my hair.

It was the last time I saw my father alive.

When we got home, Alan grabbed a sandwich and embarked on the three hour drive down to Caroline's parents, promising to come back the following day.

"If Alan can do it, why can't Chris?" I moaned to Michael, who had not long been home from work and was removing his boots at the kitchen door.

"Oh, give over, Vicky," he groaned. "He'll be here tomorrow night. Crikey, you're obsessed. Anyone would think you were his mother!"

"You have to remember, Mandy's mother's not well," appealed Mum. "Who do you suppose looks after the baby while Mandy's looking after her mother?"

"Couldn't he bring the baby with him," I argued.

"Don't be absurd! Haven't I got enough on my plate already?" she chided.

"Well, there's nothing on my plate," quipped Michael. "Pass the cake, will you?"

That night, as I was dropping off to sleep, I was roused by the noise of the telephone ringing in the hall. It could only mean one thing. With a sinking feeling deep in my gut I waited, listening with rising trepidation to soft tread of my mother's slippers on the stairs, the rise and fall of her voice and the rapid pounding of my heart. Then came another series of sounds, sounds etched on my memory for all time: a low cry; the thump of her feet as she blundered up the stairs; the frantic banging of her fists against my door. I leapt out of bed and yanked open the door. She stood mutely before me like a rabbit caught in the headlights and I knew for certain that the end had come.

"Oh Mum," I wailed. I threw myself against her rigid form, wrapped my arms around her neck and held her tightly. "Mum ... it's all right, it's all right".

I pressed my cheek close to hers and rubbed her back, caring nothing for myself and wishing only to deliver her from the jaws of purgatory into the healing hands of mercy. At the same time, Michael emerged from his room across the hall and folded us both into a shared embrace. As we stood locked together in anguish, I felt my mother's body go slack, her breath stutter and her frame convulse with a volley of inaudible sobs. My eyes glazed over and my face grew wet as our tears mingled in a mutual outpouring of grief.

A short time after, Michael called my brothers and sister. I dried my eyes and made a pot of tea. None of us felt like sleeping so it seemed like the next best option. I wanted to cry with as much vehemence as Mum had done, to give vent to my misery, but once dry, my eyes refused to weep. Instead I was overwhelmed with a dull, flat melancholy. It transpired that his body had been found on the floor of his room around 11 p.m. Evidently, he had got up out of bed to use the bathroom and had suffered a fatal heart attack. We retired to bed in the small hours and sought respite in the oblivion of sleep.

The next morning Mum had regained some of her composure. The tears came frequently but now fell noiselessly, interspersed with pockets of quiet reflection. Michael was very subdued and disposed to mourn in his own silent, undemonstrative way. I went about like an automaton, ministering a helping hand here and a kind word there, devoid of emotion and with the sensation of existing outside of myself. After lunch, we collected Dad's things from the hospital and then I had a bath and tried to read a book. Unable to make sense of the words on the page, I wandered outside to the cowshed where I ran into Walter cleaning up, and found temporary relief in good company, fresh air and exercise.

"I thought you'd had a bath," said Mum absent-mindedly, when I reappeared at the back door spattered in mud.

"I did." Although it was hard not to smile at the incongruity of this assertion, I was instantly stung by a pang of guilt. I set my face and drifted listlessly up to my bedroom to change my clothes. Crossing the room, I lingered at the window staring blankly out over the grey-green fields to the mountains beyond, meaningless black shapes against the dusky sky. I used to love this view. I shut my eyes and tried to conjure up a picture of Dad, whose image was now as remote to me as the distant felltops. On the sill stood a photograph of Rufus in a frame. I regarded it with an attitude of detachment. If I could only rekindle my sensibilities, I might thaw my frozen consciousness and tap into my emotions. Instead, it seemed the harder I tried to grieve, the more that grief eluded me.

Chris arrived just as Mum was serving up the evening meal. He looked pale and haggard, a shadow of his former self. His mood was dark and pensive. He said little during supper and sloped off to his room with a mumbled apology soon after. I washed up disconsolately, trudged upstairs and tapped on the door, determined to have it out with him.

"Come ..." His summons was officious, contentious and austere.

Conversely, this made me more, rather than less, dogmatic. I would stop at nothing to gain an audience and thrash it out. In my present state of mind, I didn't care a hoot for his good opinion. He was lying on his bed, reading 'Melody Maker'.

"Chris," I said, leaning over and tugging at the newspaper in his hands. "Talk to me, Chris."

"What do you want?" he snapped irritably. "Can't you see I'm reading?"

"Chris, what's wrong? That is, I mean, I think I know what's wrong, and it's all right, because you didn't do anything wrong … 'cause Dad said so," I blurted out somewhat incoherently.

"What *are* you talking about, child?" retorted my brother in the most condescending tone he could muster.

I felt my temper rise.

"Don't call me a child! If anyone's being a child, it's you!" I cried passionately. "You can't go on running away forever!" I stopped abruptly, clapped my hand over my mouth and sank down onto the end of the bed with my back turned. "Oh! Oh! What have I said?" I uttered in a whimper. It was a reckless assertion and a savage blow, even if true. I felt the sting of self-reproach the moment the words flew from my lips and ventured a timid apology. "That was below the belt. I'm sorry."

He put down his newspaper, sat up slowly, swung his legs sideways off the edge of the bed, shuffled up next to me and wrapped his arm around my shoulder.

"Easy, Vicks … easy." This time his tone was tender and solicitous.

Tears welled up in my eyes.

"Oh, Chris. I think I'm losing my mind. I can't seem to feel sad," I moaned. "I want to hurt like Mum but all I can feel is nothingness. I can't bear it. I can't even make a cup of tea. I keep forgetting how to. I can barely even put together a sentence."

"Oh, that!" he said with feigned carelessness. "I know *that* feeling. It plagues me most of my waking hours."

"It does?" I said, in wonder. "Why didn't you say so?"

"I told Dad."

"What did he say," I asked, intrigued.

"He told me to count my blessings," he replied morosely.

"He said that to me too …" As I recalled the words of my father I was, all of a sudden, smitten by an immense sense of abandonment. I began to tremble. "Oh Chris, I want my dad back!" I wailed and, with a heartrending sob, buried my head in his chest.

"There, there," said my brother, stroking my hair as Dad had done only the day before. "It's all right." His body heaved and started to shake. His grip on me tightened. A low gasp escaped from his throat. Then, his face in my hair, he let down his guard, opened the floodgates and together we poured out our sorrow.

"Aren't we a pair of idiots?" I said. I sat back and dried my eyes with the back of my hand.

"You're right, though. I always run away … I never got to say goodbye … and I'll never forgive myself," vociferated Chris, his voice breaking as he started to cry again. "I was a fool, a stupid, self-absorbed fool!"

"Oh, but you're not!" I protested, taking both his hands in mine. "Listen. The day before he died, Dad talked about you … and you know, he was glad you went to work instead of coming home. He said …oh, what *did* he say? Yes, now I remember … he said it was 'a commendable choice' … and he gave you his blessing." I gave his hand an emphatic squeeze. "It's all coming back to me. I thought I'd lost the capacity to think … and to feel, come to that." I smiled my relief but hastened to straighten my face.

"It's all right to smile as well as cry," said my brother in a kindly tone.

"Oh, but whenever I feel a smile coming, I get racked with guilt. I'm not supposed to be happy. I've just lost my dad."

"You can smile without being happy," he said grimly. "I do it all the time. Besides," he added, pausing to consider, "the odd smile is a very far cry from 'being happy' … and another thing; how will you grieve if you don't permit yourself to enjoy the occasional nugget of light relief? There's no pleasure to be had perched in the middle of a seesaw … no pain either. It's a monotonous ride which is only expedient when in a state of profound shock and about to topple off … although I sit there habitually." He contemplated the picture on the opposite wall, a colourful piece of 1960s word art done in his last year at school of which he was particularly proud, and took up the thread again. "You know something … I've never given it much thought before, but perhaps if I drank less and made my peace with the present, I might find some grains of happiness amongst the chaff. I was half-cut when I got the summons, so it didn't seem very important at the time; if I'm honest, I was probably just too scared to face the inevitable. Look here … I know what you said, but what do you *really* believe – black sheep or prodigal son? Heaven knows I don't deserve my father's good opinion, and if there's a trace of doubt in your mind, I want you to tell me, even if it hurts. I've been living a half-life but all that's about to change."

"I told you, there's nothing to forgive … quite the reverse. Dad spoke of you with great affection. He loved you. He loved all of us," I mused, wiping a fresh tear from my eye. "Come on, let's go downstairs and have a cup of tea." As I rose, I recollected that there was something else, something just as important, that needed to be said. This was going to be tricky, I thought ruefully, as I grappled with the words in my head.

"He did say one other thing … oh, how *can* I put this?" I steeled myself and took hold of my brother's hand. "He said … he thinks … he thinks you've been ignoring Louise. That's what *he* said, anyway … it's not my place to say," I finished hurriedly.

To my inexpressible relief, Chris greeted the remark with a contrite smile.

"Yes, I know, I'll get it sorted, I promise," he sighed. "I haven't been a very good father, have I?"

Over the ensuing weekend, we helped one another to cope during the initial stages of the healing process, which would be long and arduous. When Chris noticed a fleeting smile pass across my face, he would smile back. "It's what Dad would have wanted," he would say to me. When he withdrew into himself, I would take him by the hand and draw him back out with words of encouragement. For the most part I was calm, passive and resigned to my loss. From time to time, I would be overcome by a surge of intense grief and cry as if my heart would break, safe in my room or cradled in the arms of my brother. On one such occasion, I went into my parents' bedroom to borrow a disposable razor from Mum. It was the first time I had entered their room since my father had passed away. As I crossed to the dressing table, I was engulfed by a wave of anguish which stopped me in my tracks. In a trancelike state, I opened the wardrobe door and stared inside. There were my father's shirts, clean and pressed, his sweaters neatly folded and his socks balled together in pairs. Blinded by tears, I hauled out the sweaters, dropped to the floor, gathered them in my arms, crouched, foetal-like, with his clothes pressed against my face, and wept uncontrollably. Mum found me 10 minutes later, scooped me up, clasped me in an emotional embrace and asked me tenderly which one I would like to keep.

A week later, Dad's body was laid to rest at the tiny church of St. Michael and All Angels at Nether Wasdale. He was 58 years old. It was a beautiful day, mild with a cool breeze. The sky was daubed with puffy white clouds like celestial pillows which danced across the sun. Primroses, crocuses and coltsfoot bloomed about the graves, festooning the grass with abundant splashes of yellow and purple. Birds twittered and the scent of wintersweet hung in the porch. The little church was full to overflowing with well-wishers from all over the county who came to pay their respects to a friend and colleague whose honesty, integrity and unceasing good humour had won the hearts of many a fellow farmer and tradesman. It was clear that our father recognised the value of keeping his customers happy and took care not to reveal his flaws; his overbearing nature, his intransigence and his predisposition towards dourness, I thought affectionately, as I took my place next to Chris in the front pew. Mum broke down halfway through her eulogy and Toni had to take over. Alan got through his with relative ease. Being a teacher, he was accustomed to speaking in front of an audience. Before the end of the first verse of 'Morning Has Broken' my voice started to crack. By the end of the second one, I had lost the ability to sing altogether. I still get a lump in my throat every time I try to sing it.

At the end of the service, Chris came face to face with Julie and her father just outside the exit door. It was the first time he had seen his father-in-law since that catastrophic row more than four years ago which had marked the end of his marriage, in every sense apart from the legal one. He hesitated, then held out his hand in a gesture of friendship.

"Hello Liam. Hello Julie," he said, the epitome of grace and good manners.

Liam's taut face relaxed into a warm smile.

"Hello son," he said, taking hold the proffered hand and shaking it.

"Julie," he said amiably. "It's good to see you. Where are the children?"

Julie flushed and shuffled her feet.

"Paul's looking after them."

"Who's Paul?" asked Chris in a measured tone, which disguised his dismay but thinly.

"He's just a friend," replied Julie in an offhand way. "He's the son of Mrs. Cowley who works at one of the schools I teach at. He helps out with the childcare … and sometimes he comes over for a card game … with Dad," she qualified.

"Oh … okay," mumbled Chris, making a move to go but turning back instantaneously to address his wife again. "Look, Julie. I'd like to make amends … if I can … regarding Louise," he faltered. As I contemplated my brother not just confessing his shortcomings, but confessing them in the presence of the old gentleman generally regarded as his arch-enemy, you could have knocked me down with a feather. At that moment, my admiration knew no bounds. "I've been a pretty poor substitute for a father, and this … this … well, all this …" he stammered, with a sweeping gesture, "well, I took a look in the mirror and I didn't like what I saw." He swallowed hard, felt for my hand and squeezed it.

"That's all right, lad," said Liam gruffly. "I'm no saint, either."

I could have kissed them both there and then. Instead, it was Julie who did the kissing. With the exquisite charm which infused everything she did, she laid a hand on her husband's shoulder, leaned forward and brushed his cheek with her lips.

Chris turned crimson and took a step back in surprise.

"Heaven help me," he muttered under his breath.

I don't know whether Julie heard him or not, but she smiled anyway.

"So long," she concluded sweetly. "Take care."

The day after the funeral, I returned to London. Ray met me at the station and we shared an umbrella as we walked home together. Once inside, he ushered me up the stairs.

"Come on, get yourself showered and put on your glad rags. I'm taking you out for dinner," he announced, grinning broadly.

"Oh, are you? That's so nice," I cooed. "It's just what I need after the last fortnight. Where are we going?"

"Only the Berni," he replied apologetically. "I hope you don't mind but I'm a bit skint at the moment."

I dined on prawn cocktail, steak and chips and Black Forest gateau which was, after all, extremely palatable and the best I could hope for from an aspiring archaeologist on a modest salary.

As we sipped our coffee and sucked on Mint Imperials, Ray delved into his jacket pocket and extracted a small box.

My heart gave a little flutter. I checked myself. "It'll be another trinket," I thought, hardly daring to hope.

He rose from his seat, stepped around the table, dropped down on one knee and lifted the lid of the box.

"As I said, I'm a bit skint at the minute," he said archly. The tiny diamond that sparkled in its setting on the slim gold band might have been the Pink Panther, such was my rapture.

"Well, will you marry me?" he asked, removing the ring from the box with a flourish.

I was so astonished that all I could do was nod vigorously.

“Hold out your hand, the left one,” he commanded, with all the gallantry of a knight seeking the hand of his lady fair.

He slipped the ring onto my finger.

“Oh my God, I’m engaged!” I squealed, finding my tongue, throwing myself at his upturned face and covering it with tumultuous kisses.

Chapter 15

Life After Death

Less than 24 hours after the last of the mourners had drifted from the churchyard, Nan had taken possession of Chris's old room and would become a permanent resident at Cinderdale Farm throughout the remaining years of her life. For a woman of 74, she was remarkably energetic. With a renewed sense of purpose, she took up the reins, throwing herself into the household chores and dispensing nutritious meals whenever my mother was too tired or miserable to cook, which was most of the time according to Michael. Each burst of activity was punctuated by frequent forays to the drinks cabinet. However, Nan was blessed with an iron constitution and the only visible effect of her predilection for the bottle was her wayward sleeping habits. She would rise late and sit up drinking until midnight, but for all that she was a rock; staunch, dependable and unperturbed by every fresh episode of tearfulness she encountered (and there were many).

Meanwhile, Mum got on with the business of running the farm as best she could, assisted by Dad's right hand man Walter and our nearest neighbour, George Duffy. Michael maintained his day job and would metamorphose into a farm labourer in the evenings and at weekends, lending a hand in the fields and cattle shed and doing odd jobs.

I should have felt happier. I had a ring on my finger. I was living in a plush abode with kind and good people and doing a job I loved. Instead, I felt dejected, listless and anxious.

"It's all part of the grieving process," Mum would reassure me during our frequent conversations on the telephone. "It will pass. I felt much the same way when I lost my own father."

During the spring, I passed my driving test. It was my second attempt. The first had been on a dismal morning in January, the day after a particularly harrowing phone call in which Mum had expounded on the alarming deterioration in the state of Dad's health, as well as the relationship between my cherished older brother and the long-suffering Mandy. Feeling thoroughly frazzled, I had hastened into Ray's room and proceeded to 'offload'. Unfortunately, he was constructing a particularly complex passage in an essay on canal archaeology and I was met with a rebuff. We had argued and I had slept badly. At least I failed my test spectacularly. I stalled whilst attempting to reverse round a corner, mounted the kerb during my three point turn and nearly drove into the back of a Ford Escort at a pelican crossing. I was physically shaking and crying before the halfway mark, which might partially excuse my failure to notice that the car in front of me had stopped. To top it all, my examiner was a po-faced elderly gentleman of ample proportions who spilled over the edge of the passenger seat, making it almost impossible to avoid physical contact when fumbling for the gear stick. It was a truly mortifying experience.

On the second occasion, a sunny afternoon in April, I was met by a pleasant man in his 40s who shook my hand heartily and wished me good luck. I noted with relief, as I slid the Vauxhall Chevette into first gear, that, being considerably slimmer than his predecessor, there was no possibility of accidently brushing my hand against his right thigh. I drove proficiently, performed all my manoeuvres with the expertise of a pro and glided back to the test centre in a state of quiet confidence. I had done my homework so the theory part was easy.

That evening, Ray took me out to dinner.

"I've been thinking," he said as we waited for our first course. "How would you like to go home for a few days? We can share the driving. It'll be a chance for you to try your hand on the motorway. I should have finished my current module by the end of the month. We can go after that."

"Oh, I'd love to!" I squealed, hardly able to contain my excitement, the extent of which took me completely by surprise as it was quite disproportionate to his proposal, in itself nothing out of the ordinary. I tried to visualise myself hurtling up the M1 in the driving seat.

"Are you sure you want me to drive?" I grinned sheepishly, feeling not a little trepidation.

"You'll be fine," he smiled, helping us both to a glass of wine. "I'll just keep my eyes shut and pray hard!"

On the first Friday in May, we set off early. We took turns and the journey went without a hitch. At three o'clock in the afternoon, we pulled into the petrol station at Gosforth, a few miles from home.

"I could murder a Crunchie right now," I announced, climbing out of the car. "Want anything?"

"Get me a Curly Wurly, I'll be in in a minute," replied Ray, handing his keys to the pump attendant. "Fill her up, please."

"Good luck with that, if you value your teeth," I laughed. "Last time I ate one of those, I lost a filling!"

I crossed the forecourt, entered the little shop and headed for the counter where I knew the sweets to be. There, I was confronted by a familiar face, one little altered by the passage of time.

"Why, Avice!" I exclaimed, smiling broadly. "Do you remember me? It's Vicky. We delivered Julie's baby all those years ago. Remember … it was really snowy and the midwife couldn't get there in time. Let me think … Sarah's 10 now, it must be more than 10 years ago."

"Oh my gosh … of course I remember. I was so scared … I remember that."

"Me too … I'm a midwife now. I work in a hospital in London," I declared proudly. "How about you? Is this your main job?"

"Well, ye-es it is at the moment …" she said hesitantly, her colour rising.

"Nothing wrong with that," I interjected, sensing her embarrassment at the immense gulf between our stations in life. "Married?"

"Yes, I am as a matter of fact. I have a baby. He's 18 months old. We live just around the corner."

"Well, there you surpass me," I said with a placatory smile. I inclined my head towards the door. "It's taken Ray precisely 12 years to propose and there's no chance of a wedding until he's finished his Masters in two years' time. I'll be 27 by then! I *so* want a baby. Every time I deliver one, I turn green with envy. I've got loads of nieces and nephews but it's not the same. I want one of my own."

A slow smile spread across the face of my interlocutor.

"Do you like cats, by any chance?" she asked with a mischievous glint in her eye. "Kittens, to be precise."

"Oh … kittens, cats, dogs, all animals," I prattled on blindly, walking straight into the trap. "I love them all!"

"Maybe Ray would let you adopt a kitten … only I thought … well it's the next best thing." She glanced towards the door, leaned towards me confidentially and lowered her voice. "Mum's cat's had kittens. There's two left. She's looking for homes. You could have them both. Would you like them?"

"Oh, *would I?*" I cried eagerly. "But … well, you see the problem is that I live with Ray's mum and dad. Their house is quite posh and I can just imagine the wreckage. There's no way they'd agree to it. Such a shame, otherwise I'd have taken them like a shot." I sighed and shook my head.

"Never mind, I'm sure we'll be able to find homes for them. That's 28p for the chocolate."

As I rummaged in my purse, a crazy idea began to form in my head.

"These kittens … are they boys or girls or a mixture? What colour are they?"

"They're girls. One's black and the other one is honey-coloured. They're adorable," gushed Avice.

"Hmmm, I wonder … Mum's rather down at the moment. You knew we lost Dad in February, did you?"

"Yes, my parents went to the funeral."

"Yes, I remember …they did. Well, we lost Rufus too last year … he was our dog. It might be just what she needs to get her out of the doldrums …" I continued thoughtfully, half to myself. "Yes, it'll give her a new lease of life … and they'd be great ratters, being farm cats. I'll take both," I said decisively.

"Are you sure? Shouldn't you check with her first?"

"No, it'll be fine. It'll be a lovely surprise. Can I pick them up tomorrow?" I ventured, quite carried away by the prospect of two darling little balls of fluff.

"I-If you're quite sure," she replied dubiously.

"Yes, I'm sure," I concluded, proffering my hand to seal the bargain.

Back in the car, I had Ray to contend with.

"She'll kill you, you idiot!" he scolded. "She's got enough on her plate already without a couple of kittens tearing around the house like mad things and getting under her feet. You'll have to tell Avice you can't take them after all."

Naturally, this made me all the more determined to see my plan through to completion.

"Well it's too late now," I said pettishly. "I promised."

The following morning I made our excuses and set off for the

Cartwright's Farm at Wasdale Head with my reluctant accomplice.

Dolly Cartwright met us at the door.

"Hello, Mrs. Cartwight. We've come for the kittens," I said brightly. "This is Ray."

"Hello Vicky, hello Ray. Do come in. My, it seems like only yesterday that you were a mere slip of a thing. Avice tells me you live in London now … and a midwife. Your mother must be very proud of you." I blushed and nodded. "Come on in. I'll make a cup of tea and then you can meet the babies."

She ushered us into a huge kitchen. Gleaming pots and pans hung from shelves crammed with jars, tins and boxes in a haphazard array of different shapes, sizes and colours. A stewpan simmered on the range, emitting a savoury, aromatic scent.

"And what do you do for a living, Ray? Would you like a biscuit with your tea?" enquired Dolly over her shoulder as she filled up the kettle.

"Yes please, I'd love a biscuit, thank you. I'm studying for a Masters in Archaeology … and working at the Natural History Museum as a technician in the Geology department. I work with minerals. I clean them, catalogue them, that sort of thing."

We exchanged pleasantries while we sipped our tea and munched on Custard Creams.

"I expect you must be desperate to meet the kittens," said Dolly as I drained my cup. "Come on through; they're in the barn."

"Oh, she's absolutely gorgeous!" I cooed, cradling the little black kitten against my shoulder. "Hello, sweetheart."

"The other one's rather shy," explained Dolly, placing a saucer of milk in front of a tattered cardboard box with a hole cut into the side.

I knelt down, peered into the gloom and waited silently. A tiny whiskered face appeared at the aperture and looked cautiously out. After a minute or two, she clambered out, sniffed at the contents of the saucer and lapped it up greedily.

"She's stunning," I gasped.

She was indeed an exceptionally beautiful creature, pale ginger with a white bib and a smudge on her nose.

"She has a healthy appetite, that one," chuckled Dolly. "I'll fetch something for you to carry them home in."

"Don't you think you ought to ask your mother first?" observed Dolly, returning a short while later with a box lined with an old towel and a roll of masking tape.

"No, of course not," I rejoined merrily. "It would spoil the surprise." I placed the furry black bundle down gently in the box and carefully picked up the ginger one, who had overcome her initial fears and was sniffing at Dolly's wellingtons.

"I expect she can smell the dog … and 101 other things," laughed Dolly.

"She's so sweet," I squeaked, holding her aloft, kissing her head and popping her in the box next to her sister. "Thank you *so much*, Mum will *love* them." I closed and sealed the box.

"Well, if you say so," replied Dolly uncertainly. "But if she doesn't, please feel free to return them. I would hate your mother to feel pressurised."

"No way … they're not coming back; we're definitely keeping them!" I pronounced, picking up the box and heading for the exit.

Ray raised his eyes to heaven in a gesture that was not lost on me.

"Don't say I didn't warn you," he said with a shrug, guiding me out through the barn door.

"Victoria Jane Kelly, what have you done?" Mum stared into the box, her expression a mixture of amusement and dismay.

"They're great ratters," I countered, quick as a flash.

"Ratters? We've got rats double the size!"

"All right, maybe not yet, but they will be," I argued. "Oh Mum, look at them, though. They're adorable. You can't possibly send them back." I picked up the little black kitten and bundled her towards Mum, who held out her hands abstractedly. "You take that one. She's called Elfride. This one's Thomasin," I continued briskly, extracting the honey-coloured one and holding her up for inspection. "There. Now, how can you refuse?"

"They *are* rather sweet," said Mum, her expression softening.

"What's with the names?" chimed in Ray. "You didn't warn me about that. I thought we decided on Sooty and Ginger." He winked at Mum.

"They're characters from Thomas Hardy novels," I replied simply. "They're beautiful names. You'll keep them, then?"

"Well, I don't suppose they'll be any trouble, once they can go outdoors," she said with an air of resignation, " … and I do miss an animal about the place."

"Precisely how many cows is it you have, Mother?" teased Ray.

"More than enough, dear boy, but they don't make good housepets," laughed Mum.

"There, what did I tell you, Ray?" I said triumphantly. "Ah … this one's purring, aren't you, poppet?" I murmured, pressing my cheek against the warm, downy body of my tiny new friend.

* * *

The next time I saw Elfride and Thomasin, they were three-quarters grown. The occasion was Christmas 1979, our first Christmas without Dad. We arrived during the afternoon on Christmas Eve. After we had deposited our bags in my old room, unpacked the presents and put them round the tree, Ray nipped in the shower while I made tea. Mum was at the kitchen sink peeling potatoes.

"D'you want a cuppa?" I said cheerfully. "Where's the cats?"

"Oh … out and about somewhere," she replied flatly. "I'll have some if you're making it."

"You all right, Mum? You don't sound very … happy."

"I miss your dad," she said, with a slight tremor in her voice. "It's not been easy, you know."

"Yes, I know," I said sympathetically, slipping an arm around her shoulder.

Instead of looking up, she kept her gaze fixed on the potatoes and continued removing the skins with swift, skilful strokes like an automaton.

At that moment, Elfride trotted into the kitchen. Glad of a distraction to relieve the awkwardness, I swept her up and gave her a hug.

"Hello, darling," I chirped. "My, how you've grown. You're a big girl now."

Mum was pale, uncommunicative and withdrawn throughout the rest of the day. When the boys arrived during the evening, she greeted them with indifference and showed little appetite for socialising, preferring to immerse herself in food preparation, claiming that it would save time and effort on the morrow and brushing aside offers of help.

"Where's Mandy?" I asked Chris, when I was able to catch him alone. "Not here?"

"Nah," mumbled Chris. "Had to stay at her mum's. She's not great at the moment; her mum that is, not Mand," he added with a hint of irony in his voice. "Now scoot, Vicks, I need to shower."

"We're a bit down on numbers this year," I persisted. "I don't know if Mum said, but Toni and the kids are at Jason's parents' tomorrow, so that's five less including Mandy. Shame, that."

"On the contrary … all the more grub for me," he grinned, shutting the door in my face.

Eventually Mum loosened up after a glass or two of wine which we virtually forced upon her, but on Christmas morning she was worse.

"She's not right," said Michael, unfolding the tablecloth and throwing one end to me. "She's not usually as bad as this … and I think I know why."

"Well, obviously it's because it's her first Christmas without Dad. It's bound to be hard."

"No, it's more than that. She's been like it a lot lately. I'm going to prise it out of her." He dropped his end of the cloth and hurried out of the dining room, leaving me to lay the table.

When we sat down to our midday meal, I noticed that, although she was still quiet and preoccupied, the expression on Mum's face was less tense. We dined on venison, chestnut stuffing, roasted vegetables and red wine gravy, followed by Christmas pudding and brandy sauce. I threw scraps under the table for Thomasin, who thanked me by assailing my leg with a barrage of head-butts. During a lull in the after-dinner conversation, Michael tapped his glass with his spoon, stood up and raised it in the air.

"To Dad," he said ceremoniously.

"Dad," we echoed, raising our glasses likewise. I felt a lump rise in my throat and my eyes began to water.

I noticed that Michael was looking intently at Mum, who nodded in response. He sidled round the table and spoke to Chris in hushed tones. Chris turned to Julia, who was perched beside him, peeling the crepe paper off the cardboard interior of a spent cracker.

"Would you like to get down now, Julia? Let's take you to the toilet, shall we?"

"F'lup. Had nuff. Wee now," stated Julia, reaching for her father's hand and sliding sideways off her chair.

Sensing that 'something was up', Caroline glanced down at Leonie and saw that she was sleeping soundly in her carry cot.

"There's something I need to tell you," blurted Mum as soon as Julia was out of earshot. Michael moved towards her, clasped her hand and gave it a squeeze. "I-I've decided to sell the farm," she stammered, biting her lip and turning crimson. There was an audible gasp emanating from all four corners of the table. "I know it's not what you want, it's not what I want either, but I simply can't continue. Let me explain ... This is what Robert was afraid of all along. We've been struggling to compete with the big concerns for some time now and running at a heavy loss. To complicate matters, two of our wholesalers have gone out of business in the last year which means

I have to find new buyers for some of our produce. So far I've been unsuccessful. My labour costs have shot up as I've had to buy in more help since Robert fell ill. George has been amazing but he's got his own farm to run and I can't rely on him indefinitely. I've done the sums. The harvest should enable us to pay off most of our suppliers but we can't afford to keep running at a loss. The only hope is to quit before we go bankrupt. I still have enough left to sell the farm, settle the debts and buy a decent size home somewhere nearby, say Seascale. As a matter of fact, I've seen one in the paper that might do … I'm sorry, everyone. I didn't want to have to tell you today, but I can't bear this on my own." A silent tear trickled down her face and dropped onto her napkin.

"Oh, Mum …" I burst out, stifling a sob.

"It's all right, Vicky," she smiled, through her tears. "In a way, it'll be a relief."

There was an uncomfortable pause.

"Let's go and sit on the comfy chairs," volunteered Alan, attempting to salvage a scrap of bonhomie with a practical suggestion. Although it did little to lift our spirits, we all agreed that it was a good idea and relocated to the lounge.

Everybody tried hard to be jolly but it was difficult not to dwell on the fact that this would, in all probability, be the last Christmas we would celebrate at Cinderdale Farm.

"Let's play charades," suggested Alan, scooping up handfuls of wrapping paper and stuffing it into a black sack.

Although the mood was subdued, the game was entertaining nonetheless. Mum put on a brave face but now it was Michael's turn to act out of character. He quickly lost interest in the shenanigans and eventually muttered an excuse, wandered out and disappeared upstairs.

Half an hour later, he flung open the door and waved a piece of paper in the air, a broad grin on his face.

"Meet your saviour!" He scooted across the room, cupped Mum's chin in both his hands and planted a flamboyant kiss on both cheeks. "We're going to save the farm! I can do it. I know I can, and I will!"

"Don't be daft, Michael! Do you have any idea how serious this is?" spluttered Mum, trying hard to conceal the frustration she so evidently felt at his seeming inability to grasp reality. I was with her on that. Michael had always been a bit of a dreamer although he preferred to describe himself as an entrepreneur.

"Of course I do. I live here, right? I've seen this coming for months and given it a lot of thought. If you can't do it one way, try another. We need to carve ourselves out a niche market, and I've got the very thing. We'll go organic. Hardly anyone's doing it but there are outlets, not many but a few, who specialise in organic food. There are also customers, not many but a few, who want it. I'll jack my job in – I don't like it anyway – and work the farm. With my expertise and your book-keeping skills, we can make a go of it, at least."

"But what about the debts?" argued Mum.

"We can sell off the east field to George ..."

"If he wants it," interrupted Mum.

"Well, to someone anyway ... don't be difficult, Mum ... and use the money to get ourselves back on track. What do you say? Come on Mum, you know it makes sense."

Mum looked around the room for affirmation. I believe she was far too overwhelmed to make a decision of that magnitude single-handedly.

"Go on Mum, you should give it a go, you really should," urged Alan.

"Yes I agree, go for it," concurred Chris.

"Me too, I think it's a great idea," I piped up.

"I'll drink to that!" averred Nan. "Pass the bottle."

* * *

"I'll have red; make it a large one … no half measures, young man," hollered Nan over the general din, waving her glass at Alan, who stood by the dresser calling for orders.

The date was 21st March 1981 and the occasion was Toni's 30th birthday. The day's business had been concluded. The wider family was gathered in the sitting room behind the shop, which Jason and his brother had built as an add-on not long after they had opened the tea room at Torver. The only exception was Mandy, whose mother was now in the advanced stages of cancer and had been given a matter of months to live. A tragedy of itself, it had also resulted in Mandy's absence from all family events since Dad's passing two years ago. It was at around the same time that relations between Chris and Julie had begun to thaw, which could have proved extremely awkward had the 'third party' been present.

After I had helped get Julia undressed and ready for bed, I left Chris upstairs in Toni's room reading 'Spot the Dog' to Julia, who peeped out wide-eyed from between the sheets of the big double bed. He was reading very quietly because Leonie was already asleep in a cot in the corner of the room. As I descended, I could hear Toni singing softly to Ryan, as she put him to bed in the room next door.

Sarah sat on the sofa wearing headphones. She was gazing dreamily down at Simon Le Bon, who smiled up at her from the pages of 'Smash Hits'.

"For goodness sake, Sarah, don't be so antisocial," chastised Julie, handing her a bowl of chilli con carne. "Take those headphones off!"

Sarah scowled, yanked them off her head, threw them down petulantly and switched off her Walkman.

"This mince tastes funny," chirped Louise, pulling a face.

"It's got a little bit of spice in it, only a tad," said Julie. "Try a bit more, darling."

"Yes, try a bit more, Lou-Lou," echoed Scott, who was perched on the chair arm next to his favourite cousin.

In the last two years, since the ice had started to melt, our wider family had grown closer. As a result of this, Louise had become a regular visitor to the Kings' abode, spending almost all her weekends playing football, climbing trees and making mud pies with her two male cousins. She was a beautiful child but it was often hard to tell with her face caked in grime and her hair dirty and tousled.

"Any requests?" called out Jason, slipping a well-worn copy of 'Bridge Over Troubled Water' into its sleeve. At that moment, Chris reappeared.

"Why, Lennon, naturally," he chimed, plonking himself down in the seat Jason had vacated. "Need you ask?"

"Not the new one, please God," wailed Caroline. "I can't stand Yoko Ono. I mean to say, I'm sure she's a very nice person but whatever idiot told her she could sing wants their head examined!"

"Probably her husband," smirked Julie, wincing under the sting of her husband's tacit reproach.

Chris was a private person whose default was to keep his emotions in check, and it was testament to the reverence with which he regarded his idol that he openly cried when he learnt that the great man had been tragically shot dead as he returned to his New York home on the evening of 8th December 1980. In the end, we all agreed on 'Magical Mystery Tour' as Scott liked "the one about the walrus".

"So what's it like turning 30?" I asked my sister, when she came downstairs a few minutes later.

"Horrible, absolutely horrible!" she complained. "Look at me! I've got grey hairs sprouting all over the place!"

"I can't see any."

"I've got hundreds," she said peevishly, "and I'm losing my looks. Look at my wrinkles, Vicky, *look* at them." She held her face close to mine and pointed emphatically at her forehead.

"You look gorgeous," I laughed. "You always look gorgeous, even when the rest of us look like tramps."

Toni sighed. "Oh Vicky, there must be more to life than work and kids."

"You should think yourself lucky you've got kids," I replied tetchily.

"Yes, I suppose so," she conceded wearily. "Dad always told me I should count my blessings."

"Ha ha, he said that to everyone. Mind you, he did have a point. Come on Toni, it's only a number after all."

"Yes, a very large one," groaned Toni.

"Wait till you're 54," quipped Mum. "It won't seem so large then."

As the evening drew to a close, there was a loud knock. Julie jumped up and hastened to the door. Chris raised his eyebrows and looked at Toni with a quizzical expression on his face.

"That'll be Paul," qualified Toni. "He's ever such a sweetie. He never minds picking her up when she's had a drink or two, and he often brings Louise down at the weekend if she's teaching on a Saturday."

"Who's Paul?" demanded Chris, sharply.

"You remember Paul," I interposed. "He's Mrs. Cowley's son. She teaches at our old primary school. Julie does some music lessons there."

"Oh yes I remember now. She mentioned some Paul guy at Dad's funeral. I vaguely remember him. Blond geezer, wasn't he? Used to play cricket. Blimey, Mrs. Cowley taught me when I was a nipper. She must be pretty ancient by now. She hasn't popped her clogs then?"

"No she hasn't, and she's not even all that old. Don't be so disrespectful," I retorted.

"Hmphh … he's still hanging around her, is he? She's way out of his league," he hissed between his teeth, barely able to conceal his envy.

"Don't be ridiculous!" snapped Toni. "They're just friends, that's all … and keep your voice down, you idiot!"

A few moments later, Julie returned with Paul following after. He was tall, broad shouldered, with fair hair and a plain face.

"Hello girls," he said cheerily.

"Hello Uncle Paul," squeaked Louise, leaping out of the armchair, skipping across the room and wrapping her arms around his legs, while Chris looked on abjectly.

"Hi there," said Sarah amiably. "Can we stay a bit longer, please Mum?"

"Fine by me, you're welcome to stay for a drink," put in Toni, "unless you need to rush off."

"Thanks, I will have a quick one," smiled Paul easily. Jason got to his feet. "I'll have a beer, not too strong."

Julie glanced across the room at Chris, who was contemplating his watch with a glazed expression on his face.

"Chris, I don't believe you've met Paul," she said congenially. "Paul, this is the girls' father."

Paul ambled over to where Chris was sitting and held out his hand.

"Pleased to make your acquaintance," he said agreeably. "They're lovely girls. You must be very proud of them."

"Yeah, well that's down to their mother," said Chris sardonically. "Here, have my seat." He stood up, gave his usurper a cursory shake of the hand and turned to me. "If you and Ray want a lift back, you'll need to come now. It's getting late. Julia's got an early start tomorrow. I need to get her home to bed."

"She's already in bed," I muttered irritably.

"I mean real bed," he growled. "You're welcome to get a cab back. It's all the same to me."

"That'll cost a fortune!" I looked helplessly at Mum.

"I'm sorry, love. I can't squeeze you both in, that's unless Alan was thinking of leaving in the next few minutes."

"Nah, I'm good thanks," said Alan, getting up to refill his glass.

"Ray, what do you think we should do?" I said desperately, trying my hardest to sound casual.

"Sorry, Vicky, I don't have the dosh."

"Oh all right, we'll come now," I mumbled crossly, stomping

out to the hall and throwing on my coat while Chris went upstairs to collect Julia from his sister's bed.

"What's he got that I haven't anyway," snarled Chris, starting the car engine.

"Good manners?" I snapped impatiently.

"Did you see Louise?" he raged. "She was all over him!"

I took a deep breath and reined in my anger.

"She likes him," I argued. "She's just being a typical six year old."

"She never seems pleased to see me," he said sullenly.

"Well, maybe if you started acting like a father, she might act more like a daughter!" I spat, unable to suppress my frustration.

The wall of silence with which he met this remark spoke volumes and we drove home without a further word. Beyond the beam of the headlights, the blackness was impenetrable. The way was narrow and winding, a tortuous rollercoaster of twists and turns, ascents and descents, negotiated with the ferocity of an indignant man. Fortunately I knew my brother to be more than competent behind the steering wheel so I was not unduly alarmed.

I was also acutely aware of the torment under which he was labouring. Consequently, when I awoke the following morning, I was consumed with guilt. Had I been too hard on him? After all, it can't be easy to extend the hand of friendship to the man who has supplanted him, I reasoned, as I mulled over his embarrassing display of petulance. When we had eaten breakfast, I sought him out. He was sitting in the lounge thumbing through the Sunday paper. Mum was entertaining Julia with a game of peek-a-boo featuring Julia's favourite bear.

"Fancy a walk?" I said breezily, "only Ray's got some reading to do. Is that okay, Mum?"

Mum gave her assent.

"Yeah, sure," he said putting down the paper. "I'll get my jacket." He knelt down, wrapped his arm around his little daughter's waist, smoothed down her hair with his spare hand and gave her a peck on the cheek. "Daddy's popping out, munchkin," he said fondly. "Be good for Nanny, sweetheart."

"Bye bye Daddy, bye bye Auntie Vicky," chirruped Julia, catching a glimpse of her teddy over her father's shoulder as it emerged from behind the arm of the sofa, and dissolving into a fit of giggles.

The day was mild. The rain had given way to intermittent sunshine and the air smelt damp. I strolled down the lane with my brother at my side, filling my lungs with the earthy scent and drinking in the sights and sounds of nature. The hedgerows quivered at the light touch of the breeze. At my feet, the vegetation along the verges glistened and the tarmac gleamed, still wet from the rain. The distant drone of a hedge trimmer was punctuated by the swish of trees as they flirted with little gusts of wind, which played amongst their semi-naked boughs and whipped my hair across my face. A chaffinch twittered overhead. By the time we reached the lake, I had made my peace with Chris.

We looked down the length of Wast Water towards the three shapely peaks that command the head of the valley. A thin veil of cloud obscured the summit of Great Gable. The sun glimmered over the rim of Illgill Head, illuminating the upper reaches of the lake.

"You can't top this," breathed Chris. There was a long pause because words were not enough. Something stirred in the pit of my stomach and tears sprung to my eyes.

"I don't want to go back!" I burst out impulsively.

"Me neither, there's no rush. Let's walk on a bit."

"No, I don't mean now, I mean ever! I don't ever want to go back! I don't want to go back to London."

Chris's jaw dropped and he stared at me speechlessly.

"But I thought you loved London," he said finally, his voice incredulous.

"I thought so too, and I've tried, believe me I have. I did like it at first, but ever since Dad died I've been plagued by doubts." I sniffed and wiped my eyes with the back of my hand. "I'm so lonely, Chris. I'm like a fish out of water. The family are all very nice and kind, and Ray loves me to bits, but he's always got his head in his books and I just ... well … fend for myself … most of the time. I read, I go out with my friends, but I never feel really happy. Sometimes I don't even feel alive. Then I come home and I remember how I used to feel."

"It won't be forever, Vicks. He'll be finished with his course in a few months. Then you can get married, buy a home of your own, start a family … all those things you've always wanted."

I groaned. "Yes, but where? I want to live here. I miss … all this," I cried with a sweeping gesture. "I miss the fields and the woods, the lakes and the mountains, the bleating of the sheep, the sound of birdsong and running water, the smell of the rain. I miss Mum and I miss you guys."

"Perhaps it's because you're missing Dad," he reasoned. "That'll be what's at the bottom of all this." He gave my hand a reassuring squeeze.

"I'm not so sure," I sighed.

"Well, if you can't decide, don't decide," said Chris. "That's what Dad told me once, a long time ago, only I didn't listen."

He fixed his gaze on a distant point where the hazy hills converged and merged with the surface of the water. I knew his mind because his past lay before him, concealed within an enclave at the head of the dale, in a pretty stone cottage at the foot of Great Gable.

Chapter 16

Between a Rock and a Hard Place

Nothing captures the essence of a perfect English summer day quite as eloquently as strawberries and cream, tennis whites and the hollow slap of friendly fire which peppers the air during match day battles played out in the hallowed courts at Wimbledon Lawn Tennis Club. This I have deduced, for on the second day of July 1981 I was privileged to partake of the experience by dint of a pair of Centre Court tickets gifted to Ray's father by a wealthy client. This gentleman, a City banker, was so enamoured of his dental implants that he supplemented the very substantial cost of his new teeth with a slice of corporate bounty. As luck would have it, Ray's parents were flying out to Copenhagen that morning for a long weekend and couldn't go.

The day was fair and the grounds a short two-mile walk from home. We arrived just after midday and ate our sandwiches in the queue. Once inside the grounds, we found ourselves in a large, paved area thronging with people, most in conservative dress. The men wore shirts and smart trousers or suits; the ladies, slacks, skirts or dresses. Some sported hats. Here and there uniformed officials hovered, presumably to assist the visitors rather than for the purpose of crowd control as there appeared to be little chance of a riot. A programme vendor stood near the gate. Anji had strongly advised me to dispense with my jeans in favour of an aqua blue A-line cotton frock with broderie anglaise lace trimming around the neck, sleeves and hem, and a white cardigan embellished with fake pearls, which was provided for the occasion by Ruby. Now I understood why and was glad I had not dug my heels in when pressurised to 'dress appropriately'. I gazed at the iconic Boston-creeper-covered walls of Centre Court on the opposite side of the square, a familiar image seen countless times on televisions across the globe, hardly able to comprehend that I was actually there. Ray bought a programme and we weaved through the crowd and joined the queue for our gate. Inside the arena, we bought a drink and took our seats.

At the turn of the decade, the game was still dominated by Bjorn Borg, pin-up and winner of 11 Grand Slams including five consecutive Wimbledon Men's Singles championships. John McEnroe was hungry for the title, having conceded a narrow defeat at Wimbledon the previous year in what is still regarded as perhaps the greatest match of all time, stretching to almost four hours, in which McEnroe saved seven match points in the fourth set in a dramatic tiebreak lasting 22 minutes which he went on to win. Borg played out with one of the best sets in his career, losing only three points in seven service games and taking the title.

The first semi-final was between number two seed McEnroe and unseeded Rod Frawley from Australia, who had enjoyed three successive straight set victories. It was during the first round of this tournament that McEnroe had hurled his infamous remark "You cannot be serious!" at the chair umpire in response to a call of "Out". However, despite his reputation as 'bad boy on the block',

McEnroe enjoyed popularity on a par with his former rival, Ilie Nastase, who won the heart of many a fair maiden during his heyday in the 1970s, by virtue of his smouldering good looks and volatile temperament. Frawley put up a good fight, taking the first set to a tiebreak and pulling six deuces out of the bag before losing his serve in the third and final set. The match was not without colour, with McEnroe receiving a warning in the first set and a one point penalty in the third for 'unsportsmanlike conduct'.

As the winning shot hit the turf, we hastened to the exit to secure a place near the front of the food queue. We bought takeaway fish and chips, strawberries and cream and Pimms cups and found a pleasant spot on the picnic terrace. The food was excellent even though the portions were rather modest.

"Mmm … this is heaven," I murmured, simultaneously sipping my cocktail and munching on a strawberry. "If I could stop the clock, you know I'd do it right now." It was only then it occurred to me that I hadn't thought about Dad since midday.

Most people can count on the fingers of one hand those magical moments when the present is so perfect that the past and future cease to exist. This was one of those moments, one of a very small clutch which have a special place in my heart. Had I known then what would transpire over the next few months, that particular snapshot might have been one I would have preferred not to keep. However Ray, in his infinite wisdom, decided to spare me for the time being. Perhaps it was cowardice that stayed his tongue, but I am more inclined to believe it was an act of kindness. I never took the trouble to find out.

We returned to our seats as the evening match, between top seed Bjorn Borg and third seed Jimmy Connors, was about to commence. 28 year old Connors was keen to secure a win, having lost six Grand Slam semi-finals in two years and suffered a quarter-final defeat in the French Open earlier in the year. Borg was looking for his sixth consecutive Wimbledon title and looked to have the upper hand, having won all five qualifying matches in straight sets while Connors had been trailing two sets to love in his previous match before making an inspired comeback.

It was all the more surprising, then, that Borg crashed out of the first set 0-6 and lost the second 4-6 after equalising at 4-4, only to lose his serve again in the next game. Connors revealed snatches of his former glory, achieving a high percentage of first serves. He got lucky too on more than one occasion. Meanwhile Borg appeared to be struggling on a less than perfect surface. By the end of the second set, the odds were stacked in favour of an all American final. However, one can never write off a true champion, especially one with such an impressive record when it comes to surviving adversity. Connors faltered in the third set while Borg played with growing confidence. Borg took set four in just 28 minutes. The fifth and final set was electrifying with both players struggling to hold serve. Connors finally capitulated in the seventh game but fought back valiantly, taking the next game to deuce. Borg hung on however, by virtue of his superior serve, and took the final set six games to four.

Two days later, McEnroe lifted the trophy, ending Borg's near record-breaking run at the home of British tennis.

* * *

Three days before my 28th birthday, Ray dropped the bombshell. One Sunday evening in October, while I was ironing my uniform, he touched me gently on the arm.

"There's something I need to talk to you about … something important," he said, his face flushed and his manner edgy. "That is … when you've finished. I'll be upstairs."

Mounting the stairs a few minutes later, alarm bells going off in my head, I found him waiting outside my bedroom door.

"Come and sit down, we can talk better that way," he mumbled, nudging me through the door. He perched on the edge of the bed and signalled for me to sit down next to him.

"Vicky, I've had an offer. It's good news, at least *I personally* think it's good news, but it would mean some big changes for both of us."

"We-ell?" I replied uneasily.

"You've heard of the Mary Rose?"

"The Mary Rose? … er, I'm not sure, to be honest."

"It's a 16th Century Tudor warship. They found the wreck in the Solent about 10 years ago. There's a massive excavation project going on. They've found literally thousands of artefacts, bones too, all kinds of stuff, and they're planning to raise her off the seabed next year if everything goes according to plan." Something in my face made him hesitate.

"And …?" I put in, my heart sinking.

"They've put together a team to restore and preserve the finds and they're looking to recruit more people with the right skill set. Back in the summer, I happened to mention to one of my lecturers that I did my degree at Portsmouth and he reckoned I'm exactly what they're looking for. The Masters is practically in the bag and I've been working at the museum for eight years now. I'm getting a bit bored, to be honest. Anyway, to cut a long story short, he sent a recommendation down to the people at the Mary Rose Trust and they've offered me a job. It would be a big step up for me and the money's heaps better. Of course we'd have to relocate to Portsmouth but being my old stomping ground, I've got a few mates down there already. The houses are much cheaper so we could buy our own place … What do you think?" he finished breathlessly.

"I … I don't know what I think," I stammered. "This is all so sudden."

"It's the chance of a lifetime," he said, barely able to conceal his desperation to gain my approval.

Unsurprisingly, this failed to have the desired effect. Nobody likes to be put on the spot.

"Why didn't you tell me before? I thought we were a team," I said reproachfully.

"There didn't seem any point," he countered. "Not till I had a job lined up."

I sighed audibly. "All my friends are here. It took me ages to settle in London, and now you want to up and move again."

"Don't be angry, sweetheart," he coaxed, wrapping his arm around my shoulder. "You don't have to make up your mind right now; they're not recruiting for at least six months."

"All right, I'll think about it," I concluded, with an air of resignation. "I don't want to talk about it right now."

We lapsed into an uncomfortable silence.

"I'm not cross with you," I continued reining in my frustration. "More shocked than anything. I'm sorry. I *will* think about it, I promise."

"Thanks, Vicky." He gave my shoulder a squeeze.

"Come on, let's go downstairs." I extricated myself from his friendly grasp with a faint sense of relief as I was still feeling peeved with him. "They're showing a TV adaptation of 'Brideshead Revisited' and I don't want to miss the beginning."

Over the next few weeks, I made an earnest attempt to reconcile myself with a move to Portsmouth. I listed all the advantages, talked to colleagues who had visited the city and even borrowed travel guides from the library expounding on its many attractions. I couldn't find fault with the plan. I also knew I had it in me to make new friends, as I had done this without difficulty when I had moved to London four years ago. However, try as I might, for some inexplicable reason, I found it impossible to warm to the idea and had got no further in terms of a decision when I received a telephone call from Chris two weeks before Christmas. He called to tell me that Mandy's mother had finally passed away. This was an event which was to have far-reaching effects, although I didn't know it at the time.

It was now well over three years since Mandy had assumed the role of sole carer. In that time, she had not been up to the farm. Julie, on the other hand, was always present, and I had noticed, with not a little consternation, that Chris was becoming increasingly attentive towards her. Paul was still on the scene. He almost always dropped off and picked up Julie and the girls, and usually stayed for a quick drink before they departed, but never came in the capacity of a 'plus one'. Julie was perceptive and very proper in her manners, could sense the rivalry between the two, and would no doubt have advised Paul not to overplay his hand. I fervently wished Chris could learn to show the same restraint, especially in front of four year old Julia, who was no fool and apt to tell her mother everything.

We drove up on Christmas Eve and arrived just after six. Michael let us in.

"Hi sis, hello mate," he said hurriedly, pecking me on the cheek and giving Ray's hand a brief shake. "Sorry, bit busy. Make yourselves at home." He retreated into the front room and closed the door.

I peered into the kitchen.

"I can't find Mum. Let's get the overnight bag out of the car and take it upstairs. Might as well do it now as later. The presents can wait."

Ray wandered over to the telephone which stood on a small circular table in the hall.

"Mind if I ring Mum and let her know we got here all right? You know how she worries."

"Go ahead. Chuck us the keys, will you? I'll get the bag."

I heaved the large navy blue canvas holdall from the boot of the car, lugged it up the stairs and dumped it in front of my bedroom door. As I reached for the doorknob, it spun between my fingers and the door flung inwards.

"Hi, chicken," grinned Chris from the doorway, surveying me with amusement. "Merry Christmas! Bag a bit heavy, is it? Shame, that. You're downstairs!"

"That's not fair," I wailed. "This is *my* room. I *love* this room."

"It's every man for himself, as you well know," he said jovially. "Mine's taken. If you want your old room back, you'll have to take on the old bird," he chuckled, inclining his head towards the bedroom in the opposite corner of the hall which had been given over to Nan. "I'm not turfing her out. She's got squatters' rights and besides, she's deadly when she's under the influence."

I scowled and picked up the bag with an effort.

"Here, mind my present!" he called out after me.

"What makes you think I've got you anything?" I retaliated, waddling down the stairs with my load.

"Can someone get the door?" Mum was basting the turkey. Mandy was washing up the breakfast things. I was sitting at the kitchen table with Ray peeling sprouts. Chris was removing some orange and white plastic components from a box which Father Christmas had left for Julia, who was watching him with eager anticipation. Michael was finishing his toast. Nan was still in bed.

"I'll go," said Michael equably, stuffing the remaining morsel into his mouth and depositing his plate in the sink. Moments later he returned with Julie and the girls in tow.

Sarah had grown into a tall, slender 13 year old with fair hair, blue eyes and freckles. Louise, now eight, had dark glossy hair, large tawny eyes and perfectly aligned features, all the hallmarks of a beauty in the making.

"Hi Julie, what a lovely surprise!" exclaimed Chris, blushing deep red, whereupon he leapt up and proffered his hand. "Merry Christmas!"

Julie, always the soul of discretion, glanced uneasily at Mandy, took a step back and shot him a warning look.

Chris hesitated and turned towards his daughters.

"Hello, young ladies, what a lovely surprise." He hugged the elder girl affectionately, knelt down and wrapped the younger one in an awkward embrace. "Julie, can I get you a drink? Tea? Coffee? Some festive bubbly? You're not dashing off, are you?" he gushed, turning his attention back to his wife.

"Thank you, but I won't stop," she replied uncomfortably. "I've left father in charge of the turkey and … well, you know what he's like … he'll probably forget to take it out of the oven and it'll be burnt to a crisp," she added with gaiety which sounded forced and did little to smother her embarrassment.

"Oh, but before you go, hasn't Lou got one of these? Here, have a quick look for me, will you? I can't work out how it goes together. Please, Julie," he pressed. "It should only take a couple of minutes." He motioned towards the chair alongside his own.

Julie glanced down at the pieces scattered on the table.

"What's it supposed to be?"

"It's Sindy's caravan."

"Sorry. Mine's the older version. This one looks different," she said bluntly.

"Would you have a look anyway?" he persisted. "They're probably very similar."

Julie looked apologetically at Mandy, who was watching from the sink with a glazed expression on her face, and sat down reluctantly.

To her credit, Sarah tried her best to diffuse the situation. She was genuinely fond of Mandy and possessed wisdom beyond her years.

"Hi Mandy," she smiled, approaching her. "I haven't seen you for absolutely ages. I'm so sorry about your Mum. You must be devastated."

"It's all right," Mandy answered tremulously. "It's a bit of a relief, to be honest."

"How's Bella?" continued Sarah. "Is she here?"

"Yes, she's upstairs in her basket. Would you like to see her?"

"Sarah, would you be a treasure and go and get the presents for your mother? They're under the Christmas tree, the two big bags at the front," interrupted Chris from his position at the table. "They're silver with red writing."

"Yes, in a minute, Dad."

"Can you get them now?" he huffed. "She's in rather a hurry."

Sarah shrugged helplessly and disappeared out of the door.

Mandy dried her hands and slipped out after her. I followed Mandy to the door but she shook her head and scurried upstairs. A few seconds later, I heard the door to my room close softly. Julie watched the proceedings with mounting vexation and then addressed Chris sternly.

"Was that Mandy in the corner? Oh, Chris, you might have introduced us! Honestly, where are your manners? Whatever must she be thinking? Go and fetch her!"

Chris muttered under his breath and departed hastily, his face the colour of beetroot. By the time he returned, Sindy's caravan was complete.

"She's not coming down," he grumbled. "She's not in a good place. Her Mum passed away a couple of weeks ago. Ah … you've finished it."

"Yes, I know that," retorted Julie, ignoring his closing remark. "Well if she's upset, you'd best leave her be. It's hardly surprising. The poor child's sorely in need of some TLC. I hope you're looking after her."

"Thanks for fixing the caravan," he mumbled sheepishly.

"It was simple," declared Julie haughtily. "A child of four could have worked it out. Perhaps you should have asked Julia to help you." She threw him an exasperated look, got up from the table and bid a hasty retreat.

It took most of Christmas Day to grab a few moments with Chris alone. As I watched Mandy withdraw further into herself as the day wore on, I became more and more determined to have it out with him. Eventually, out of sheer desperation, I stationed myself outside the bathroom door when he felt the call of nature and accosted him as he emerged.

"Is Mandy all right? She's hardly said a word all day," I asked casually, staking out the turf on which to pitch my campaign.

"Of course she's not all right," he hissed. "She's just lost her mother. Was there anything else you wanted to say?"

I took a deep breath. "Julie's right," I ventured. "She badly needs looking after and she's out of her depth. We're not exactly sober company. Are you sure you should have brought her?"

"I gave her the choice," he snapped. "She wanted to come."

"She's hardly the sort to keep you from your family at Christmas. She's way too nice for that. *Even you* wouldn't have had the heart to leave her on her own. She *knows* that. It's obvious she only came because of you."

"Shhh … they'll hear us!" he interjected. "Come in here." He tugged me roughly by the arm into Nan's room and closed the door. "She could have gone to her sister's," he argued, once inside.

"I expect she was thinking of Julia. She loves it here."

"Anyway, what do you mean? '*even* me'."

"Please let's not argue. Don't be so defensive. I'm tired of fighting with you. Please, Chris."

I sat down heavily on the edge of the bed and waited. He looked at me with contempt, wandered over to the window and stared out. In the silence that intervened, I mulled over a way to break the deadlock and eventually got up and stood alongside him. Dusk was casting her inky veil over the sleepy hinterlands between the mountains and the coast. Here and there, faint specks of silver twinkled upon a canvas of charcoal blue suffused with fiery orange where it dipped below the western horizon. I reached for my brother's hand.

"Do you remember back in '67, when we stood at this very same window and you told me you'd just got married to a girl I'd never met?"

"It seems like light years away. I was so full of hope," he said dolefully. "Life was simple then."

"Speak for yourself. I thought the world was collapsing around my ears … I feel a little like that now."

"Don't be silly, Vicks. These are my problems, not yours," he said fondly, giving my hand a squeeze.

"No … no, this is about me. This whole moving to Portsmouth thing. It's doing my head in."

"I thought it was all decided," he said incredulously. "Don't tell me you're contemplating not going. This is the chance of a lifetime for Ray."

"Oh, he'll go," I said bitterly. "It's just whether … whether I go too."

"Vicky … we *are* talking about Ray, aren't we? The only guy you've ever loved, ever since you were … what? 13? Why, I'd follow Julie to the ends of the earth."

"And what about Mandy?" I cried out impetuously. "What about her?"

"That was below the belt," he chided with a wry smile, "but I take your point. Seriously, hun, don't blow your only chance for happiness. Take it from me … I know."

"And what will you do, Chris?"

"Nothing," he said morosely. "Julie's moved on. You know something, I thought things would get better after Mandy's mum died. I've hardly spent five minutes with my girlfriend in the last six months … but it's worse now. She mopes day and night and barely says a word to me."

"But Chris, you have to give her time, she's not herself and you never show her any kindness. You were beastly to her this morning and you know it! It was embarrassing!"

"Yes, I know. I've had my knuckles rapped … *not* that I needed telling," he conceded grudgingly. "I can't help myself, you know."

"Then walk away. Stop fuelling the fire," I said with a touch of severity in my voice.

"And what will you do?" he asked me.

"I don't know," I sighed. "Come on, let's go downstairs."

The next morning, after breakfast, Chris announced his intention to pick up the girls from their mother's. They were to spend Boxing Day at the farm.

"Go and fetch your coat, sweetheart," he said, wiping the

crumbs from his mouth with the back of his hand. Julia hopped off the chair next to her father and scampered upstairs.

"I thought Mum was going," I said pointedly, fixing him with a significant look.

"No, I'll go, she's busy," he said airily, feigning innocence.

"Oh, would you? That would be very helpful," clucked Mum.

"I can go with Ray," I said hurriedly, rising from my seat.

"Will everyone stop telling me what I should and shouldn't do!" exploded Chris, glaring angrily at me, shoving back his chair in a gesture of defiance and stomping towards the door. "I'll see you later."

I looked despairingly at Mandy and raised my eyes to heaven. She smiled weakly but I could see that she was on the verge of tears.

"Fancy a walk, Mandy?" I said after an interval. "We could take Bella down to the lake. She would love it. Wouldn't you love that, pumpkin?" I cooed, addressing the shaggy little creature curled up on a blanket in the corner of the kitchen.

"If you like," she said meekly, hugging herself and staring down at the little dog.

"Let's go now, it's a lovely morning," I said brightly.

"Yes, you're right, she would like that," she rallied. "I'll get my coat."

"I'll stay and give you a hand, Mum," offered Ray diplomatically.

The day was cold, crisp and crystal clear. The sky was duck egg blue. Shafts of pale, golden sunshine spilled over the ridge, beamed on us askance and doused our cheeks with feeble warmth. The frost sparkled on the tarmac and clothed the vegetation in a mantle of silver. A flock of starlings gossiped in the leafless boughs above our heads.

Near the foot of Wast Water is a shingle beach where we stopped to throw stones for Bella, who was darting in and out of the shallows like a whirling dervish.

"Time is a great healer," I mused, watching the light play on the water and suddenly becoming aware, perhaps for the first time since the death of my father, that the pain was almost gone.

"Some wounds not even time can heal," said Mandy mournfully.

"I thought that too, just short of three years ago when I lost Dad, but I'm all right now … I think," I concluded, swallowing the lump in my throat.

"What makes you think I'm talking about my mum?"

"As to that," I replied, after a long pause, "I wish I had some words of encouragement for you, but I'm at a loss. The boy's obsessed."

"She's his wife, after all," responded Mandy, "the mother of his children. I don't see how I can compete, Vicky … with her; with all this loveliness, and with the family; no offence, but I just don't belong. You understand, don't you?"

"Yes, of course I understand; and none taken. To be honest, I'm in the same boat, more or less. Ray wants to cart me off to Portsmouth and I don't want to go. London's bad enough but at least I've got my friends … and his parents."

"I thought you loved London!" she exclaimed, completely taken aback.

"Why does everyone think I love London? Oh, it's all right I guess, but it can't hold a candle to this … and I hate living so far from Mum … and Toni, Michael even. That's the worst part. What do *you* think I should do, Mandy? But hey, I'm forgetting. This is about you, not me."

"Me … huh! What am I compared to Julie?" she said despondently, "other than a scrap of nothing out of the ordinary. I mean, she's gorgeous, she's accomplished and she's a genuinely nice person. I've only seen her twice and both times I felt dowdy and inept the minute she walked through the door. It's not her fault. I can't blame him for loving her."

"But he loves you, Mandy. I know he does. And you're not dowdy, or inept."

"Maybe he did once, or maybe I was only ever a distraction, someone to fill the void. We're almost strangers now. Mum's illness didn't help but it was always on the cards. We never had all that much in common. Oh, how *could* I have been so blind? He never *would* entertain a divorce. I should have seen the signs."

"But he loves you; he told me so," I insisted. "Granted, he's treated you abysmally, but he's not a bad person. He's confused and he's misguided and sure he's missing the cheerful, carefree Mandy he fell in love with. And yes, he's fixated on Julie … but he's not a complete fool. Hopefully he'll see all this … oh, how can I put it? … detachment … for what it is, just a phase. And of course there's Julia. That's got to count for something."

"Ah, Julia. She worships her dad. She likes her half-sisters too. So you see, I can't compete, can I?"

It was difficult not to agree so I let it go at that.

"For what it's worth," volunteered Mandy later, as we were heading home, "if I had such a loving family and lived in an amazing place like this, I would never want to leave. Can't Ray get a job up here?"

"I wish it was that simple," I said ruefully.

"Don't go, Vicky. I honestly don't think any man is worth it … but then I'm probably not the best person to ask."

By the time Chris got back home with the three girls, I was setting the table for lunch. He put his head round the door with an apologetic smile.

"You took a long time," I said with a hint of accusation in my voice.

"Ah, well … I stayed for coffee, and we got talking. You know how it is."

"Yes, I know how it is," I said brusquely, studiously ignoring him and laying down the cutlery with more force than necessary while he continued to hover at the door. On the other hand, it seemed futile to chastise him repeatedly for neglecting Mandy and only served to drive a wedge between us. Since there was nothing to be gained by going over the same old ground, I looked up at him and softened my tone.

"I guess we're all of us caught between a rock and a hard place."

"Don't worry, pigeon. It'll all pan out. I'll be kind to Mandy, I promise." I raised my eyebrows. He blushed deeply and smiled penitently. "My wife insists on it. Now isn't that ironic?"

He crossed the room, kissed me on the forehead and ruffled my hair, and for a second I felt like a child again. Instinctively, I leant into him but at that very moment he stepped away. I lurched forward and caught hold of the edge of the table.

"Ha ha! Drunk again? Now promise me you'll go to Portsmouth, Vicks."

"I can't promise you that," I said, recovering my balance and grinning, "and I'm not drunk. Chance would be a fine thing."

Chris was as good as his word, and for the remainder of their stay, he was considerate, attentive and affectionate towards Mandy.

"Would you mind very much if we stopped off at Rose's on the way back to London?" I asked Ray, the following morning. "I'd like to catch up with her."

"Sure we can," said Ray amiably, so I telephoned Rose and arranged to have lunch with the family en route.

We set off after an early breakfast and arrived at the Victorian semi-detached red brick villa in the Manchester suburb of Levenshulme just before lunch. 15 year old Deborah opened the door. With her mother's prepossessing looks, an abundance of chestnut-coloured hair and a statuesque physique inherited from her father's side, she probably had the capacity to floor a man at 20 paces with a flash of her big, brown eyes.

We dined on cold turkey, ham, sausage rolls, crusty bread, pickled onions and chutney.

“Would you like another cup of tea and a slice of home-made Christmas cake to see you on your way?” asked Rose, rising from the table.

“Do we have time, Ray … please? Half an hour can’t hurt.” There was something I wanted to ask Rose.

Ray looked at his watch. “If we leave now, we’ll hit the M25 right in the middle of the rush hour. Yes, let’s stay for cake. Could you direct me to your toilet?”

I heaved a sigh of relief at the opportunity this provided for me to have a private conversation with my friend.

“Straight up the stairs, mate. First on the left,” said Leslie.

“Let me help with the clearing away, Rose,” I chimed in, determined to seize the moment, whereupon I jumped up and started stacking the plates.

“There’s no need, really Vicky. Go and sit down,” she protested.

“I’ve been sitting down in the car for three hours!” I laughed. “Please, I insist.”

I followed her into the kitchen, pushed the door to behind me with my elbow and put the plates down on the draining board. Rose was filling the kettle. I sidled towards her and put my mouth close to her ear.

“Rose, Rose, I need to talk to you about something. Can we go out in the garden … or somewhere we won’t be overheard?”

“Have a care, child! It’s freezing out there!”

“Please Rose, it’s really important!”

“All right, dear, I’ll think of something.” She patted my arm and winked conspiratorially.

“I got a lovely new dress in the Boxing Day sales, didn’t I, Les? Would you like to see it, Vicky?” enquired Rose blandly, draining her cup.

“Don’t bore the poor girl. What’s another dress? You’ve got dozens already. I don’t see what’s so special about this one,” put in Leslie cynically.

"I'd love to see your new dress," I said politely. "Shall I come up?"

"Yes, do. I can show you the one I got last summer too. You remember, Les, the one with the poppies on."

"Women …" growled Leslie, as I preceded Rose out of the lounge. "They bleed you dry. Take my advice, sonny. Don't get married."

We retired to the sanctuary of Rose's bedroom where I was afforded a cursory glance at her new dress.

"Now what is it you want to talk to me about?" she commenced, perching on the edge of the bed and signalling to me to do likewise.

"I don't know what to do, Rose. Ray's been offered a fantastic job in Portsmouth starting in the summer but I don't want to go. I wouldn't dream of stopping him but I can't bear the thought of yet another move … *and* it's even further from home. I've tried to get used to the idea but it feels all wrong. It was different when I moved to London. I had Anji and Bill; I guess you could say they were surrogate parents. But I don't know a soul in Portsmouth. Ray's got a few friends down there. I'm not sure if that's a good or bad thing from my perspective. It depends if they're the 'let's all go down to the pub' type or whether they've got nice girlfriends I could get to know. Also, what worries me even more is that it's a project … they're raising some warship. What's going to happen when it's all over? As soon as I've put down roots, he'll be wanting to gallivant off somewhere else, I shouldn't wonder."

"Have you tried talking to him?"

"Oh, I've talked to everyone," I sighed. "That just confused me even more. Chris says go, Mandy says don't. I think on balance, most people think I should go."

"Vicky, let me give you some advice," said Rose tenderly, placing a reassuring hand on my back. "Intelligent women like you don't make bad decisions when it really matters. Every decision you make will be the right one *at the time*. It will merely take you along a different path and lead to a different outcome. I'm not talking about a better or worse outcome, just a different one. We are, none of us, clairvoyant so there's no point agonising over the decisions we make after we've made them. Better to live with them and move on. Whatever course you choose will be the right course and you must remember that if you ever start to doubt yourself. Of course, sometimes things happen that force our hand; births, marriages, deaths, that sort of thing."

"You can't tell me what to do then," I said glumly.

"Good gracious! Of course I can't. You'd probably do the opposite anyway. People are so contrary. Try listening to your gut instinct. It's rarely wrong."

"Okay … I-I-I'll try," I said uncertainly. "Thanks, Rose."

"That Deborah's a looker," announced Ray, as we joined the main road.

"For shame, Raymond Elphick!" I gasped in mock horror. "She's almost half your age!"

"Oops, I had her down for 17 at the very least," he said, turning crimson.

"She's 15 and still in school; you pervert!" I rejoined merrily.

"Well, she certainly had me fooled."

There were road works on the M1 and by six o'clock we had only got as far as Toddington Services.

"We've still got a fair way to go. Let's stop for a break," proposed Ray.

We pulled off the motorway, parked the car, entered the amenity building, chose a table next to the window in the restaurant area and ordered coffee.

"Shouldn't we be making a move?" I suggested, half an hour later.

"Yeah … I guess so," said Ray absent-mindedly but then proceeded to stay put and appeared to be making a study of the fingernails on his left hand. Another two minutes elapsed.

"Well? What are we waiting for?" I was beginning to feel a little irritated.

Suddenly, without warning, Ray reached across the table and clutched at my hand, which was resting on the table next to my handbag.

"Vicky … *darling*," he began earnestly.

I stared at him with unbridled astonishment. Evidently he was about to say something very significant. He stopped short, as if unsure whether to continue.

"Go on," I urged him. "Spill the beans."

"You know, we've spent a lot of time together over the last few days. It's been great and I've loved every minute of it. You know, I'd almost forgotten what an amazing girl you are. It's far too easy to take people for granted, but I'm not going to let that happen again. I want to marry you, Vicky, and I want to do it this year. Let's get married in the autumn. We'll move down to Portsmouth in the summer and tie the knot, say, third week in September. What about the 18th? That's a Saturday."

"Oh my gosh, I don't know what to say!"

"Yes would be good."

"Well … yes! Of course, yes!" The words tumbled from my lips of their own volition. It was only after I had uttered them that the full import of what he had said dawned on me.

"Oh, thank you, thank you, you've made me the happiest man on earth," declared Ray, leaping to his feet, pulling me from my chair, flinging his arms around my waist and lifting me bodily from the floor, much to the amusement of the customers at the nearby tables.

"Put me down, you idiot! Everyone's watching," I squealed, wriggling like an eel. "They'll be plenty of time for all those shenanigans when we're married!"

"Have you still got your heart set on a small wedding?" asked Ray, as we embarked on the final leg of our journey.

"Yes, I don't want anything fancy. We could hold the ceremony in St. Paul's Church … you remember St. Paul's? … the one where Toni got married. Then have a little party at the farm, in the garden if the weather's nice."

"Don't you want to 'queen it' for the day? Most girls would jump at the chance."

"No, can't say I'm interested. Anyway, it's what Dad would have wanted. He was forever falling out with Toni over her expensive tastes … he was very frugal and nearly had kittens over her wedding bill. And besides, Mum can't affort a lavish affair."

"Oh, that's no problem. My folks'll chip in."

"Yes, I know that, but I couldn't ask it of them. They've been more than generous already, so we'll do it on the cheap and then they're not under any obligation. If there's anything left, we can spend it on the honeymoon."

"Honeymoon, eh?" grinned Ray. "Did you have anywhere in mind?"

"Well, yes I did actually … um … I'm not sure you'll like the idea," I said timorously.

"Okay, what harebrained scheme have you come up with now?" chaffed Ray.

"I want to go to Scarborough," I said coyly.

"Scarborough? Isn't that a bit of a dump? Don't you want to go somewhere exotic?" exclaimed Ray with an expression of dismay.

I burst out laughing. "Oh, don't worry. I don't want to go on the astro slide, or go to the zoo or the Fun House or hit the clubs, or anything like that. Anyway, Scarborough's not a dump … at least it wasn't when I last went."

"And when was that, pray?"

"Oh … er … 1967 … I think," I giggled.

"Oh, come along, Victoria. It'll be awful. Full of bingo halls, amusements and chippies."

"I like fish and chips," I protested. "Anyway, there's some lovely local walks. Seriously, Ray, it's a nice place. I used to go every year when I was a little girl. It reminds me of my dad."

"Oh, all right then, suit yourself" conceded Ray, with a scowl and a shrug. "We'll go to sunny Scarborough … only next year we'll go somewhere decent."

* * *

On the first Sunday in April, when I returned home from my night shift, there was a message from Mum, who had tried to call me late the previous evening.

"That's unusual," I commented to Anji, who was making breakfast. "I hope there's nothing wrong."

"She said there was no need to bother you at work so it can't be anything urgent," reasoned Anji. "Would you like a hot drink?"

"Yes please, decaf coffee. I'm off to bed once I've called Mum."

"Vicky, oh, thank goodness you've called." Mum's voice fluttered down the line, anxious and breathless. "It's all kicked off. Mandy's packed her bags and gone to live at her sister's. Chris is at Alan's. He's in a terrible state. He blames himself entirely."

"Oh my God … but she'll come back, surely. It's just temporary, right?"

"No, no, dear. He was very clear about that. She told him on Friday night she had decided to leave him. They stayed up all night apparently but she was adamant. She says he's better off without her, she says she's a hindrance … she even said she was an incompetent mother."

"Crikey, what about Julia?"

"Chris has Julia. That's something at least. To give Mandy her due, she hasn't been neglectful in that respect. I gather she'd already approached a neighbour, a lady whose daughter is a friend of Julia's, and presented Chris with the contents of her Post Office account to pay for the childcare for the next few weeks until they've got something more permanent in place. He's beside himself. Thank goodness he has Alan and Caroline to take care of him."

"And Julia … is she all right?"

"Surprisingly well, actually. She's a bit of a Daddy's girl and Mummy's promised to see her as often as she can. Four year olds are quite resilient, you know. I'm more concerned about Chris, to be honest. But I mustn't keep you talking. You must be exhausted after your night shift."

"Well I am rather tired, Mum, although I doubt if I'll get much sleep."

"A word of advice, child. Don't call him, at least, not just yet. He's still in a state of shock. He knows you'll be worried sick … he told me that … but he did say he was intending to ring you when he feels a little more like talking, probably in the next few days."

"All right, Mum. I'll be patient, but it won't be easy. Bye for now."

On Tuesday evening, to my immense relief, I finally got a call from my brother.

"Hey, Vicks. You all right, sweetheart?"

"Yeah … yeah … I'm okay, at least I think so. How about you?"

"Well obviously not great in the circumstances," he responded gloomily, "but I'm getting by, you know, one day at a time an' all that."

"I'm so sorry. You mustn't beat yourself up over it. It won't do any good, you know."

"If you mean it won't bring her back, you're probably right," said Chris morbidly. "I miss her already. She's a sweet girl."

"An absolute gem," I concurred.

"Listen, Vicky. There's something I need to tell you. I've handed in my notice and I'm moving back north. That is to say, 'we'; Julia and me."

"Oh …"

"Is that all you can say, Vicky? '*Oh*'. I thought you'd be pleased."

"Well, yes, I am pleased … I am really. I'm just … well I don't know what I am. You should go, though … definitely," I gabbled, wondering why I didn't feel in the least bit pleased.

"Jesus, you're hard to fathom."

"Sorry ... er … where are you going to live?" I asked distractedly.

"D'you remember Simon? That mate of mine over on the coast. He's agreed to put me up for a few weeks and Mum said she'd have Julia till I've got a place of my own. I've got a week's holiday owing so I'll only lose two weeks' pay if I leave this Friday."

"Oh, that soon? Chris, are you sure you know what you're doing? I mean, thi-is i-isn't a kneejerk reaction, is it?" I said tentatively.

"No, of course not. As a matter of fact, I've been thinking a lot lately about moving back home so I asked Simon a while back … he's still working at the old firm in Whitehaven … anyway, I asked him if there was anything doing and they've offered me a job, see?"

"Did you mention any of this to Mandy?"

"Well, yes I did actually. Er … it would have been about a fortnight ago," he said hesitantly. "She likes Mum, and I thought …" he trailed off.

"You thought you could play happy families with your wife and daughters while she stood on the sidelines," I said coldly. "Oh, Chris, have you no conscience?"

"She wasn't all that keen on the idea," he admitted.

"… And you're surprised she ditched you? It was ill-advised … *and* ill-timed," I scolded. "You've definitely blown it this time."

"Please don't start, Vicky. Mum's given me the third degree. So has Caroline. I've been an absolute monster; I'm well aware of that. It was stupid and reprehensible but I can't undo the past. I've apologised to Mandy, grovelled even, put it down to temporary insanity, but she's having none of it. If it's any consolation, I'm paying for my sins. I've never felt so rotten in my life."

"I'm sorry … and I didn't mean to have a go at you," I said anxiously, recalling the fragile state of his emotions. "Nobody's perfect, least of all me. You won't do anything silly, will you? Oh, I *wish* I wasn't so far away."

"Don't be daft, I'm not a complete dunderhead. Look, I have to go, Vicks. Julia wants her bedtime story."

"All right. Take care … and keep me posted. Bye Chris."

Ray was upstairs, getting changed. I started to recount the conversation with my brother.

"Would you like to go home for a few days?" suggested Ray, who sometimes possessed an uncanny ability to read my mind.

"Funny you should say that. I finish nights next Tuesday morning. I thought I could get the train up later, after I've had a sleep and come back … um … Friday. Would that be all right?"

"Sure," he said genially. "Shame I can't join you but it's Easter hols and two of the team have already got time off, so I'm snookered. Sorry Vick."

It was after nine when Michael picked me up from Barrow-in-Furness rail station, a good hour's drive down the coast but the only option available, as the last train to Seascale had already departed. When I got home, Mum had gone to bed. Chris and Nan were in the lounge, drinking whisky.

"Hi guys. Chris, what a lovely surprise! I thought you'd be at Simon's."

"Nah, that's next week," drawled my brother, "when I start my new job."

"Give us a shot of that," I grinned, dumping my case on the floor and throwing myself onto the sofa.

"You hate whisky!" spluttered Chris.

"Well I feel like a drink," I said emphatically. "I'm cold, damp and frazzled."

Suffice to say, I felt a great deal better after a couple of glasses of whisky and a cheese sandwich; and just a mite tipsy. Nan retired at midnight but I was in no mood for bed.

"Ah, my little Jiminy Cricket. It's good to have you home," said Chris, topping up my glass.

"Why do you say that?" I giggled.

"The voice of my conscience … self-righteous, infuriating, but rarely wrong."

"I wish I had as much confidence in myself as you have in me," I said ruefully.

"Tsch, Vicky. You're one of the most together people I know. Great job, great fella, great prospects …"

"Then why do I feel torn in two?" I burst out involuntarily.

"Whoa, take it easy, sis," enjoined Chris, shuffling up next to me, sliding his hand along the back of the sofa and scooping me into his arms.

"Don't mind me. It's the drink talking," I mumbled, pressing my cheek against his shoulder, since I was at that very moment suppressing a sudden and quite unexpected urge to cry. "I'll be all right when I've sobered up."

With the aid of Elfride, who had begun to take an interest in the proceedings and thought it might be helpful to nibble at a loose strand of hair, I soon began to feel better.

"Up you get, you're squashing me," he said presently, manhandling me into a sitting position. "Come along, there must be something the matter." He looked into my face expectantly.

"Only the usual … Portsmouth," I said wearily.

"Ah … that old chestnut," he groaned. "Look here. I've got to be honest, Vicks. You don't seem all that keen on getting married. Are you sure you really want to? Marriage is a big deal, you know. It's not a decision to be taken lightly."

"Huh, that's rich coming from you! Yours was a lightning affair, if you remember."

"I have no regrets," he said sanctimoniously.

I pulled a face and picked up my drink.

"Hey, you'd better make that your last," he cautioned. "On second thoughts, I think you've had enough already." He prised the tumbler from my grip like a protective parent. "You're sharing with Julia. I'm sleeping here and I'm all in. Go on, scat!"

With my brother's imprint on my face, neck and shoulders, I mounted the stairs, undressed silently and clambered into bed. The sheets felt cool against my skin. A playful wind chopped at the old stone walls, hurling swathes of rain against the window pane like handfuls of tiny pebbles. I could just discern the soft, silvery sound of my little niece, wheezing as she slumbered in the bed opposite mine. With whisky coursing through my veins and the friendly patter of Cumberland rain murmuring in my ears, I had ceased to care what the morrow might bring and felt profoundly content. I was cocooned in the safety and comfort of my childhood home. I curled up under the duvet, abandoned myself to the present and drifted into unconsciousness.

Part Three

Water Under the Bridge

Chapter 17

The Catalyst

I woke up early as usual. The grey light of dawn was trickling through the curtains. A blackbird warbled in the cherry tree outside my bedroom window. The gutter beneath the eaves was dripping copiously, drumming a tuneless melody on the sill. I propped myself up on my elbow and peered at the travel clock on the bedside cabinet, a gift from Ray on my 24th birthday, not long after I moved down to London. 5.15 … I rolled over onto my back, closed my eyes and tried to piece together the remnants of a dream that was slipping from my mind.

I dreamed I was walking along a causeway over a limitless expanse of water, enveloped in white mist. I knew that I was dead and felt completely at peace. Ahead of me, a pool of white light beckoned me into its epicentre. As I drew nearer, the mist began to thin and I thought I could discern the face of my brother Chris. Suddenly I found myself in a crowded street, standing at the entrance to a concrete subway blighted by litter and graffiti. I entered the subway and stepped through a scissor gate into a steel-lined lift. The gate closed with an eerie clunk and the lift hurtled downwards. Terror gripped me and my dream became lucid. I tried to shout out – I had learnt to wake myself up like this – but the words got stuck, as they often did when I was grappling to free myself from a dreamscape. With a violent jolt, the lift hit the ground, I regained my voice and scrambled into consciousness in state of profound fear.

I soon became aware that my head was throbbing; probably the after-effects of last night's over-indulgence, I thought remorsefully. My brain felt foggy too, but that was par for the course. The dream didn't help, but six months spent agonising over my future had long since deprived me of the ability to think rationally, even in the cold light of day. I leaned over the edge of the bed, fumbled in my handbag, downed a couple of aspirins and lay in the half-light, mulling over the past and contemplating the future, a process which had become embedded into my morning routine. The harder I searched for the answer, the more my mind wound around in ever-decreasing circles, until it became so knotted up that I felt confused, helpless and angry. It always ended this way; indecision would lead to frustration, frustration to resentment. Resentment, as I well knew, was a dangerous precedent apt to lead me down the wrong path. Hence I lingered aimlessly at the crossroads, month after month, unable to move forward.

After what felt like an interminable length of time, but what in reality was about 45 minutes, I heard my mother shuffling down the stairs. Impulsively, I clambered out of bed and descended to the kitchen.

"Vicky, you're up early! I thought you'd be exhausted after your journey," gushed Mum, putting down the kettle, shambling across the kitchen and giving me a cursory hug.

"I couldn't sleep," I grumbled. "Might just as well have a coffee. Better than staring at the ceiling, getting bored."

"How was the journey, dear?"

"All right." I picked up Thomasin and pressed the side of my face to her head, finding comfort in this simple act. Unfortunately, she was hungry and in no mood for a cuddle so my pleasure was short-lived.

"How's Ray … and the family. Are they well?"

Yeah, they're all right."

I sat down at the kitchen table and watched my mother making coffee, wondering how much she missed my father.

"Are you all right, sweetheart?" she asked presently. "You seem rather subdued."

"I've got a headache, that's all," I sighed.

"That's as may be but you can't pull the wool over my eyes. You're the world's worst patient! When my Victoria Jane gets a headache, she wears it like a badge. What's the trouble, child? Is this about Ray?"

"Oh Ray!" I said vehemently. "You know, Mum, I'm actually really cross with Ray and at this precise moment I don't care if I never see him again! He's *never* stopped to consider whether I want to move to Portsmouth. As far as he's concerned, it's a fait accompli. It's not fair."

"No, it isn't fair, Vicky."

"Well, it's not his fault," I cut in defensively.

"I didn't say it was his fault. I was merely echoing your sentiments," explained Mum patiently.

"Well, I can hardly *not* go, can I?" I said sulkily. "This Mary Rose thing is massive. He'd never forgive me if I dug my heels in. He'd probably hate me forever!"

"Well, I don't think he'd hate you, but he might be rather disappointed."

"I can't do that. It's not an option … end of…," I said decisively.

"So what are your options?"

"Get married and move to Portsmouth … or move back home," I moaned.

"Do you want to get married?"

"It's what I've always wanted. Besides, it would break Ray's heart if I didn't go through with it … anyway, all my friends are married."

"He'd survive … and as for getting married because your friends are all married … I've never heard such a ridiculous notion!" she chided, spooning the coffee into the cups.

I shrugged, picked up yesterday's newspaper and pretended to read it. It was easier than trying to converse whilst nursing a sore head.

"Do you want to come back home?" she continued at length.

"I'd come home in a flash!" I said unequivocally, "but Chris thinks I should get married … that is, he did, only I'm not so sure now. Mum, do you miss Dad?"

"Of course I do, but I have my family," she smiled. "Are you excited by the prospect of your marriage, Vicky?"

"No, not really, if I'm honest," I said miserably, "but losing the only man I've ever loved … that's just unbearable."

"You have your family too, child," said Mum, handing me a cup of steaming hot coffee. "Now, would you like some toast?"

"Is Michael in the cowshed?" I asked my mother, wiping the crumbs from my mouth with the back of my hand.

"Yes, he's been up for hours," replied Mum.

"I think I'll throw some clothes on and go and help him. There's no point going back to bed and I'll go insane if I don't find something to distract me."

"Good idea, love. I'm doing bacon and eggs for nine o'clock, when the family are all up. You'll want some, I expect."

"Of course; good old Mum," I said, depositing my empty plate in the sink and giving her a peck on the cheek.

"Oi! Less of the old!" she retorted with a grin.

"Chris, will you walk down to the lake with me?" I asked my brother after a hearty breakfast.

"Oh God, do I have to? I've got a banging headache," he groaned.

"Serves you right!" quipped Mum. "Goodness knows how much whisky you consumed last night, you, your sister and my erstwhile mother."

"Traitor!" hissed Chris, scowling at me.

"Can I come?" implored Julia.

"No, Julia, not this time," said Mum firmly. "Chris and Vicky want to have a chat … about grown-up things," she added, tipping me a wink.

Chris raised his eyebrows, pushed back his chair lazily and sauntered out.

"I'll be ready in five," he called back, disappearing upstairs.

The day was cool and very still, the sky overcast and the air heavy with moisture. We walked down the lane together in silence, listening to the sound of birdsong, the bleating of lambs and the intermittent plink of water droplets as small currents of air shook them from the saturated vegetation. The verges were brimming with spring colours; speedwells, forget-me-nots, lilac and white cuckoo flowers and red campions; sunshine yellow dandelions, buttercups, cowslips and celandines; daisies like tiny stars; all waiting cheerfully for clouds to part. The smell of the damp earth was heartwarming and familiar and the ground beneath my feet felt solid and dependable, conflicting with my precarious mental state so that I felt like a tightrope walker with a safety net beneath me.

"You're very quiet; hung-over, by any chance?" said Chris, giving me a playful nudge.

"No … no it's not that. I had this dream last night. It was horrible, that is, it ended horribly." I told him all about it.

"Well, I don't claim to be a psychologist but that sounds pretty straightforward to me," he said, after an interval. "Clearly you have a choice to make. You feel you need to choose between Heaven and Hell. I'm honoured you see me as some kind of deity but I can assure you I'm anything but! According to Freud, the sea is your emotions. They seem remote, obscured from you. You're out of touch with them. The sea was calm, right?"

"Yes, calm as a millpond."

"Well, that's something at least. Then there's death. Obviously that doesn't mean an actual death. It means change. The rest … the second half … that speaks for itself, although I don't think Portsmouth is as bad as all that."

Shortly afterwards we arrived at the shore. A fine mist hung over the water and obscured the mountains that guarded the gateway into upper Wasdale, giving the scene a surreal quality. I half expected the Lady of the Lake to pierce the smooth, glassy surface of the water with an outstretched arm and hold aloft the sword Excalibur. I gazed up the length of the lake, reached for my brother's hand, hardened my resolve, stepped over the threshold inside my head and took my first, faltering step along the road into an unchartered future, a road which I suddenly knew that I must travel alone. I opened my mouth to speak but no words came, only a huge, heart-rending sob that burst from the pit of my stomach and shattered the quietude. Without a word, for words were not necessary, Chris threw both arms around me and squeezed me tight. I buried my face in his anorak until I found myself gasping for air.

"I'm frightened, Chris. I can't do this alone," I whimpered, when I had got my tongue back.

"You're not alone, kitten. You have me, and Mum, Toni, and Michael. We'll take care of you."

"Wast Water looks rather melancholy today," I mumbled forlornly peeping over my brother's shoulder at the listless, grey water quivering under a blanket of cloud.

Chris turned to face the lake with one arm still entwined around my waist. "She's subdued, I won't argue with that, but it all depends on your perspective. What looks like melancholia to you looks very much like serenity to me."

I wiped my tear-stained face with my sleeve and stood motionless, focusing on a patch of silver glinting on the sleepy lake, my vision blurred from crying so that all definition was almost lost. All my life I had marvelled at the remarkable beauty and astonishing depth of this shimmering trough of liquid crystal. Now I narrowed my gaze and tried hard to imagine the utter calm at her centre. In that moment I found peace of mind. My reverie was broken by a sharp gust of wind. I watched an arc of ripples gliding easily across the surface of the water, while I stumbled on blindly with one foot stuck in the past and the other on the brink of a precipice.

Soon after, the wind got up and it started to rain. We lingered on the shore, absent-mindedly watching the raindrops dancing on the water, the surface now transformed into a myriad of tiny rings. With a sinking feeling, I looked down despairingly at my left hand.

"Chris, do you think I'm making a terrible mistake?"

"I don't know, Vicky. Just go with your gut instinct but for God's sake make up your mind. You've been drowning in doubt for far too long now. You can't go on like this."

I considered again the transformation on the surface of the lake, agitated now like my own emotional state. With an effort, I reconnected with the tranquillity at its depths; that part untouched by superficial change. It was then that I saw stability, instilled in me by the love of my family and the constancy of this lovely valley that held me under its spell.

"Yes, the lake is serene," I murmured, almost inaudibly. "That comes from within. I'd like to come home."

"I thought you and Ray were pretty solid," said Chris resumed presently.

"We're not the same people anymore," I said morosely. "Ooph, I'm getting cold."

"C'mon, let's walk," proposed Chris, releasing his hold on me and clasping my hand.

We trudged along the shore and halted where a shallow stream scurried across our path; a cheerful incessant thing. We picked our way over the stones, with the lively chatter of the water a welcome contrast to the bleak silence that hung in the damp air. Chris came to a stop and gazed thoughtfully down at the little tributary.

"What a charming little spot." There followed an elongated pause. "Nature has encapsulated your essence."

"That's a pretty speech. You have the soul of a poet. Whatever do you mean?"

"Simply put, it's an association of ideas. I mean that, in essence you're bright and energetic, like a babbling brook, as opposed to slow and ponderous like a large river or still and reflective like a millpond; inspired by poetry certainly."

"Poetry?" I echoed, surprised.

"Yes, you see, I've been dabbling in Wordsworth lately. Julie likes Wordsworth – Mandy hates poetry – but coming back home, well you know … I thought I'd give it a go. Plus I dug out my prog albums as I didn't feel much like listening to anything jolly. Some of the lyrics are magnificent; on the other hand, some are plain nonsense. Then last week Sarah showed me this amazing piece of work she did in English, bursting with metaphors and stuff – she's a smart girl. Well, it got me thinking. It helps while away the long hours of solitude shut in my room, where I don't have to pretend I'm okay. I used to quite like English, you know – Shakespeare and the classics. That and Art, the rest was a bore."

"Wow, I never knew you had it in you," I breathed, genuinely impressed.

"Oh, I'm a veritable ocean of untapped talent," he laughed wryly. "That aside, a stagnant pool probably best describes your present state of mind … or a wet November morning in a Manchester suburb, which amounts to the same thing. There. I'm a philosopher too," he grinned.

"Yes, I *am* painfully aware that I haven't been myself lately. I can see now that I've been keeping my emotions in check, basically to avoid facing the facts," I replied, starting to cry anew. "When you talked about my dream, you said I'd lost touch with them. You're absolutely right … that's exactly how I feel!"

"Ha! Don't flatter me," cut in my brother. "I'm rarely right, it was just a lucky guess."

I hesitated, searching for words to convey my feelings, or rather my lack of them. "It's like my brain's reached saturation point," I continued after a short pause. "There's no room left in it for anything … happiness, sadness, logical thought, definitely not decision-making, although ironically I *have* made a life-changing decision today … generally I overthink things and end up incapable of deciding on anything. I wish I didn't, but I can't help it. Oh God, now I'm getting really wet." I shivered and pulled up my hood.

"You'd better get used to it. It's not called the Lake District for nothing," said my brother with an attempt at levity. "Has London turned you soft?"

"I don't know. I don't even know who I am," I groaned, "and before you remind me I'm a babbling brook," I added, with a half-smile, "I'm not sure that's a good thing."

"I never said 'babbling' but you hardly need me to give you a character analysis. You can be active to the point of irritation and to be fair you do talk an awful lot but that's part of your charm. Look, this is just a blip. You'll be back to your usual self in no time. Incidentally, if brooks really could babble, you can bet they wouldn't waste time agonising over their future. You should definitely stop doing that."

"So your advice would be to make a decision, stick to it and go with the flow, if you'll pardon the pun," I concluded.

"Well, I'm no expert but I've learnt through bitter experience that inaction, the failure to reach a decision and act on it, can sap your energy and block your capacity to think coherently until, as you very succinctly put it, your brain gets saturated. I should know. My track record's appalling when it comes to making decisions. I'm convinced, having dealt with the death of Father and wasted years hankering after Julie, that procrastination is infinitely more destructive than grief, which tends to run its natural course and gets better with time. Metaphorically speaking, since we're drawing parallels, if you built a dam across this lake, in time you would flood, or in your words saturate, the whole valley … d'you understand what I'm getting at?"

The rain was heavier now. I sidled closer to my brother, leaned hard into him and he wrapped his arm around my waist.

"In the same vein," he continued, tugging affectionately at my hood, "as you yourself said, the rain does dent the surface but it doesn't penetrate the depths. You're a tough cookie, though you may feel a little bruised right now … they're surface wounds. Come now. Don't cower under that hood. Are you going to embrace the storm or let it engulf you?"

"You're right, of course."

"Ha! Right again! I'm on form today! In a nutshell Vicks, now you've come to a decision, you can start to rediscover your calm and move forward. You'll be all right, I promise you."

My eyes were drawn towards the rocky promontory where I had had my first kiss with Ray 15 years ago and my heart sank.

"I can't help feeling I've wasted half my life," I said ruefully. "28 years old and nothing to show for it."

"On the contrary kid, a river is like life, another pearl of wisdom courtesy of your philosopher brother. It starts off small, then other streams and rivers connect with it and it gets larger. It's the same with people. Take Ray. Imagine how different your life would have been if you'd never met him. At least you've seen a bit of the world. You're a different person now, much more confident and self-assured, though you may not feel it right now. So you see, there's no such thing as wasted time. Come along, even *I'm* getting cold. Let's walk on a bit."

I ambled along the shore with my brother, holding his hand, throwing stones in the water and making idle conversation between bouts of crying.

"So … if I'm a babbling brook," I said good-humouredly, "Mum … what's she then?"

"A roaring fire on a winter's night?" said Chris. "Dad's a rock, naturally. God rest his soul. Now you try. Toni, what's she?"

"Hmmm … a box of expensive chocolates. Your turn. Mandy?" I suggested, instantly regretting my lack of tact. "Sorry, that wasn't fair."

"Oh, that's all right. I would say … let's see … a sunny afternoon. Okay, now you have to do Ray."

"Oh God, I don't know … a shiny new car?"

"Really?"

"Yes, really. A fine prospect but too smart for me."

"Nonsense, Vicky," he said, tightening his clasp on my hand. "Don't do yourself down."

"Julie?" I ventured timidly.

"A rare orchid," said my brother decisively. "Nan?"

"Oh, that's easy, a bottle of cheap wine," I smirked. "No offence but she doesn't have much finesse!"

At length we turned round and headed for home.

At the front door, we paused while Chris searched in his pocket for his key.

"How do you feel now?" he said, giving my hand a squeeze.

"I don't know … empty … flat … numb … maybe a tad relieved, a little more human I guess … mentally exhausted, like when Dad died," I said heavily. "I suppose I'll have to tell Ray," I added, stating the obvious. "That'll be the hardest part."

"It might not be as hard as you think," said my brother tenderly, turning the key in the lock. "I shouldn't be surprised if he already has an inkling of what's in your mind. He's quite perceptive and you're easy to read. Come along, I'll make you a cup of tea."

"I'll be sorry not to go to Scarborough," I said despondently, as I sat on the sofa with Chris and Julia in the early evening, sipping an illicit glass of wine and watching 'Postman Pat'. "I was looking forward to that."

"When were you thinking of going?" Chris enquired, after an interval.

"19th September, all booked," I said dismally. "I guess that's another thing I'll have to cancel."

"I'll come with you."

"*You*?" I replied, astonished.

"Well, why not? I quite fancy Scarborough. I used to like it when I was a kid. It'll be nostalgic."

"Can I come? Can I come?" squealed Julia, who didn't miss a trick.

"No, Julia, you can't come. You have school," said Chris, patting his daughter fondly on the knee. "I suppose I could take Louise, though," he said thoughtfully. "She'll be in second-to-top class by then. It can't do any harm to take her out for a few days. Sarah, being Sarah, won't want to miss school. You know how studious she is. I don't think they'd agree to it anyway. Secondary schools can be a bit funny like that."

"That's not fair!" piped up Julia. "I want to miss school."

"Now Julia," said Chris, wrapping his arm around his daughter's slender shoulders and pulling her close. "You *live* with Daddy. We see each other every day. Louise spends hardly any time with Daddy. I owe it to her. I'll take you to Scarborough some other time, I promise. Perhaps I could ask Mummy to come up and stay while I'm away. Would you like that?"

"Mmm …" grinned Julia, nodding enthusiastically. "I want to see Mummy. When I can I see Mummy?"

"In two-and-a-bit weeks. You can spend a whole three days with her, poppet." He turned to address me. "I'm taking her down to Alan's for bank holiday weekend. Mandy's offered to go up and stay with them. It's easier that way. Oh … and I've been in touch with Louise's school so I'm just waiting to hear. They're not exactly over-subscribed so I can't imagine I'll have any trouble getting her a place. Julia's quite excited. She loves her half-sisters." He lowered his voice. "Mandy's quite different from Julie. She's more … how can I put it? … accommodating."

Two days later, I boarded the train down to London with a heavy heart. I felt emotionally drained and cried often, in public as well as in private, including several times during the long, miserable journey back to the place I had already ceased to regard as my home.

Ray met me at the exit to the tube station.

"Why Vicky, what's the matter?" he cried, hugging me affectionately. "You look terrible. You're as white as a sheet."

"I'm all right, I'm just tired. It's just … oh, you know how it is … family stuff," I lied, skirting the issue. "What's for dinner? I'm starving." Nothing could have been further from the truth. However, I could sense an invisible wall between us and it was the only thing I could come up with that sounded relatively natural. As I had earned the reputation of having a better than good appetite, it worked a treat.

"We've got chicken biryani. How's the family?"

"Oh please, Ray. I don't want to talk about it right now," I said irritably. "Ask me later."

"All right, keep your hair on," he said playfully. "Are you working tomorrow?"

"Yes, you know I am. I told you." I said wearily. "I'm on earlies."

"Would you like to eat out tomorrow," he prattled on undaunted, "as long as it's not too late?"

"Yes, that would be very nice," I smiled, glad of the opportunity to broach the subject closest to my heart on neutral ground.

"I fancy pizza, I mean *real* pizza, not like the ones you get at the supermarket."

"Sure," I said distractedly.

"Okay, I'll book the San Lorenzo. It's only 10 minutes on foot … meaning we can both have a drink," he winked. *I'm going to need one*, I thought cynically.

For the first time in living memory, I was thankful to be working the next day. It was better than the alternative, which was akin to trying to act normally in the company of an intended victim whilst contemplating the most painless method by which to commit a murder.

When the hour of reckoning arrived, I was still no closer to finding the kindest words with which to deliver the killing blow.

We ordered drinks and I tried to read the menu, which was in English but might just as well have been in Italian, as it made little sense to me. When the wine arrived, I gave up, put down the menu and filled a large glass for myself and one for Ray. There was no time like the present.

"Ray, there's something I have to tell you. It's about Portsmouth." I took a large gulp of Chianti and braced myself. "I've thought about it, honestly I have, and I've tried and tried, but … I can't go, I just can't. It feels all wrong … and I miss my home … and …" My voice cracked, I caught my breath, let out an involuntary gasp and made a grab for his hand. "I'm sorry." Tears welled up in my eyes. "I'm going home." I pressed my eyes into the back of my free hand, unable to look him in the face. There was an uncomfortable silence.

"Vicky, you're not serious. You're just having a wobble, right?" he said incredulously.

"I can't go through with it," I mumbled, without looking up. "Please don't make this harder than it is. It's killing me already."

"We can talk about this," he said, after another awkward pause. "We can make it work."

By now my tears were falling fast. I felt shaky and sick. With difficulty, I extricated my right hand from Ray's firm grasp, fumbled with the ring on my left, removed it with an effort, glanced up briefly and pushed it across the table.

"You'd better have this back," I blurted, between sobs. "Now do you believe me?"

He stared at the ring in disbelief. "This isn't happening," he said, shaking his head.

I reached out blindly, picked up the ring, held it out to him.

"Please Ray. Let me go," I implored. "Don't make me hate myself more than I already do."

"Oh my God, you really mean it," he said, his voice taut, staring down at it.

"Ray, please try to understand. I love you but …" I broke off, put the ring on the table, drew in my breath and steadied my nerves. "Me and you, we're like chalk and cheese. You're brave and ambitious. All I want is to put down roots in the place I love, with safe and familiar people. Portsmouth is just the tip of the iceberg. There'll be other assignments, perhaps even further from home. Suppose they ask you to work abroad? It was fine when we wanted the same things, but now we're poles apart."

"I'll come with you. I'll move to Cumbria," burst out Ray, clutching my wrist.

"And join the three million unemployed? Is that what you want, because honestly, Ray, I don't think it is."

"You're right, of course," he conceded dolefully.

"Look, if it helps, I feel like a cad. You can hate me if it makes you feel better. God knows, I hate myself."

"I don't hate you … I-I don't understand you," he said in bewilderment. "How can you write off the last 15 years? At least stay here in London. Forget Portsmouth. I'll stay on at the museum. We'll get married and buy a little house out of town."

"I want to go home," I wailed. "I can't help myself."

Ray shook his head and stared down at the table. We lapsed into silence.

"That's that then," he said eventually, releasing his grip on me, biting his lip and fixing his eyes, which were red and blotchy, on the menu. "What do you want to eat?"

"We can still be friends … and I'll visit," I ventured, touching him lightly on the hand.

"How can you be so cavalier?" he said tetchily.

"Of course, if you'd rather not …" I faltered, suppressing a sob.

There was another interval of silence.

"Would you rather leave now? I don't seem to have much of an appetite," I said miserably, gazing blankly at the menu.

"And go home looking like this?" he snapped. "Come now, Vicky. Boys don't cry."

"All right, I'll have a Hawaiian," I muttered, refilling my glass.

"How do you feel now," I asked timidly, as we waited for the waitress to bring the bill.

"Bitter, angry, confused," he said grimly. "Like I've been hit round the head with a sledgehammer."

"I'm sorry, I-I don't know what else to say," I stammered. "For what it's worth, I'm hurting too."

I got out my purse.

"I'll pay," he grunted. "I know you're hurting, Vicky. I'm sorry too." He smiled weakly and his eyes glazed over.

"You had no idea then, what was in my mind?"

"Well, I think maybe I did a little; I just didn't want to acknowledge it, even to myself," he said with a sigh. "You never told me outright you would be coming to Portsmouth with me. I just chose to carry on assuming you would … but lately I've been having doubts, especially since the Chris thing blew up. This is about Chris, isn't it?"

"No, Ray. It's not about Chris, it's about me," I countered. "Chris is just the catalyst."

The following day, I handed in my notice. I spent the next four weeks going about in a trancelike state. Sometimes, in the privacy of my bedroom, reality would hit me and I would cry silently, then reapply my make-up, go downstairs and make small talk. After his initial petulance, Ray put his own feelings to one side and was unceasingly kind, affectionate and sensitive. He knew I was battling with a guilty conscience and did his best to alleviate it by treating me as he would a very dear friend. He gave me the freedom to process my emotions and didn't press me when I lost the thread of the conversation, clammed up or felt the urge to leave the room.

The day I moved out is probably still one of the unhappiest events in my entire life, exceeded in magnitude only by the passing of my father and the day following Toni's wedding, when I had convinced myself that Chris had met with an accident or sought a way out. The fact that the pain was largely self-inflicted made matters worse. As I packed my things into the boxes Anji had obtained from the supermarket, red-eyed and sick at heart, I began to wonder whether I was making the right decision but my gut instinct held me firm to my purpose and by two o'clock I was ready to depart. Bill had paid for a man and van. He was wealthy, knew that Mum was strapped for cash and was keen to reassure me that the family respected my decision, referring to the cost as "a drop in the ocean" and insisting that nothing was too much trouble.

"Keep in touch. You will come down and visit, won't you?" said Anji, as we congregated in the hall to make our sad farewells.

"Yes of course, when I'm feeling stronger," I gulped, fighting back tears.

"No hard feelings?" said Bill, shaking me by the hand warmly.

"No hard feelings," I nodded.

Ray was standing just inside the open front door.

"Vicky ... dear, darling Vicky," he murmured, throwing his arms around my neck and pressing his cheek against mine. "If you change your mind, you know where to find me." He held me close, stroked my hair and smothered my face with kisses. We both started to cry. "Now go, before you break my heart," he said, his voice thick with emotion, as he released his grip on me and nudged me gently over the threshold. "Knock 'em dead!"

I stretched out my hand and clutched onto his, for one brief, unforgettable moment. Then, steeling myself, I turned my back on the past, climbed into the van and waved goodbye.

* * *

I spent my savings on a cheap mini and got a job at West Cumberland Hospital, where I ran into my old friend Donna. Donna was quirky, funny and gregarious. She was also single, which made her a particularly desirable companion. She had long since shed her gothic garb and had lately donned the mantle of a New Romantic. When our nights off coincided, she would drag me into bars and clubs frequented by men dressed as women and women dressed as men, who flaunted hairstyles and make-up which were louder than the music. We had so much fun that I almost forgot how unhappy I was.

However, my favourite evenings were the ones I spent holed up in the cosy little two-up, two-down in Ulverston where my very best friend Wendy lived with her doctor husband and three-year-old son. Only with Wendy could I be completely myself. Donna was relentlessly merry, whilst my family were forever trying to fix me. Wendy was unerringly patient and kind, never judged me or advised me, nurtured me, distracted me and lightened my mood. I passed many a night that summer curled up under a blanket on her sofa after a delicious meal, a glass of wine and a game of scrabble, sometimes because I felt too tired or too emotionally fragile to drive home, at other times because I was marginally over the limit.

By this time, Chris had moved into a small maisonette in Seascale with Julia so I had my old room to myself. It was just as well, since I was still prone to episodes of depression and often had the urge to retire to the privacy of my bedroom and have a good cry. Coming home to Mum's at 28, unmarried and childless, was a hard pill to swallow, especially for someone in my profession, although the fact that Michael was also unmarried and childless was some consolation. Chris and Julia would come over and partake of Mum's excellent culinary skills several times a week, especially on Sundays when we always had a roast dinner. After lunch, we would walk off our meal with a trip down to the lake. As the summer drew to a close, I began to see a glimmer of light at the end of the tunnel.

* * *

Fate was smiling on us the week we went to Scarborough and we had wall-to-wall sunshine. We stayed at the Crown Hotel on the Esplanade overlooking the South Bay. We had neighbouring rooms which faced east. The sun would flood in every morning, filling them with light and warmth. Sometimes we would head for the beach to walk, relax or play ball games. We swam in the North and South Bay pools flanking the headland, where we spent many happy hours when we were children. There were boating lakes, a water chute, cliff lift, miniature railway and Tree Walk Wonderland in beautiful Peasholm Park. Scalby Mills had been treated to a facelift with the installation of an immense astro slide which dwarfed the fairground rides and penny arcades which had enthralled me as a child. Another new addition to the vast array of visitor attractions was the Marineland and Zoo, much to the delight of our young companion. Once, we ventured out of town and took a long, leisurely stroll in nearby Wykeham Forest. Our timing was perfect, for on Friday we witnessed history in the making when Scarborough beach was host to Britain's first ever elephant derby, in which a quintet of the noble beasts competed in a race. Louise laughed until the tears rolled down her face.

Everywhere we went, Louise was met with glances of admiration or outright compliments, which fell from her like water off a duck's back. She was an exceptionally beautiful child but a very level-headed one who didn't regard herself as especially pretty and craved only the approval of her cousin Scott, whom she talked about incessantly.

On the final day of our holiday, we were sitting outside the café at the Mere watching Louise, who had attached herself to a couple of older boys who were waiting in the queue for the pirate ship.

"You know, Chris, I think she's got a little crush on Scott," I volunteered.

"Don't be ridiculous, she's only nine," scoffed Chris. "She's far too young to be thinking about boys."

"Course she's not! Look at her, the little scamp! They start young nowadays, not like when we were kids. I blame 'Top of the Pops'. Some of those videos are quite explicit, you know."

"He's her cousin," argued Chris. "Nobody fancies their cousin!"

"Whyever not? People used to marry their cousins all the time. You should try reading Jane Austen."

"That's weird," he said, pulling a face.

"No it's not, it's sweet. I don't suppose she'll marry him, but I do think she's got a crush on him."

"Yeah, so you keep saying … oh well, maybe you're right," he drawled, leaning back on his chair and stretching out his legs. "Every time I go over to Toni's, Louise is always there, which is quite nice actually, as I barely knew the child for the first few years of her life. Now we get along great. On Saturdays, I often make a point of going over, just so I can get a glimpse of the little darling, and I'm rarely disappointed; not that I see much of her; she's usually up a tree, or building a den, or something." He tilted back his head, yawned and closed his eyes. "Ahhh … this beats work."

"Scarborough's nice, isn't it? Thanks for coming," I said with genuine warmth.

"Pleasure's all mine," he answered sleepily. "A dump, is it? Ray's loss is my gain. The boy's a fool."

"Perhaps." I shivered and pulled my cardigan around me.

* * *

Early in the spring of 1983, Nan died suddenly of acute liver failure brought on by many years of excessive drinking. She was 79 years old. Mum was upset but coped remarkably well, perhaps because she feared a long protracted illness and felt she had got off lightly; perhaps also because life's hardships had made her resilient; undoubtedly because she had plenty of support from her offspring, with two of them living under the same roof and two more living not far away.

* * *

On the first day of April, after dinner, we were sitting in the lounge as usual. I was reading; Mum was mending her stockings;

Michael was watching the Nine O'clock News. Suddenly he let out a loud yelp.

"That's my Polly!" He leapt from his chair, ran towards the television set and gesticulated wildly at the screen. "Look! There in the background, the one with fair hair wearing a black dress and holding a camera."

"She's not *your* Polly; she's never even been to stay," I taunted, with a pang of envy.

"What's she doing on TV?" enquired Mum mildly, glancing up from her darning.

"She must be down at Greenham … You know, CND, the Women's Peace Camp. She gets involved … not all the time … depends if she's got any work," explained Michael, sitting back down.

"Why are they dressed as teddy bears? Not Polly, I mean the ones climbing over the fence," I asked, intrigued.

"They're doing it to highlight the threat of nuclear weapons to future generations of children," replied Michael loftily. "It's a clever strategy … teddy bears in a military setting … they're using imagery to make a point … they're striking a contrast between military might and the innocence of children. I bet she'd come if I asked her," he added peevishly, after a pause.

"Why don't you ask her then?" I goaded. "I bet she won't come."

"I bet she would," he retorted. "I'd put money on it."

"A tenner says she doesn't," I said impetuously.

"Victoria, have a care!" cried Mum.

"Done!" He jumped up again, grabbed my hand and shook it vigorously. "I'll ask her. I'll ask her tomorrow."

I burst out laughing. "Don't be silly, Michael. How are you going to find her amongst all those women? There'll be thousands of them. Anyway, it may have escaped your notice but you're the wrong gender. What are you going to do? Storm the camp in one of my frocks?"

"Michael, you're not serious," said Mum in disbelief.

"Course I'm serious. That's the beauty of this job; flexible working hours. I can scoot off for a day or two. The cows won't mind. Walter can see to them."

"It's 300 miles away," persisted Mum.

"I know that, Mum. I fancy an adventure. I've never done anything outrageous, never done much at all … and I do so want to prove my annoying little sister wrong!" he said gleefully.

"Oh, Michael!" she exclaimed, unable to conceal her exasperation at his harebrained scheme.

"Mother, I'm 30 and I'm going," he said decisively.

"Where will you sleep?"

"Dunno, in the car I guess. Faint heart never won fair lady."

Michael left early the following morning and returned two days later, grinning like a Cheshire cat.

"You'll never guess what? She's coming," he said triumphantly, sauntering into the kitchen and throwing his jacket over the back of the chair. "I'll have my 10 pounds now, if you please?"

"Oh my God, you're joking!" I shrieked. "However did you find her?"

"Oh, it was easy," he said breezily. "I asked about a bit, found the spot where they scaled the fence, then managed to talk to some of the women about the place. Word got out and eventually someone told me she'd gone to join the human chain. I figured if I drove all the way from one end to the other, I'd spot her. It worked!"

"Human chain?"

"Yes, Vicky, human chain. The campaigners have formed a chain 14 miles long, all the way from the American airbase at Greenham to the ordnance factory at Burghfield. It was amazing. They reckon 80,000 people turned up. They were all holding hands, singing and chanting 'Ban the bomb' and stuff."

"Oh right, I didn't know that," I said indifferently.

"Oh, Victoria! Do you realise, the world's nuclear arsenal has the capacity to wipe out most of the western world in a mere 20 minutes?" he cried passionately. "How can you be so blasé? Don't you ever watch the news?"

"Not if I can help it; it's depressing. When's she coming, anyway?"

"Not yet. Not till harvest. I offered her a job. We're always short-handed at harvest time. We could do with a bit of extra help."

"You did *what*? That's cheating!" I exploded.

"Let's just say it was an inducement," said Michael nonchalantly. "There's nothing in the rules about *how* to get the thing done. I know she's always short of cash so I used my initiative. Don't try and wriggle out of it; we made a bargain."

"What does she *do,* Michael? Doesn't she have a job?" said Mum anxiously.

"She takes photos. She's a freelance photographer."

"Oh, like ... for the newspaper, you mean. That's what she was doing at the camp, presumably."

"No Mum, she's an activist ... a campaigner. She was there because she believes in nuclear disarmament. Her photos ... they're kind of ... arty. Flowers, trees, still life ... mostly nature but not always. Sometimes she photographs people. She sells them at craft fairs and suchlike. She took that glorious photo of a guitar on my bedroom wall. There's not much money in that kind of work though. That's why I offered her a job."

"Oh dear, she's not *very* militant, is she?"

"No, not particularly, and she's awfully nice," he said, turning crimson.

* * *

"Hello Mum, Vicky ... this is Polly."

On a balmy evening on Saturday 17th July, Mum was peeling potatoes at the kitchen sink and I was shelling peas at the table. Michael stood in the doorway with an attractive girl of about my age. She was remarkably small, with long, ashy-blonde hair which she wore loose and straight with a heavy fringe. She was wearing a Bob Dylan tour T-shirt, jeans and brown tooled-leather calf boots. She reminded me of Marianne Faithfull.

"Hi guys, it's great to meet you at last. I've heard so much about you, all good," she grinned.

"Hello, Polly dear," smiled Mum. "Would you like a cup of tea?"

"D'you have any herbal teas … camomile, peppermint, that sort of thing?" she said brightly.

"Er … no … I don't think so," said Mum apologetically.

"Oh, that's fine. I'll have a rummage around in the garden. I'm sure there'll be something I can pop in a mug with a bit of hot water."

"Sure, come through … it's this way," said Michael, ushering his fair companion through the kitchen and out of the back door.

"She'll be cheap to keep," I smirked, as soon as they were out of earshot.

"Victoria, don't be so disrespectful! Honestly … people complain about the older generation being stick-in-the-muds, but you youngsters …"

"All right, it was just a joke," I said tetchily. "Probably what she's used to, to be fair. I expect they eat and drink whatever they can get their hands on down at the camp. You never know, we might be glad of her expertise if the harvest is a total disaster and we're in danger of starving," I giggled. "I wonder what other wacky ideas she's got up her sleeve."

"Tsch, Vicky, stop it!" tutted Mum.

Polly returned a few minutes later with a handful of fresh basil, Michael bringing up the rear.

"Do you have any honey?" she enquired, as she helped herself to a mug from the draining board, stuffed in the leaves and filled it with steaming hot water.

"Of course," said Mum, wiping her hands on her apron.

"Don't worry, Mrs. Kelly, I'll get it. Just tell me where I can find it."

"It's right above your head, as a matter of fact … there, on the bottom shelf on the left."

"Thanks, Mum." She picked a teaspoon up that was lying on the worktop, ran it under the tap and spooned the honey into her tea.

"Oh, what a beautiful animal!" she cooed, gazing down at the little black cat that was winding itself around her legs. "What's her name?" She bent down, gathered the unsuspecting creature up into her arms and planted a kiss on its head.

"She's called Elfride," I replied.

"Elfride? How divine! I shall call her Elfie," she purred, burying her face into the nape of the cat's neck.

"I'm starving. What's for dinner?" demanded Michael, helping himself to a large slice of fruitcake. "Want some, Pols?"

"Cool." She peered into the tin. "Ooh, is that lemon? Could I have a piece of that one instead … just a small piece."

"We've got pie and mash, peas, carrots and boiled onion," replied Mum. "Polly, is there anything you don't eat?"

"Er … well, as a matter of fact, I'm a veggie. But don't worry. I'll just have the vegetables and make myself a couple of fried eggs."

"Are you sure? Oh mercy, I feel so unprepared. Michael, why didn't you tell me?"

"No, really, it's fine. Don't go to any extra trouble. I can sort myself out. Which one's my room?"

"You're having Nan's old room," said Michael, hurrying out into the hall and bending down to pick up her case.

"Leave it, Mike. I'll get it," she trilled, depositing Elfride at her feet and hastening out of the door.

What she lacked in stature, Polly made up for in spirit. She was confident, energetic and very self-sufficient. Throughout the harvest she worked tirelessly. She went out in all weathers and would come back caked in mud with a smile on her face, even when the work was dull and the weather foul. She rose early and helped around the house as well as in the fields, asking for nothing but a small wage in return. She often prepared her own meals, using home-grown produce which Mum was glad to provide, for she valued Polly's services highly. She was a gifted and innovative cook, who could whip up a vegetarian feast from a hotchpotch of leftovers and taught us to appreciate the delights of alternative cuisine.

Polly was sociable and enjoyed a night out as much as the next person. I introduced her to Donna and they instantly hit it off. Although their interests were very different, each appreciated the other's uniqueness and the three of us quickly formed a little clique and would regularly don our glad rags, go out and paint the town. Michael dubbed us the three musketeers.

Polly was entrepreneurial too. It was she who inspired Mum to launch her own little cottage industry under the name 'Kelly's Kitchen' and sell her own jams and chutneys, cakes and biscuits in my sister's tea room in Torver. It was she who urged me to take the plunge and become a community midwife. It was she who encouraged Sarah to develop her talent, pursue her dream and become a professional violinist. But that was all several years down the line.

On the last weekend in August, Polly and Michael made their annual pilgrimage to Reading Rock Festival, where that year Black Sabbath and Thin Lizzy took centre stage. Over the years, Mum had become more liberal in her attitude to recreational sex and hardly turned a hair when the pair departed armed with a single tent, or even when Polly's bed appeared not to have been slept in, which was 50 per cent of the time.

As summer turned to autumn and harvest time came to an end, Polly announced her intention to move back home. Michael begged her to stay but she was far too free-thinking and independent to make a life for herself on a little farm in a far-flung corner of England.

"I'll be back," she said gaily, as she kissed me and Mum goodbye and clambered into Michael's car, bound for the station at Seascale; "next year … for the harvest. I've had a brilliant time but I really do have to get back to Greenham. They're planning something big in December. I wouldn't miss it for the world."

45 minutes later, Michael returned with a hangdog expression on his face.

"What's up, Michael? Missing your girlfriend?" I teased.

"Shut up, Vicky," he snapped. "If you were a boy, I'd thump you."

"Come now, Michael; she didn't mean any harm by it," said Mum in a conciliatory tone. "I'm sorry it didn't work out. Vicky, you can be so insensitive sometimes," she continued, rounding on me. "You know how he feels about Polly."

"Didn't work out?" I looked more closely at my brother and noticed that his eyes were red.

"You might as well know, Vicky, I asked her to marry me. You can guess what her answer was."

"You *never*!" I gasped. "Oh my God! You're a dark horse. What did she say?"

"Well obviously she said no," he said impatiently.

"Oh I'm sorry. I mean … I really am. She *will* come back though, won't she?"

"Yeah, she's coming back. That's something at least," he sighed, with an air of resignation.

I confess I couldn't help but feel incredibly relieved. Being human, I found solace in the fact that I was not the only Kelly child to have hit a wall in pursuit of love. I possessed a selfish desire to keep close with Michael and feared the competition. Besides, I genuinely valued his companionship for it filled a gap.

* * *

The first time I saw Ray again was in November 1983, 18 months after I had ended our 15 year relationship and four weeks to the day after my 30th birthday. I stayed with Mandy and her sister in

Balham as the thought of sleeping in my old room at South Park Road was unendurable. We decided to keep the terrain neutral so we settled on a trip to the Lord Mayor's Show. The prospect of seeing Ray again filled me with both anticipation and dread. It kept me awake for many a long night during the preceding weeks and by the time the hour of reckoning was almost upon me, my stomach was churning and my legs trembling. I was fearful lest his nearness should re-open old wounds and terrified that I would fall for him all over again.

We met under the clock at Waterloo Station where we exchanged a tentative embrace. Then, in a gesture that superstitious folk would describe as prophetic, he handed me a box containing a smooth, round marble paperweight with a beak, tail and rosy-red breast.

"It's a robin," I grinned. "How sweet!"

"Happy birthday, Vicky," he said bashfully.

"Christmas, more like!" I laughed. "Thank you, it's lovely."

Ray was in excellent spirits and we quickly fell into easy conversation. I sensed a subtle difference in him; there was more worldliness about him. Perhaps it was because I was acutely aware of the void between the simple country midwife and the up-and-coming archaeologist with his sights on the prize. Though it pained me to admit it, I was secretly relieved that I had not been supplanted and inwardly rejoiced at his status as a single man as it kept my pride intact.

We walked up Stamford Street, over Blackfriars Bridge, entered Blackfriars Station concourse and made our way to a small terrace part way down a concrete stairwell exiting onto Queen Victoria Street to await the arrival of the procession. The weather was mild and cloudy, much the same as it had been on that memorable morning 17 years ago when we had first made our acquaintance. Our plan was a well-chosen one. The parade was uplifting and gave us something impersonal to talk about. We had a late lunch at the Eden Restaurant in Holborn and then walked down to the Embankment. As the dusk fell, we took our places on a little promontory half a mile up-river and waited for the fireworks to commence. The Embankment was swarming with people but we chose our spot well. The firework display was stunning and for a breathtaking half hour our ears were assaulted by a tumult of bangs, pops and whistles and our eyes dazzled by a glittering spectacle of swirls, sparkles and showers that splashed the sky in an explosion of light and colour that rained down into the Thames. The air reeked of sulphur and as the last dying embers shimmered in the blue-black Heavens, I noticed for the first time the blanket of thick smoke that hovered over the river as well as over the heads of the rapturous onlookers.

We crossed Westminster Bridge, continued on to Waterloo and boarded the Northern Line together.

"This is my stop," I said to Ray, as the tube approached Balham Station.

"Hey, Vicky, it's been great to see you." He followed me towards the door, caught me by the shoulders, spun me around and planted a kiss on my cheek. "We must do it again."

"Yes, definitely," I agreed, steadying my voice. "It's been nice, it really has."

"Cheerio then, pipsqueak. Safe journey," he grinned, releasing his hold on me.

"Thanks, you too. Send my love to the family," I called back as the doors slid shut.

As I walked briskly back to Mandy's flat, I was conscious of the lifting of a very great weight I had hitherto been unaware of. Was it guilt or was it regret that had kept me fettered to the past? Probably both, I concluded. An irresistible urge to smile gripped me. At the risk of looking foolish, I indulged my whim and was gratified by its pleasing effect on the passing foot traffic, some of whom reciprocated with a nod or friendly greeting. It was a good end to a great day.

Chapter 18

The Treehouse

1985 was a good year. Encouraged – nay coerced by Polly during her second visit to Cinderdale Farm the previous summer, Mum had launched a small business creating jams, pickles and chutneys for sale in Toni's tea room, and in the space of a year was beginning to see a small profit. For some time, I had been dabbling with the idea of becoming an independent community midwife and it was in 1985 that I struck up a friendship with a new colleague called Karen who shared my aspirations. Two years later we left the NHS and went into private practice, and remain business partners to this day. However, that was by no means all, for on Saturday 13th July, Toni hosted a garden party to mark the event that came to be known as 'the day rock and roll changed the world'. It was also a day which brought startling revelations that would have far-reaching consequences.

The stage was set. The rambling garden behind King's of Torver was flooded with summer sunshine. The sky was azure. Puffy, white clouds sailed overhead and were reflected upon the shining surface of the sloping glass panels atop the huge greenhouse adjoining the homestead. The borders were crammed with vegetation which, on closer inspection, was mostly of the edible kind. A large kitchen garden brimming with produce was visible through a gap between the greenhouse and chicken shed. A light breeze revelled amongst the leafy branches of the fruit trees in the orchard beyond. A small clutch of hens pottered around on the grass, clucking cheerfully and foraging for scraps. Birdsong competed for airspace with the clamour from the small portable television which had been positioned on a wooden bench on the lawn. At the rear of the garden was a small copse of ancient trees, some housing nesting boxes only visible to the keen-eyed observer. Perched within the boughs of the largest tree was a rough wooden construction with a small aperture about four feet high, from which was suspended a rope ladder. This was Scott and Ryan's treehouse, where the pair were currently holed up with Louise.

While the international stage played host to a myriad of recording artists from all four corners of the earth, who came together in response to the plight of the Ethiopian people by giving their services freely in a global music event called Live Aid, the Kelly family were enacting a drama of their own. As Status Quo took to the stage at noon, to the roar of 72,000 spectators who packed Wembley Stadium, Toni strolled casually across the lawn to where I was seated around the television with Mum, Jason, Julie, Sarah, Michael and Polly who had come up to spend a few weeks helping on the farm.

"Would you come and help me with food please Vicky? Be a pet," she said with a meaningful glance.

"Sure," I replied, wondering what was up. I rose and followed her inside. "What do you want me to do?"

"Would you mind cutting up these tomatoes for me and putting them in the bowl there … and that cucumber there. Hey Vicks, you'll never guess who rocked up last week!"

"I've no idea. Mel Gibson?"

"Unfortunately not, but you're on the right lines. They're both drop dead gorgeous," she grinned, turning crimson.

"I can't imagine ... Harrison Ford?"

"Come on, be sensible. Someone I used to know."

"I really couldn't say. Have I met him?"

"Yes, lots of times," she replied.

"Oh, I don't know. I give up."

"Why, Phil, of course!"

"Phil? Oh! Toni, how *could* you? That man's got more front than Brighton! I hope you didn't give him the time of day."

"As a matter of fact, Vicky, he was very humble," she rejoined righteously. "He's having a terrible time. He's married to Joanie, you know. They've got four kids but he's as miserable as sin."

"Serves him right," I shrugged.

"Oh, Vicky, how can you be so heartless?" she chided.

"What goes around comes around," I said carelessly. "He threw you over twice for the platinum predator and you feel sorry for him? For shame, Toni!"

Just then, the doorbell rang and Chris arrived with Julia, now a pretty, brown-haired seven-year-old.

"Hi ladies," he said cheerfully, giving us both a peck on the cheek and popping a cherry tomato into his mouth. "Have I missed anything?"

"Oi, hands off!" scolded Toni. "If you mean the TV, it's just started," replied Toni, as the Quo pounded out their third and final number. "Can I get you a drink?"

"Yeah, I'll have a beer."

"There's McEwans over there on the side ... or you can have some of Jason's home brew, if you're feeling brave," added my sister with a wink, "or we've got Fosters."

"I'll pass on the home brew, thanks!" laughed Chris, helping himself to a can of McEwans. "Where's Lou?"

Through the patio doors, the back of Sarah's head was clearly visible above the rim of a plastic garden chair. Julia was wrestling with a folding chair, which was almost as large as she was, while Mum supervised the operation.

"She's in the treehouse …"

"With the boys, no doubt," interrupted my brother, raising his eyebrows. "That girl's incorrigible."

"Scott's sweet on her," grinned Toni confidentially. "It'll end in tears."

"Too right," concurred Chris. "She has at least a dozen suitors in first year."

Chris picked up a kitchen chair with his free hand and sauntered outside.

I followed him out and sat down on the grass.

"Hi guys," he drawled. "Oh …. happy birthday for yesterday, Julie." He put down the chair between his mother and daughter and ruffled the latter's hair affectionately. "Hi Sarah."

"Hi Dad," Sarah smiled back.

"How do you plan to spend the next two months, now you're a lady of leisure?"

Sarah had just left school and was waiting for her 'O' level results.

"Me and Jen are going down to Manchester next week to stay at Uncle Alan's for a few days," she said without taking her eyes off the television, where a dapper Paul Weller was delivering a soulful ballad to a captivated stadium. "After that, I've no idea. It's so boring here; there's nothing to do."

"Well, it won't be for long, Sarah," put in Julie. "Aren't you going to tell Dad your news?"

"Oh … yes of course. I thought you'd already heard. I've been offered a place at Chetham's School of Music, in their Sixth Form. Isn't that fab?"

"Chetham's? That's in Manchester, isn't it? Wow! That's some commute," he jested.

"Yes, right in the centre. It has some of the best facilities in the country and an amazing reputation. Lots of students go on to become professional musicians. I'm so excited, I can hardly wait!" she said, her eyes shining.

"That's terrific, darling!" said my brother warmly. "Where will you live? Will you board?"

"Good grief, no! Far too expensive! Uncle Alan and Auntie Caroline are putting me up. I have to earn my keep though, worst luck. Apparently I have to babysit Leonie. Ugh … I can't stand six year olds." She scowled.

"Don't be so uncharitable, Sarah. I expect she's a dear little thing," retorted Julie with a faint note of reprimand in her voice.

"I expect she's a pain in the neck," rejoined Sarah gaily. "However, it can't be helped. It'll be worth it to get a decent education in a proper music school. Honestly Dad, the buildings are amazing, quite palatial, and there'll be lots to do. There's literally nothing round here, just mountains and lakes, which are all very pretty but I'm hardly likely to meet Curt Smith tramping the hills!"

"Well, good luck to you, Sarah. You've clearly inherited your mother's considerable talents," concluded Chris, seizing the opportunity to pay his estranged wife a sly compliment.

Julie blushed. "Nonsense, she's ten times better than me."

"Well, I guess we'll never know, since you had the misfortune to marry me, thus putting an end to whatever musical career you might otherwise have aspired to."

"I wouldn't swap my family for all the fame and fortune in the world," replied Julie amicably. "Would you mind fetching me another drink please, Chris? I didn't have a drop yesterday so I intend to drink twice as much today!"

"Sure, what's your shout?" he said, getting up.

"I'll have a white wine, please."

"Would you like a spritzer? Presumably you're driving. You need to take care."

"Now why would I want to water down decent wine?" laughed Julie. "Besides, Paul's picking me and the girls up. I didn't bring the car."

She held her empty glass aloft. As he reached out to take it from her, she extended her fingers and brushed his knuckle with the lightest of touches.

"A-ah … Any particular variety … of wine, I mean," he stammered awkwardly.

"No, I'm not fussed, as long as it's chilled," she purred, laying back in her deck chair, hitching up her skirt and stretching out her long, slim legs in a most flirtatious manner.

"Mum? Sarah? Anyone else for a drink?" babbled Chris, visibly flustered.

"Wine for me too, please," said Mum.

Sarah held out her glass. "I'll have a coke thanks, Dad."

"You can get me a Fosters while you're at it," called out Jason.

"Nothing for me, thanks. I'm driving," mumbled Michael.

"Julia? Where's Julia?" said Chris, looking wildly around.

"Gone to the treehouse," I said. "Lucky someone's keeping an eye on her."

"Ginger punch for me, please," said Polly brightly. "D'you need a hand?"

"It's all right, I'll go." I clambered to my feet, collected up the empty glasses and scurried indoors.

Chris was retrieving a bottle of Chardonnay from the fridge.

"Jesus! Julie … she's such a minx," he confided, raising his eyes to heaven. "I don't get it. One minute she's as sweet as honey, then she has to go and throw her boyfriend into the mix. I can't make head nor tail of her. And another thing … how come he never comes to *any* family events, *ever*? I could understand she might not want to bring him along after the first date, but we've been separated for 11 years and they've been an item for at least half that time. I can't deny I'm sore at losing her but I would hope I'm not that small-minded."

"Perhaps he's wary of you," I volunteered. "You weren't particularly polite to him at Toni's 30th, when he stopped in for a drink. If you recall, you gave me and Ray our marching orders and we all departed in a hurry. I've never been so embarrassed. We had a blinding row in the car."

"Oh God, yes I remember," he groaned. "It was a miracle we got home unscathed. I was driving like a maniac."

"She's probably just being friendly," suggested Toni. "What makes you think there's more to it than that?"

"Dunno … body language?" I flashed him a knowing smile and his colour rose. "Now she's made me forget who wants what. Any idea, Vick?"

I reeled off the orders, we poured the drinks and he took them outside while I stayed behind to help Toni lay out the buffet in the dining room adjoining the large kitchen.

"So … about Phil? Where did you have the misfortune to bump into him?" I demanded, as soon as Chris was out of earshot.

"He came into the shop to buy something, though I can't for the life of me remember what it was. I couldn't believe my eyes! Apparently, they've moved to Broughton. They were over in Bootle before that, which is why we never saw them, but now they're literally 15 minutes away."

"Oh, great!" I said sarcastically. "Then I don't suppose you've seen the last of him."

"Absolutely not! He loved the set-up, was extremely complimentary and promised he'd be back."

"Complimentary towards what? The fruit and veg or the proprietress?" I said cynically. "Either way, he's bound to have an ulterior motive, the lying hound. Just be careful, that's all."

"Vicky, you of all people! You're constantly preaching about how we should forgive and forget, and all that. Yet you can't spare a modicum of compassion for a guy who made a couple of mistakes which he's never ceased to regret."

"Is that what he told you? As I said, be careful."

"I happen to be very fond of Phil and intend to be extremely pleasant to him any time he cares to put a bit of custom our way," she said indignantly. "Besides, it's good for business. Now let's change the subject before I lose my patience. I thought you of all people might understand. Would you mind popping out and telling the others the food's ready?"

In the garden, Bob Geldof was holding the crowd spellbound with an impassioned performance of 'I Don't Like Mondays'. To my astonishment, Chris had relocated his chair and was now sitting beside Julie. When he saw me, he excused himself, got up and ushered me back indoors.

"Entirely her idea," he said in a low voice. "She started asking me about my work. Sarah was getting annoyed 'cause we were talking across her, so Julie insisted I sat next to her so we could chat."

"Well that's interesting," I said, intrigued. "You must keep me posted. Hey, food's ready. Would you mind alerting the family? I thought I'd attempt to climb the rope ladder and round up the little people!"

I performed the operation with surprising agility for an inexperienced 32 year old with two left feet. Soon we were all seated around the television enjoying a delicious lunch of cold meats, cheeses, pastries, home-made bread and a multitude of different salads, whilst being entertained by an impressive array of talented and popular musicians, including the likes of Ultravox, Spandau Ballet and Nik Kershaw.

During lunch, Scott sat a little away from the others and I observed that he was rather quiet and not at all hungry. At about half past three, Sting took to the stage, dressed all in white and bearing a remarkable resemblance to a Greek god. His stunning, acoustic rendition of 'Roxanne' showcased his voice to perfection but my attention was diverted when, out of the corner of my eye, I saw Scott slipping surreptitiously back into the trees. Although it was plain that something had upset my nephew, his mother was too busy playing hostess to notice, while his father was a little the worse for drink. I knew Scott to be a serious and sensitive boy so I meandered down the garden to the copse and mounted the rope ladder for the second time that day. Scott was sitting with his back against the wall, cradling his tortoise Strider on his lap. I put him at his ease with a few random questions about his pet and then proposed a trip to the shed to get some feed for the chickens.

"What's bugging you, Scott?" I enquired, handing him a plastic cup to decant the pellets into. "You hardly ate a scrap. Strider's eaten more than you in the last five minutes and you can bet the chickens will!"

"Have you ever been in love, Auntie Vicky?" he said shyly.

"Yes. Why do you ask?"

"How did you know … that you were?"

"Well, I found I was thinking about that person a great deal, almost all the time in fact, and I wanted to spend as much time as possible with them, and I wanted to … um … sit next to them and hold their hand and stuff."

"Oh."

"Do you have feelings for someone?" I asked, knowing the answer full well.

"We-e-ll, I *think* I'm in love with Lou," he said coyly, "but she doesn't care for me and she's gone all funny lately. She's suddenly started to wear lots of make-up and paint her nails. She got these pink, shiny tights. They were a birthday present from Mum and Dad … and these ridiculous woolly sock things she wears round her ankles. All she talks about is this boy said this, and that boy said that, and how she wants to look like Madonna. She's not coming round next weekend. She said she's going to the cinema with friends. One of them's called Tom. She's always talking about him. I think she fancies him." He pulled a face. "She got mad with me because her tights got muddy. She said how it was my fault 'cause she only came to the treehouse so as not to upset me but she really wanted to watch TV instead."

"I'm sure she didn't mean to get angry," I said tenderly. "She was just venting her frustration at dirtying her nice new leggings, and perhaps she would have preferred to watch TV but didn't want to let you down. Most young ladies are more interested in pop music than climbing trees. It was kind of her to make that sacrifice for you but it probably wasn't easy for her."

"What do you do if you love someone and they don't love you?"

I hesitated. "Well, you might feel a bit sad at first, but then that person stops being so important because other things come along to occupy your mind, until eventually you find that you might not have thought about that person all day, and you mind less if you don't see them very often."

"Mum says Lou's turning into a teenager. That's why she's changed."

"Your mum is right, but you'll change too, in a couple of years' time, and then the age difference won't matter anymore. The difficulty is that girls grow up faster than boys and she's already older than you so you're bound to notice it even more. Be patient, Scott. You have a very strong and special friendship with your cousin and she's very fond of you. Things will get better between you again in a year or two, which isn't as long as it sounds. You like football, don't you, Scott?"

"Yes, why?"

"Maybe we could ask Dad to take you to a match, to take your mind off things."

"Lou likes football. Do you think she would come?" he said, brightening.

"Well that wasn't quite what I had in mind but there's no harm in asking her. Some would-be teenage girls like football and I suspect she's one of them. She'd probably prefer that to climbing trees! And you'd have the advantage over Tom," I said with a conspiratorial wink, "unless he's got a season ticket for Carlisle United!"

I knelt down and gave him a long, affectionate hug. When I stood up and stepped away, I noticed that his eyes were red.

"Come along, let's feed those chickens," I said, wiping his eyes with the corner of my shirt. "Try not to let her see you upset. She has a kind heart and she'd hate to think she was the cause of it."

Back in the garden, the drink was flowing and Chris and Julie were reminiscing.

"Huh, Bryan Ferry," guffawed Chris. "You had a massive crush on him, if you remember, Jules. Does he still fire you up, eh?"

"Mmm," murmured Julie dreamily. "Hey, isn't that David Gilmour on guitar."

"Yeah, course, weren't you listening or were you too busy ogling Mr. Cool?" teased Chris. "Maybe they'll do a Floyd number. It would be a massive improvement on this tuneless racket." He nudged Julie playfully and she reciprocated with a well-aimed kick in the shins. "D'you remember we used to sit up half the night listening to Pink Floyd with the lights down?" he continued, unfazed.

"Oh gosh, yes, 'Echoes'. We practically wore the record out! D'you have a copy of 'The Final Cut'? I nearly bought it but a teacher at one of the schools where I work said not to bother, so I didn't."

"It's not great. Have you got 'Brothers in Arms' yet?"

"Dire Straits? *Oh my God*, I can't believe you asked me that!" squeaked Julie. "I got it yesterday from Paul. Would you like me to record it for you?"

"Oh … er … no, it's all right," mumbled Chris, flinching at the mention of his rival's name.

"It's no trouble … or you can borrow it if you'd rather, once I've had a chance to listen to it," she persisted, "or if you prefer, you can come round and we'll listen to it together. It'll be just like old times. Do, please. Father has mellowed beyond recognition. He'd love to see you again."

"Go on, Dad," urged Sarah. "You can see my room. Me and Mum decorated it last summer."

"Yeah, go on, Dad," echoed Louise, who was sitting on the lawn reading 'Just Seventeen' to the chagrin of her mother, who felt it was rather racy for a 12 year old. "It'll be fun. You can thrash Mum at Trivial Pursuit! She *always* wins."

"Be a sweetheart and come over. I won't take no for an answer." Julie was adamant.

"Well, I won't argue with three women," said Chris in a tone of mock resignation.

"Good, that's settled then. You and Julia can come for Sunday lunch. How about a week tomorrow?"

"Sounds good to me," he shrugged. He shot me a significant look. "Top up, anyone? Hey, where's Julia?"

"In the treehouse," said my sister and I in unison. "With Ryan," added Toni with a snigger.

After a short interval, I joined him indoors.

"See, told you," proclaimed Chris, snapping the ring pull off the last can of McEwan's. "That girl wants to have her cake and eat it."

"Well, personally, I think it's about time you and Julie reconciled your differences. You've got loads in common and she's right about Liam. He's definitely mellowed with age. You should definitely go, and the children would love it. Fill it up." I passed him my half-empty glass.

"I wonder what the state of play is between her and Paul," he mused. "I still think it's weird that she never invites him along."

"If it bothers you that much, why don't you tell her it's okay," I suggested.

"Yeah, I guess I should. It's the least I can do, since she's being so liberal with the olive branch today. Yes, I'll talk to her," he said decisively. "I could ask her if she wants him to come over later and stop by for a drink and a bite to eat, since I'm on a roll."

"You'd better check with Toni," I cautioned.

"Don't be daft! Toni won't care. There's bucketloads of food!" he scoffed. He stuck his head out of the open patio doors. "Here, Jules! Can I borrow you a moment?"

Julie breezed in and put her glass down on the worktop. "Well?"

"Julie, would you like to invite Paul over tonight? He might like to come over for a drink and a bite to eat. I don't mind, really I don't."

Julie looked nonplussed. "Why would I want to do that?"

Chris hesitated. "I just want you to know that there's no hard feelings."

"I know that. I'm sorry, am I missing something?" she said, with an air of bemusement.

"We *are* talking about the same person, aren't we? Paul, your boyfriend."

"My *boyfriend*?" she cried incredulously. "Oh my God! You think Paul's my *boyfriend*?" She emitted a spontaneous peal of laughter.

"Well, yes. I mean … we all did," said Chris, taken aback.

"Let me get this straight. Everyone thinks we're an item?" she said, suppressing a further outbreak of mirth with difficulty.

"Well, what were we supposed to think? He's always driving you here, there and everywhere."

"Yes, we have a business arrangement," interrupted his wife. "You see, he's teetotal and he's cheaper and more reliable than a commercial taxi, so when I fancy a drink I pay him for the fuel and give him a bit extra for his time," she finished, attempting, but not altogether succeeding, to conceal her amusement.

"But he's constantly round at yours. You can't deny that," argued Chris.

"I wouldn't dream of denying it. He plays chess with Father. They enjoy each other's company, and sometimes we play board games on a Sunday night." She reined herself in with an effort.

“Anyway, I’m not his type.” She dissolved into a fit of giggles.

“You’re drunk,” barked Chris.

“No, I’m not … well, not that drunk,” she parried, feigning pique.

“What’s so funny?” demanded a bewildered Chris.

“I told you, I’m not his type,” she insisted.

“How can you be so sure?” He was beginning to lose his patience.

She crossed the room and flung both arms across his shoulders. “Let me put it simply. You’ve got infinitely more chance of a date than me, though I think he prefers Michael!” Her face creased into a grin.

“Oh … you mean …”

“Yes, he’s homosexual, a lovely man and my very best friend, but nothing doing in the bedroom. How about we kiss and make up?” she said, offering him her cheek.

“You never said,” complained Chris, but giving her a peck nonetheless.

“You never asked,” she replied simply.

As the afternoon progressed, each new act was greeted with fresh gasps of admiration. In the space of 12 minutes, U2 sealed their reputation and took their place in the top flight. Queen’s explosive four-song set was later voted the greatest live performance of all time in the UK. I was keen not to miss David Bowie and with military precision emerged from the patio doors with a plateful of food just as the maestro was walking on stage in a pale grey suit, oozing sophistication and brandishing a smile that would melt an iceberg. Hot on his heels were the Who, who powered through a bunch of classic songs with their customary vigour. As the light began to fade, Elton John took to the stage in a half-hour showpiece, the longest of the day. Aided by George Michael on vocals, he wowed the audience with an electrifying performance of ‘Don’t Let the Sun Go Down on Me,’ which remains to this day one of my favourite ever songs. Just when I thought the quality could get no better, the legendary Paul McCartney took his place at the piano and delivered a truly uplifting rendition of 'Let It Be', which made the hairs on the back of my neck stand on end and sent the spectators into rapturous applause.

Just after 10 p.m. the audience dispersed. Meanwhile, across the pond at the JFK Stadium in Philadelphia, they were still hard at it but we were all beginning to flag. Shortly after, Paul arrived to pick up Julie and the girls.

"See you next Sunday, then?" smiled Julie, offering her husband her hand.

"Just try and stop me," he grinned, ignoring her outstretched arm, sweeping her into the air and giving her a bear hug.

"Oi … steady on, put me down" she giggled, flapping her feet and wriggling like an eel.

* * *

The visit was a great success. Liam was as keen as his daughter to let bygones be bygones. He welcomed his son-in-law into the cottage with open arms and made a tremendous effort to put him at his ease. Bitter experience had taught him the pitfalls of expressing his views, which were often controversial by modern-day standards, in so forthright a manner. Hence, although he did not altogether relinquish his strongly held opinions, he saw the futility, as well as the potential damage, of inflicting them too forcibly on others and recognised the value of restraint. From that moment on, the pair began to rediscover their love and a year later Chris moved back into his matrimonial home with Julia, where he has remained ever since.

In the meantime, I was contemplating a career as an independent midwife, and in 1987 I took the plunge, together with my friend and colleague Karen who was keen to start her own practice and was looking for a partner. I was encouraged in this bold venture by Polly, as well as by my long-time friend and mentor Rose, who even went so far as to loan us a tidy sum to get our business off the ground. We had both found it increasingly frustrating that, having established good relationships with expectant mothers, the system did not permit us to assist them in the labour ward unless this happened to coincide with our shift. As private midwives, we would be able to provide care to these women before, during and after birth, mostly in their own homes. With guidance and advice from the Independent Midwives Association, who proved to be an invaluable resource, we started to explore our options, including how to advertise our business and what fee to charge for our services, as well as the legal requirements around private practice such as how to insure ourselves against risk. Polly proved to be a crucial source of information. As a freelance photographer, she was already au fait with matters such as publicity and taxation. All midwives, even independent ones, must have a supervisor to ensure that they are operating safely and we were fortunate in that we happened to be allocated a highly experienced and very supportive one.

We got off to a slow start but secured enough clients to keep the coppers trickling in. Our clientele was by no means confined to the wealthy; some were amongst the very small cohort who had been unfortunate enough to suffer one of those very rare bad experiences at the hands of the NHS and were looking for an alternative. Having both been practising for some years, we had plenty of contacts and eventually gained ourselves a reputation, largely through word of mouth, and made a decent living at it. I'm still practising independently though currently considering taking a prolonged break from the front line and trying my hand at teaching midwifery, as the economy has taken a downturn and purse strings are being tightened, meaning that less people are now opting for private healthcare.

In hindsight, Michael's decision to 'go organic' at the turn of the decade was a visionary one, for the '80s was a decade that bristled with social conscience. Environmental issues, animal welfare and body image took centre stage and dominated the media, and events like Live Aid brought wider-world issues to the fore. Organisations such as Greenpeace were reaching out to a new generation of young adults. The sinking of their ship 'Rainbow Warrior' in 1985, although a travesty which caused outrage amongst environmentalists, did at least raise the profile of the charity and all that they stood for, and increased their membership. By the mid '80s, disposable income was on the up, especially amongst more well-to-do households, so that discerning shoppers were starting to make choices based on quality rather than merely cost.

As early as 1987, UKROFS was established by the Ministry of Agriculture to ensure minimum standards in the organic sector in response to consumer trends. At the time of writing, the British Government has begun to acknowledge the benefits of organic farming, both to health and to the environment, and is starting to offer financial support to producers such as ourselves via the Organic Aid Scheme. Whether growth in the market for organic produce can also be attributed to the Salmonella scare and BSE crisis in the late '80s is a moot point, but grow it did, and our profit margin, though modest, is sound and improving. Michael believes that even seemingly unrelated events, such as the Chernobyl nuclear reactor disaster, probably sparked interest amongst consumers, for it highlighted the ease with which pollutants can be absorbed into the food chain. However, since he has always been vehemently opposed to nuclear power, it's hardly surprising that he holds this view.

* * *

On Saturday 24th June 1989, Louise turned 16. During her teens, she had remained a frequent guest at the smallholding in Torver, to the extent that she was almost regarded as the fifth member of the King family. As I had predicted, the 18 month age gap between Louise and her favourite cousin Scott eventually ceased to matter and now the pair were as thick as thieves. They shared a passion for rock music, enjoyed going for walks together, watching football and playing Dungeons and Dragons.

Scott had developed into a tall, lean 14 year old who took pride in his appearance. He liked to keep himself in shape and worked out at home using weights. On Thursday evenings he attended Cadets. His smart bearing and quiet, reflective nature lent him an air of maturity beyond his years. Louise was a practical girl. She lacked her older sister Sarah's academic bent and had never learnt to play an instrument, preferring more active pursuits such as performing stunts on her BMX bike and skateboard to impress numerous would-be suitors. For all that, she never went out without make-up, permed her hair at 15 and ripped holes in her jeans because it was the hip thing to do. She had a flair for cooking and made herself indispensible to her aunt, baking cakes and pies for sale in the café in exchange for cash. It gave her an excuse to spend more time at her cousins' and kept her in hair mousse.

Liam, although to all intents and purposes a changed man, had never quite succeeded in letting go of his anger at Jason, or indeed his precious ideals with regard to conception out of wedlock, and harboured a private grudge concerning the King family which he couldn't quite rid himself of. Fortunately, Julie was a perceptive woman who had wisdom enough to play down the strength of his granddaughter's attachment to her cousin and his family, and even resorted to sidestepping the issue with an occasional white lie if her father was in a particularly bad mood. Hence, they bumbled along comfortably most of the time. However, when Toni begged Julie to allow her to hold a birthday party for Louise at the smallholding, which Julie considered an excellent idea due to the size and location of Toni's spacious house and grounds compared with her own small cottage, it felt to Julie rather like treading on eggshells when she revealed their plans to her father. Liam was well aware that he was in no position to make a stand but grumbled nonetheless. On rare occasions when his guard was down, he would curse his prejudices, which were so deeply ingrained that they interfered with his reasoning despite his best endeavours to stifle them. All the same, the prospect of attending the shindig was one step too far.

True to form whenever my sister was organising an event, Louise's party was a grand affair complete with non-alcoholic cocktails on the lawn for the young people to imbibe, prior to a buffet in the marquee followed by dancing until midnight. I arrived with Mum just after 7.30 and we made our way through the house to the garden. The weather was balmy and the evening sun tinted the grass with beams of deep gold. Most of the guests were already making merry on the lawn, while a succession of Stock, Aitken and Waterman hits thumped out of the PA system, which had been hired for the occasion. I lost no time in reminding my sister how much alcohol was consumed illicitly at her own 16th birthday bash. She laughed and said there was "nowt she could do about it", if they chose to smuggle it in. I surveyed the throng and eventually spotted my niece talking to a couple of girlfriends, with Scott at her side. I struck out through the mêlée of precocious damsels and dashing young blades, bearing her present.

"Happy birthday, Lou," I grinned, holding out a gaily-wrapped box.

"Hi, Auntie Vicky," she beamed. "Ooh … is that for me?" She ripped off the paper. "Wow, an instant camera! That's brilliant, thanks! I've been wanting one of these."

"And there's the film to go in it. Catch you later," I said, handing her a second package and scooting back indoors to the sanctity of the kitchen, where 35 reverted to a mere number rather than a measure of my advancing years.

As I stood at the counter with my back to the patio doors pouring myself a drink, I heard the sound of footsteps behind me and felt the pressure of a hand on the small of my back. I started and dropped the glass, which landed on the worktop, rolled off and shattered on the floor. In the same instant, I spun round and found myself face to face with Phil. He looked noticeably older; his face bore the hallmarks of a lifestyle of excess and his hair was streaked with grey, but he still possessed the same slim, muscular physique and dishevelled good looks that had been known to beguile even the most staunch and level-headed of females. I wondered if I was about to become his next victim.

"Well, well, if it's not Nurse Kelly." He spoke in a low voice, as smooth as silk. I felt my colour rise. "Did I startle you, or are you just overwhelmed to see me again after all these years?" He slipped his arm around my waist and put his face close to mine. I scowled and tried vainly to wriggle free but my back was against the kitchen cupboard. He gripped my side hard and fixed me with a wolfish smile. "Look, sweetheart, can't we be friends? It's patently obvious you're still sore with me. I don't blame you. I was a louse, made a mess of everything and I've paid for my misdemeanours 10 times over. Have pity on me, for Christ's sake."

"Get off me," I squealed without conviction, aiming my knee at his upper leg but lacking both the impetus and the resolve to deliver an effective blow.

Quick as a flash, his free hand found its way into my hair and somehow became tangled in it.

"Ha! Got you!" he grinned mischievously.

"Let me go, you octopus!" I squawked, tugging uselessly at the clenched fingers clutching my waist.

"Ah, come on, Vicky, water under the bridge an' all that. You can't possibly be angry with me after 15 years. I made it up with Toni ages ago and she's the one that got hurt, not you, so I haven't a clue what your problem is. However, problem or not, you could make an attempt to be civil for her sake."

"Since when have I been uncivil, unless civility means giving you a licence to molest me?" I said archly.

"All right, all right," he countered, adopting the tone of an injured man, releasing me from his grasp and holding both hands in the air in an attitude of surrender, although still standing far too close for comfort. "Blimey, I was only trying to be friendly. No need to be so touchy, or are you afraid your fella will catch you in the arms of another man?"

"I don't have a *fella,*" I said acidly.

"What! A cute little trick like you? I don't believe it!" He rummaged in his jacket pocket and produced a packet of Marlboros and a lighter. "Want one?"

"No thanks, I don't smoke," I replied tersely.

He lit a cigarette, took a drag, exhaled slowly and held out his hand. "Mates?" he said equably.

"I'll think about it, if you get that thing out of my face." I coughed and we exchanged a handshake. "Now, if you don't mind, I'd like to pour myself another drink, since that last one hit the deck, thanks to you. I guess I'll have to clear it up," I sighed. As I turned my back on him, his outstretched fingers drifted up and settled on the nape of my neck. I should have expected that. "You never give up, do you," I hissed with as much venom as I could muster, which amounted to precious little, since my sense and sensibilities were at odds.

He withdrew and strode out through the patio doors.

While I was sweeping up the broken glass, Toni came into the kitchen.

"What happened?"

"Phil *happened,* that's what," I said pointedly. "He nearly gave me a heart attack! What the hell's he doing here?"

"He comes round all the time. He's a friend of Jase, they're drinking buddies, and it so happens that his nephew's doing the sounds. I hope you were nice to him."

"We made it up," I said resignedly. "Where's Joanie? Not here, I take it, since he was rather free with his hands!"

"At home with the kids, I would imagine. Honestly, he's harmless, Vicky. Take no notice of him. All mouth and trousers," she said airily. "Need some newspaper for that?" Without waiting for an answer, she disappeared into the utility room, emerged bearing a copy of yesterday's Daily Mail and dropped it on the floor beside me. Then she poured herself a drink and made her exit.

Just before 11 p.m. as I was returning to the garden from the bathroom, I saw Phil again. He was standing on his own outside the marquee smoking a cigarette. He noticed me crossing the patio and hailed me.

"Hey, Vicky! Would you mind grabbing me a lager on your way out?"

"Any particular type?"

"I'll have a Bud," he called out. I returned to the kitchen and helped myself to a can of Strongbow on the way back outside.

"I thought you were on the wine," queried Phil, as I gave him his drink.

"I fancied a cider." I snapped off the ring pull and took a draught.

"Let's go for a walk round the estate," he suggested, reaching for my hand.

"What for? It's pitch," I laughed and took up the proffered limb. The alcohol had made me magnaminous.

"Exercise?"

"Don't be silly, you're sozzled. But just to prove there's no hard feelings, we'll do a circuit of the garden," I giggled. "*However*," I added with emphasis, "any funny business and I'll scream the place down."

"I believe you would," he said agreeably, marching me off towards the vegetable beds.

As we were strolling up the garden, I thought I spotted two shadowy forms disappearing into the copse.

"Did you see that?" I gasped, pretending astonishment. "D'you think they're ghosts? We could be ghostbusters!"

Phil burst out laughing. "You're plastered!"

"No I'm not! Well, maybe a bit merry," I smirked. "Let's go and round them up." I quickened my pace.

"Whoa, Vicky, they're just teenagers, doing what teenagers do. Leave them alone."

"I know that," I said impatiently. "Joking aside, I'd rather they didn't 'do what teenagers do', as you so eloquently put it, in my sister's back garden. This is a birthday party, not a knocking shop! Perhaps if we rustle about a bit and snap a few twigs, they'll hear us and scarper."

"You're actually asking me to go into the woods with you and 'rustle about' a bit?" he chortled. "Hallelujah! And there's me thinking you didn't like me!"

"Be serious, Phil. It can't hurt to make our presence known."

"If you insist," he shrugged.

We entered the copse. All was still and quiet until we neared the treehouse, where I noticed intermittent flashes of light emanating from the pencil-thin gap around the door.

"Someone's in the treehouse," I said in hushed tones.

"Blow the treehouse! This is far too good an opportunity to waste," said Phil salaciously, steering me towards a small clearing half-hidden by the trees.

"Behave yourself!" I scolded. "Come on, let's make a noise, stamp on a few twigs or something," and we did so.

"They're coming out!" said Phil in a hoarse whisper. "Quick, behind the tree."

From our rudimentary hiding place, I peered through the gloom. I watched open-mouthed as Scott clambered down the rope ladder, followed by Louise.

"I think they've gone," said Louise breathlessly. "Phew, that was close."

"No, wait a minute," said Scott. "I can smell smoke. Shush a moment." He panned the glade with his torch. "Behind that tree there, I can see a light."

Phil threw his cigarette on the ground and crushed it. The undergrowth crackled noisily beneath his feet.

"That's done it," I groaned.

Scott advanced and I realised we were scuppered so I stepped forward followed by Phil. Louise's jaw dropped.

"W-we weren't doing anything," she stammered, like a child on the verge of tears. "Don't tell Mum and Dad, they'll go mad!"

"Please don't tell anyone," begged Scott. "We were only kissing." Something in the tone of his voice, together with his inherent honesty, convinced me that he was telling the truth. "And we were only there literally a minute or two," he qualified.

"Yes, I know," I reassured them. "We saw you sloping into the woods. It's all right. I won't tell your parents. You have my word, only please do take care and don't get carried away. You're playing with fire." I turned to Phil. "If you dare say anything, *ever*, I'll kill you," I said fiercely.

"Thanks Auntie, you're a legend," smiled Scott.

Louise merely flung her arms around my neck and pressed her cheek against mine.

"By the same token, I'd rather you didn't mention *this*," I said, inclining my head towards my partner in crime, as we all walked back to the marquee together. "There's nothing in it, we were just walking around the garden and came to investigate. However, it wouldn't look good."

Phil chuckled. "Yeah, just walking around, more's the pity."

Chapter 19

Wild Love

The year was 1990, the month March. The wind howled around the farmhouse and the rain lashed at the window panes. All the family were in bed except me. I was sitting at the kitchen table, writing up my case notes, to the low drone of the late night arts programme on Radio 2. All of a sudden, my ears were assailed by loud and urgent knocking at the front door. I leapt up, rushed down the passage in a state of agitation, fumbled with the key in the lock and after several attempts, for my hands were shaking, released the deadlock and peered cautiously around the edge of the door. My sister stood on the doorstep, soaked to the skin, her face flushed with cold. Her teeth were chattering and she was shivering from head to foot.

"Oh my God, Toni!" I cried, ushering her inside. "What's happened? You'll catch your death."

I heard a door click open upstairs and Mum appeared on the landing.

Toni stood motionless. Her shoulders were hunched and she was hugging herself and staring straight ahead as if in a catatonic stupor.

"Toni, oh my goodness, what's the matter?" gasped Mum, flying downstairs.

My sister started, put her keys down slowly on the hall table and hesitated.

"It's my … yes, my car, that's all. It's okay, Mum. Don't get up on my account."

"Are you hurt? Have you had an accident?"

"No … no, nothing like that, Mum. I'm fine, really I am." She smiled weakly. "I … I sort of got stuck. And then I had to get help only it was a long walk … and the weather's shocking."

"Go and get yourself warm and dry, dear," said Mum. "Can I get you a cup of tea?"

"It's okay, Mum, I'll do it," I said. "You have to get up before me. You can borrow my dressing gown, Toni. D'you want me to run you a hot bath? You must be chilled to the bone."

She gave her assent with a halfhearted nod, wandered into the kitchen and sat down at the table with her head in her hands.

"Are you sure you're all right?" I enquired, "only you seem rather upset and … well, you're here, not at home … which is … unusual, to say the least."

She looked up sharply. "Please don't quiz me. I don't want to talk about it right now; I don't even want to think about it."

I put the kettle on and went upstairs to run a bath.

When I came down she was standing in the hall by the telephone.

"Are they all in bed?" she asked hurriedly.

"Yes, why?"

She lowered her voice. "I need to make a couple of phone calls. Would you mind very much not listening in? I'll tell you everything, I promise, only not now. I need to get my head straight."

I thought this was rather an odd request but agreed readily and shut myself in the kitchen with the radio turned up lest I should be tempted to eavesdrop. Five minutes later she re-entered. I handed her a steaming hot cup of tea.

"Best get out of those wet clothes," I advised. "Go and warm up. You'll find my dressing gown hanging on the back of my door. I'm guessing you're sleeping here tonight."

She nodded. "There's just one thing I need you to do for me. If anyone calls, *anyone at all*, I'm not here and you don't know where I am. I don't think anyone will but please, please don't breathe a word. Will you wait up for me?"

"Yes of course. Have you had a row or something?" The suspense was unbearable.

"No, not exactly. Well … something like that," she sighed.

"I'll make you up a bed in the spare room … unless you want to sleep in my room."

"Oh yes please, if you don't mind," she said gratefully. "I'd rather not sleep on my own tonight."

"When she came back downstairs, her expression was tense and drawn.

"Warmer now?"

"Mmm … can we talk?" She sat down at the kitchen table opposite me.

"Sure," I said, pushing my notes aside.

"Oh Vicky, I've been so stupid," she cried. "I've done something really bad."

I reached across the table and took her hand in mine.

Her face contorted and her whole frame started to shake.

"Don't fight it, take your time," I said gently.

A half-stifled sob escaped from her lips, she gave vent to her tears and eventually took up the thread.

"It's not been easy for me, you know Vicky," she began. "I know you think I have this picture perfect life, but nothing could be further from the truth."

"Oh, Toni, I had no idea you were so unhappy. What's made you so upset?"

"Everything," she said miserably. "Marriage, kids, middle-age, the business … look, whatever I'm about to tell you, please hear me out and try not to be judgemental. What I need right now is a bit of sympathy, not someone pointing out what I should have done differently."

"I wouldn't dream of doing that," I said tenderly, squeezing her hand affectionately.

She took a deep breath and composed herself.

"Well to start with, Jason's been absolutely foul lately. Oh, I know it's not his fault, but he's so touchy I hardly dare open my mouth for fear of getting into yet another argument. I'm not the best at holding my tongue when he gets unreasonable. I know I should ignore his tantrums and let him get on with it, but I can't. We're at each other's throats all the time."

"Why's he being like that, do you think?"

"Well I do know he's terrified the business will go under. Interest rates are sky high, they've doubled in the last two years and we're struggling to pay the mortgage, to be honest. If we lose the house, we lose everything. He thinks we're heading for another recession and he's probably right. We survived the last one back in '81 … just, but it hit us hard. Who's going to pay our prices when you can get the stuff at half the cost in Tesco's? And as for the tea and cakes, that's the first thing people cut back on when times are tough.

"Then there's Louise. When we took her onto our permanent staff last year, Julie had a hell of a time talking her grandfather round, who seems to rule the roost. He hates me, you know, and since we've been skirting round the issue for years, he had no idea she was already working in the shop and helping out with the baking. That didn't help when it came to getting him to see reason. If the business collapses, we'll have to let her go. God only knows how he'll react; hate me even more than he already does, I would imagine.

"Then there's Scott. He's acting so strangely. He spends hours in his room with his headphones on."

"He's just being a normal teenager, I would say."

"No, it's worse than that. He's edgy, like something's worrying him. He's better when *she*'s here of course, almost like his old self. He's very fond of her."

"You mean Louise, I presume."

"Well, yes, and if she wasn't his cousin, I would say he was smitten, but I can't imagine anyone falling for their cousin and to be honest I daren't even entertain the thought, given this ridiculous family feud that old misery guts seems determined to prolong. I did ask him recently, Scott that is, but he told me I was being stupid!"

"Perhaps he's hankering after some other girl," I suggested, recollecting the incident last year in the treehouse and lying through my teeth. "He's probably too embarrassed to talk about his feelings with you. He's at that difficult age. Or perhaps he just doesn't like the arguing," I added as an afterthought.

Toni shrugged. "Who knows? To be honest, I wouldn't blame him if he was developing feelings for her, although I don't for a moment think he is. I mean, she's stunning, isn't she? And that's another thing. Look at me? I don't want to sound bitter or anything but I can't bear the thought that she's more attractive than me, *much* more attractive. I'm not used to playing second fiddle. Do you have any idea how it feels to be outdone by your niece? It's mortifying."

"Not much difference from being outdone by your sister, I would think," I said, wincing. "You were always heaps better looking than me. You still are … and you still don't look a day over 30 to be fair."

"But the reality is Vicky, I'm 40 next year," she moaned.

"Look, you still haven't told me what you've done. Did you have a massive argument with Jason and walk out? Did he threaten you, only you sound like you're on the run?"

"Good God no! Jason wouldn't hurt a fly," she rejoined, horrified.

"Well, what then?"

"It's worse than that … oh Vicky, I've been such an idiot," she groaned. "I'm really struggling with the prospect of turning 40 and I wish I didn't envy Louise so much, but I do and that's that." She dropped her voice and stared down at her hands. "Someone's been paying attention to me. I was flattered. Nothing happened … well almost nothing," she said, turning crimson.

"Oh, Jesus Toni, tell me it's not Phil."

She looked at me despairingly.

"Toni, he's a predator! How could you be so blind?"

"Yes, I know, I know, but he's … well you know what he's like."

"Yes I know," I conceded. "What happened?"

"Of course, he's always popping in and out of the shop."

"Yes I can imagine … any excuse," I said sardonically.

"A couple of weeks ago, I had to go out back to the stockroom and get some stuff he wanted … off the top shelf, some chutney I think. I asked him to come round the back and hold the ladder. I know I shouldn't have done it; I knew where it would lead. As I was coming backwards down the ladder, his hands … well put it this way … he made absolutely no attempt to keep them in check; quite the reverse, and when I got to the bottom and he was standing there right behind me, I turned round and … oh Vicky, we just started kissing and couldn't stop! After a couple of minutes the shop bell rang, thank goodness. Well it wasn't 'thank goodness' at the time – it was actually really frustrating – but afterwards I figured it was just as well as I was in no state to fend him off. I went out and served the customer and told him to wait in the stockroom. I was terrified someone might catch him in there but luckily we got away with it. We waited till the coast was clear and off he went with his chutney."

"Crikey, Toni. What were you thinking?"

"Well, I wasn't, was I? Anyway, the next day he rang but Jason was there so I pretended it was a wrong number. Not sure why, as to be fair he could have been calling to speak to Jason about something. He's his mate, after all. I didn't think of that till afterwards; probably my guilty conscience. Then the day after he rang again but this time Jason wasn't there. He told me he needed to talk to me and would I meet him somewhere? First of all I said no but eventually I capitulated and told Jason I was meeting Jean in Ulverston for a pizza this evening. We arranged to park up on the verge under the Hawk. It's very off the beaten track. Honestly Vicky, I don't know why I agreed to it."

"Surely you knew he wanted more than just a chat," I said incredulously.

"Of course I did. I'm not a complete imbecile! I knew what I was doing … but I did think he cared for me. I've been questioning my marriage lately and when you do that, it's easy to convince yourself you'd be happier with someone else, especially if that someone is as charming and attentive as Phil. You have to remember, we go back a long way and he was very young when he developed a taste for Joanie. I thought he might be a reformed character."

"Reformed characters don't act covertly. Did I ever tell you, he made a pass at me last year?" I blurted, wishing fervently that I could retract the words the instant they escaped from my lips. "I'm sorry, there was no need for you to know that," I added hurriedly.

"Oh my God! I had no idea." Toni stared at me agape and started to cry anew. "I wish you'd told me. I might have acted differently. Still, it's too late now."

"I'm sorry. It was nothing. For what it's worth, I do know how persuasive he can be," I said, feeling my colour rise.

"Anyway, this evening …" She hesitated. "Could I have some buttered toast, please? I've only just realised how hungry I am."

"Of course you can," I smiled, rising.

"Well, you might as well know everything," she continued resignedly, talking to my back. "We walked up the Forestry Commision track, about 10 minutes I think. It was raining. I was complaining about Jason and he was complaining about Joanie and told me he was thinking of leaving her. We were walking very close together; he had his arm around me. Then he told me there were some ruined farm buildings over the little footbridge, and said he was getting wet and there might be somewhere we could shelter, so that's where we went. I was starting to feel a bit uncomfortable with it all but we were getting really wet. Anyway, we tucked ourselves into a little alcove in one of the buildings and it all started to happen, but pretty quickly I changed my mind. All I could think about was Jason and the kids, and sitting on the sofa at home with a glass of wine and the TV on. I told him to stop but he told me I was being ridiculous, and got annoyed and said it wasn't fair to drag him out on a wet night for nothing. Then I started to panic. I didn't let on though. I just told him I wanted to go home and got up and started to walk back to the car. He followed me but we didn't say a word to each other all the way back. I was trying to turn my car around but it got stuck in the mud, so I asked him if he could give me a push. First of all, he said it *wasn't his problem* and then when I asked him again, he said 'You don't get something for nothing.' I was furious. After that, there was no way I was going to compromise myself, even if my life depended on it, so I told him to go away ... only I didn't put it quite as politely as that. Well he took me at my word and left me there, stranded."

"Unbelievable! So what did you do then?"

"I tried a few more times but the car was well and truly stuck and I knew I wouldn't be able to do it on my own, so I walked back to the junction. There didn't seem much point walking back the way I came as I didn't remember seeing any farmhouses on the way, so I turned right down the hill. It just seemed easier than walking up the hill. I thought it might lead to Broughton and I was right as it turned out, but fortunately I found a farm about a mile down the road. They got the tractor out and we went back up the lane and they towed me out. Honestly, Vick, they were amazing … so kind and helpful. I'm not sure they would have been if they'd known what I was doing there. Anyway, then it dawned on me that I couldn't go home soaking wet and covered in mud. I was supposed to be eating pizza with Jean. I asked the farmer, who said I was right about it being the road to Broughton and I know my way here from there … and here I am … only Jason thinks I'm with Jean. I told him I'd had too much to drink and decided not to drive back, then told Jean to cover for me. That's why I needed to make those phone calls. To cap it all, the heater's not working in my car. Trust me; 45 minutes can seem like hours when you're freezing cold and wet and suffering from shock. I can't believe I got myself into this mess. How could I be so blind?"

I handed her the toast and sat back down. "You had a lucky escape. Are you going to tell Jason?"

"I don't know what good that would do," she replied. "I'm over Phil now and no-one in their right mind would tell their best mate they've been fraternising with his wife. I suppose I'll have to be pleasant to him to avoid any awkward questions, but I won't be inviting him back to the stockroom," she said glumly. "Why hurt Jason unnecessarily?"

"Because it's dishonest? Won't you find it hard to live with yourself, knowing what happened and having to pretend everything's normal?"

"I'm sure I'll manage. Eventually it'll probably cease to matter. It's not as if anything happened, other than a kiss and a fumble. Look, I haven't actually decided yet but I'd rather not risk another scene. Jason's got enough on his plate already. I'll see how I feel in the morning." She finished her toast and yawned. "Come on, let's get some sleep."

We had no trouble convincing Mum and Michael the following morning that Toni had merely got her car stuck in the mud somewhere nearby and had decided to come back to the farm because she wanted to get out of her wet clothes as quickly as possible. We told them not to mention the incident, on the grounds that Jason could be over critical of Toni's driving and she wanted to avoid an argument. They both seemed satisfied with that. Toni was beside herself with remorse but took a grain of comfort from the knowledge that she had found the resolve to halt the proceedings before they had crossed the finishing line. After breakfast, she went home a wiser and more introspective woman, believing she had got off lightly with a warning. However, fate saw fit to decree a harsher penalty by far and Toni's trials were a long way from over.

A few days later, Toni caught a severe cold. She wasn't one to baulk at the first hurdle so, aided by copious amounts of flu remedy, she continued to go about her daily business. She baked pies and cakes, ran the shop and did the book-keeping as usual, whilst determining to try harder to be a more loving and supportive wife and mother. Her natural inclination was to carry on regardless and her guilty conscience made her even less disposed to make waves. A week later, when she should have been getting better, she developed a high temperature, hacking cough and chest pains. On Good Friday she took to her bed and slept for most of the day.

I was finishing my lunch the following day when the telephone rang. It was Jason.

"Vicky, I need your advice," said my brother-in-law. "Toni's getting worse. She hasn't had a bite to eat since Thursday evening and when I took her up a cup of tea just now she said she felt tight-chested and could barely summon the energy to sit up. She was coughing in her sleep most of last night. Do you think she's got a chest infection?"

"Call an ambulance," I said without hesitation, "and keep me posted. I would hazard a guess she's got pneumonia."

Toni was admitted to Furness General Hospital, where they ran a series of tests and confirmed my hurriedly-made diagnosis based on seven years' nursing experience before training as a midwife. They put her on a course of strong antibiotics and kept her in, as any deterioration in her condition could have very serious consequences. The next day, when I went to visit with Mum, I was horrified by what I saw. Toni's face was ashen and her lips were tinged with blue. Her breathing was shallow and uneven. A cannula was attached to her right hand, from which an infusion tube snaked up to a bag of saline solution above her head. I wasn't too alarmed by the drip as I knew it to be usual practice in acute cases of pneumonia. Her weak attempts at making conversation were peppered with bouts of coughing. Every now and again, she would ask for the oxygen mask next to her bed to be passed to her. As I watched her taking deep draughts of air to ease her breathing, I recollected all too vividly sitting at my father's bedside the day before he died, and my heart quailed. Evidently Mum's thoughts were running in the same groove.

"It's just like your dad all over again," she wailed, as soon as we were out of earshot. She started to cry.

I knew I needed to stay strong for Mum's sake so I reined in my emotions, gave her some words of comfort, which sounded hollow and unconvincing, and offered to drive home.

During the afternoon, I was called out by a client who had gone into labour. I managed to get through the delivery without crumbling but as soon as the baby's mother diverted her attention from me to her newborn, tears welled up in my eyes. I excused myself, asked to borrow the lady's phone and called Karen out to take over. I was in no fit state to work that day.

The next two days were interminable, as if walking through fog with boots of lead. By now, Toni had been put on a ventilator and was slipping in and out of consciousness and talking gibberish. Meanwhile, I had completely lost my appetite and had barely slept. Being self-employed was a mixed blessing. I had no wish to let my clients down so I soldiered on. On the one hand, work forced me to abandon my morbid reflections and afforded me glimpses of normality. On the other, it put an immense strain on my already overtaxed mind and body, so that after three days I was physically and mentally exhausted.

Just when I thought I could endure no more, Toni turned a corner. When we arrived that evening, she was sitting up, with a cup of tea steaming on the table next to the bed. Jason sat beside her, holding her hand. I burst into tears and smothered her free hand with kisses.

"It's all right, Vicky, I'm not a china doll," she said hoarsely, releasing both her hands and stretching her arms out towards me.

"Oh Toni, I was so scared," I cried, leaning in, wrapping both arms around her shoulders and kissing her tenderly on her cheeks and forehead."

"I'm going to get well," she smiled, "but the doctor says it's going to be a long road. It was touch and go."

"She's a trooper," said Jason with a broad grin, "and I've been an absolute beast. This has been a real wake-up call, eh Toni?" He turned to address Mum. "She's going to need some help around the place. Even if she was in a fit state to work, I can't have her running around like a headless chicken anymore. No wonder she crashed, poor love. She never stops … partly my fault," he added sheepishly. "I put too much pressure on her but all that's going to change."

"Family trait," said Mum with a meaningful glance in my direction. "She puts pressure on herself. Her sister's the same. You'll have a job getting her to sit down, once she's up and about again."

"Seriously though, Marion, do you know anyone good who could pitch in? It might lead to a permanent job but I couldn't guarantee that. It does rather depend on the economy. I'm not sure we'll even be solvent this time next year, but I've learnt that there's more important things in life than paying the mortgage!" He looked affectionately at his wife.

"Oh my goodness! Is it really that bad? Jason, why didn't you say something?" exclaimed Mum.

"Pride, I guess," he shrugged. "Besides, I couldn't expect you to bail us out. You've probably got more than enough money worries of your own."

"Well I couldn't stand by and watch my daughter and son-in-law go under. If need be, I'd sell off some of the fields. I nearly did once, you know, but Michael had other plans. He's a genius at making the most from the least and a wizard at playing the stock market. He's made some tidy cash from shrewd investment decisions. He used to terrify me with his speculations but now I just let him get on with it. He's never made a bad one yet."

"He has heaps of time to analyse the market," I put in wickedly, "since he never does anything else!"

"Don't say mean things about your brother, Vicky," chided Mum. "He's made the farm what it is since we lost your father. I'll see what I can do, Jason," she continued, "… I'll make some enquiries. There might be some local lad who would be glad of a bit of paid work."

"Or lass," I said indignantly.

"Point taken," agreed Mum.

Soon after, the bell rang to signal the end of visiting hours. I put on my coat and turned to bid Toni goodbye. Jason was gazing down at her, his hand resting on her arm, with what I can only describe as love in his eyes. I felt that familiar pang of envy, which I quickly dismissed, grateful that my sister had escaped with both her life and marriage intact.

The following Saturday, I ran into Janice. She was riding her horse in the lane. I was on the way back from an early morning call. I pulled in, wound down the car window and hailed her, and we exchanged pleasantries.

"Your Mum told me Toni got rushed to hospital," she said presently. "Is she all right?"

"Yes, she's on the mend now, thank goodness, but she was in a critical state for a couple of days. She went home yesterday but she's still very fragile. She had pneumonia … which reminds me.

You don't happen to know anyone who's looking for a job, only she's not likely to be well enough to work for a couple of months at least? Poor Louise – that's my niece – she's managing the shop as well as doing all the baking. Jason and the boys are all doing their best but he's worried he'll get behind with all the other jobs and the boys should really be concentrating on their school work. They need someone who can do a bit of everything."

"Funny you should say that," beamed Janice, "but my baby brother – well he's not exactly a baby, he's 20, but he's a lot younger than me – anyway, he's due to finish polytechnic next month. He's been doing Electrical Engineering at Lancashire but he hasn't got a job lined up yet. I expect he'd be glad of something to tide him over. You remember Jamie?"

"Yes of course I remember Jamie – nice lad. Would you mind asking him? I'll mention it to Toni."

"Champion. I'll ask him tomorrow. He phones every Sunday."

"Do let me know if he's interested and I'll give you Toni's number. I should be in all day tomorrow unless I get another call-out. The last one was a false alarm – indigestion. Catch you later!"

I wound up the window and she trotted off down the lane.

Every Sunday evening, we would decamp to the lounge and eat our tea on our laps in front of the television. We would dine on hunks of home-made bread, ham and cheese, Mum's chutneys and preserves and either freshly-baked cake or warm scones with a generous dollop of jam and cream, sometimes both. That Sunday, as I was loading the tea trolley and Mum was making drinks, we heard a light tap on the kitchen window. Janice rarely came in by the front door as it was quicker to walk across the field and come in by the back door, although she tended to jog everywhere.

"I'll get it, Mum," I said, crossing the room.

"Come in, Janice, you're just in time for tea," I laughed, gesturing towards the trolley brimming with food.

"I won't stop," she panted. "I just wanted to let you know that I spoke to Jamie and he's definitely up for it so I've come to get Toni's number."

"Sure." I wrote it on a slip of paper and she bounced off down the garden.

A few days later, I went to visit my sister. It was a beautiful spring day. The sky was cloudless and the sun shone down, infusing the crisp air with its warmth. I parked in the yard and walked round to the back of the house, since Toni was still feeling very frail and I figured it might save her a trip to the front door. Scott was in the back garden with a retractable metal rule in one hand and a pencil in the other. A large sheet of plywood lay on the grass at his feet. Atop the chicken coop behind him was a beautifully structured wooden framework consisting of two neat rows of rafters which met at an apex along the centre of the half-finished roof.

"Hi Scott. I thought you'd be at school. What's that you're doing?"

"Re-roofing the chicken shed. School's next week," he replied amiably.

"It's very good. I didn't know you were into carpentry."

"Neither did I but we've all got to start somewhere," he grinned. "Dad showed me the rudiments and left me to get on with it. Since Mum's gone and got herself laid up, we've had to muck in, which is fair enough. I'm pretty proud of it."

"I thought you might be in the shop with Louise," I ventured, cautiously.

"Oh … yeah … well … she's asked her mate to come over." I raised my eyebrows. His colour rose and he lowered his voice. "Look, you might as well know, Lou's broken it off … not that we were ever an item as such," he began hesitantly, "but I always thought of her as my girl and I believe she felt the same. However, it was doomed to failure so we've put an end to it. For a start, her grandfather would never have condoned a match. To make things worse, one of my *so-called* buddies found out about us and blabbed, and now apparently I'm a psycho or a weirdo or some such thing 'cause I've got the hots for my cousin. When I told Lou they were giving me hell at school, she was mortified. As if that wasn't enough, when I told her I planned to enlist next year, she said she didn't want to be an army wife – too much stress and too much moving house. To give her her due, I could end up dead or on the other side of the globe. It's a chance you take but it's something I've got to do. Anyway, to cut a long story short, when Mum went into hospital last week, she ended it, whatever 'it' was. Oh God, Auntie, it was awful! Dad walked into my room and caught me crying like a baby. I told him I was upset about Mum. Well obviously I was, but that was a different kind of upset … like I was all tense and edgy. With Lou, it was different, more like being smashed over the head with a sledgehammer."

"I'm so sorry, Scott."

"Thanks. Anyway that's why I'm giving her a wide berth, which is pretty hard since she comes to work here six days a week. I've told her I need some space and said to Dad that I'd prefer to do some outdoor maintenance jobs as I needed to learn some practical skills so I'm better prepared when I join up. Clever of me, that was. He fell for it so here I am, re-roofing the chicken shed."

"It must be very hard for you," I said, completely at a loss for anything helpful to say.

"I can't say it wasn't a massive shock," continued Scott, "but because Lou is older than me, between you and me, I've always had this dread that she would outgrow me. She did once before when she started secondary school but I caught up. So naturally that was my gut reaction when she ditched me, but she was very sweet and explained that it was nothing to do with our ages, just her pain-in-the-neck grandfather and the whole army thing, so there it is. I'll survive." He averted his gaze, pulled out the retractable rule and knelt down on the grass.

I took my leave, entered the kitchen by the patio doors and went through into the lounge.

Toni was sitting on the sofa with her feet up, with a blanket wrapped around her shoulders and another draped over her legs. She was pale but smiling.

"Jamie's been in touch," she said soon after I had arrived, "so thanks for that. He can start in three weeks. We'll manage till then."

"Glad I could help. I hope Jason and the boys are taking good care of you."

"They've been smashing. I've barely lifted a finger since I got home. I saw you were talking to Scott. He wants to join the army, you know. Did I ever tell you that? I think," she continued, without waiting for an answer, "that was another thing that made me do … what I did. It felt like rejection. I can see now that I was wrong. Jason says it's the mark of a great mother, one who has instilled in her son the confidence to fly the nest and make his own way in the world. I never thought of it like that. I thought I wouldn't be able to bear it, Scott being hundreds of miles away in the line of fire, but now that me and Jason are back on track, I know I'll cope, though it won't be easy."

"I … assume you haven't told Jason what really happened?" I asked cautiously.

"I'd rather forget all about it," she sighed, "only that's pretty hard to do, given the state I'm in. I really don't see what's to be gained. Oh, I know it's wrong to lie and cheat and I should do the honourable thing, but he's got enough to cope with already. Don't you think it would be kinder to say nothing? Besides, not much happened and Phil definitely won't drop me in it. He might be a chancer but he's not stupid. He knows Jason would kill him! Sometimes a white lie is less painful than the truth, don't you agree?" persisted Toni.

I recalled the fear on the faces of my nephew and niece the previous summer as they emerged from the treehouse. Then

I recollected the boys with whom I had shared the occasional moment of intimacy when Ray and I were living at opposite ends of the country.

"I suppose so," I smiled, reaching forward to give her ankle a squeeze.

"This is all my fault," she continued. "If I hadn't been so reckless, I wouldn't have been out in that weather and none of this would have happened."

"Nonsense, you can't catch pneumonia from getting cold and wet, I learnt that much at nursing school. It's a complete myth. Sure, it can make you more susceptible, but you must have been in contact with a virus."

"It's karma," she said morosely.

"Don't be ridiculous! You've just been unlucky. I'm dying for a cup of tea. Can I get you one?"

"Yes please," she called after me, as I disappeared through the door into the kitchen.

"Do you ever wish you'd got married and had kids, Vicky?" she asked me later.

"Maybe once in a blue moon. Most of the time I don't give it much thought nowadays. I love my job and I've got a great family; a lot to be thankful for. I'm certainly glad I didn't move to Portsmouth."

"Ray still single?"

"Yeah, he is actually. We keep in touch. In a way, I'm glad about that. I know it's selfish of me but I think I might find that really hard to swallow."

"Do you think you'll ever get back together," she said.

"I doubt it. He'd have to want to move up here and that won't happen."

"Do you think Michael will ever marry?"

"What is this … 20 questions?" I laughed. "No, I don't think he's the marrying type and Polly's *definitely* not! Maybe that's why he's fixated on her. Subconsciously, he probably knows she's unattainable. That makes her a safe bet. They still dabble, you know," I giggled.

"Oh my gosh, Vicky, you're hilarious!" shrieked Toni gleefully. "Dad would turn in his grave!"

"Mum just turns a blind eye. It's 1990 after all and Polly's a real asset around the farm. She cracks me up. I only wish she was here full time and not just when it suits her. I wonder how many other men are reaping the benefits of her liberal nature!"

"Oh Vicky, don't be such a cow," smirked Toni. "Pass me my tea, would you?"

At six o'clock I kissed my sister goodbye and set off home. I couldn't help but feel a little disappointed, though I had no right to be. Any hope I had secretly nurtured of a union between my nephew and niece, which might be instrumental in healing the rift between their two families, was all but lost. On an impulse, I pulled in at the roadside, rummaged in the glove compartment, pulled out a battered cassette and slotted it into the player. It was the soundtrack to my favourite musical. The name of that musical was 'West Side Story'.

Chapter 20

The Icing on the Cake

Louise Marie Kelly and James Gabriel Duffy were married on Saturday 9th May 1992 at St. Paul's Church, Irton, in the parish of Eskdale.

Soon after Jamie had taken up a temporary position at King's of Torver, it had become very apparent that he was growing fond of Louise. Jamie was not unlike Scott in appearance. They were both tall and fair, although Jamie was broader, his hair was a shade darker and his eyes were hazel, while Scott's were blue. Consequently, I wasn't particularly surprised when I learnt that the attraction was mutual. Meanwhile, Scott immersed himself in his GCSEs and attended Cadets avidly outside school. He could hardly fail to notice that he had been usurped in the affections of his childhood sweetheart but he bore it like a Trojan. Perhaps he was already arming himself for greater challenges than an aching heart, as he contemplated a career in the armed forces. Still waters run deep. To give the couple their due, they played down their attachment until Scott joined up the following summer, then announced their engagement shortly after.

As the big day approached, I started to feel a little apprehensive. The venue was the very same one at which the bride's father and grandfather had almost come to blows 18 years previously and the forecast was for rain. When Julie received a call three days before the wedding informing her that the vicar had sustained a fall and broken his leg and the service would be conducted by a cleric from a nearby parish, I began to feel quite tense.

As we trickled into the church, the clouds broke and the sun came out. The tarmac sparkled and the nodding vegetation glistened as if studded with tiny emeralds. The verges were crowded with swathes of cow parsley which danced in the playful breeze. Birds twittered gaily and the sweet scent of honeysuckle lingered just inside the entrance gate. Things were looking up.

I took my place next to Mum in the second pew from the front. The visiting curate was a short gentleman of about my own age, with dark curly hair and a benign countenance, who looked vaguely familiar. At one point he glanced in my direction and fixed his gaze on me for an instant. I thought I glimpsed a modicum of recognition in his face but the moment passed unmarked and he went about his business. Presently, the church organist struck up the Wedding March, we all rose, the rear doors were opened and Louise walked slowly down the aisle on the arm of my brother. Louise was the sort of girl who would have looked good dressed in a bin bag. Today, she wore a gorgeous off-the-shoulder 'mermaid' style dress of white beaded lace, with a plunging V-neckline and figure-hugging contours, which fanned out at the knee. Her chestnut hair was scooped into an elegant bun and her eyes shone beneath the chiffon veil that floated in front of her face and behind her back as she glided towards the altar. I thought I had never seen a more beautiful bride, although my sister scored a close second. Next came Sarah, Julia and two friends, wearing dropped-waist pink taffeta dresses that ended at the knee.

The service went without a hitch and we all filed out into the spring sunshine. Scott was standing with his family in military attire.

"Scott, you look great," I squealed, breezing up to him. "How's army life?"

"It's good, thanks," he smiled. "Lou looks amazing."

"You must tell me all about it. Can we walk and talk? I need to warm up. I got quite cold in there and it's blowing a gale out here."

"You want to try the barracks, if you think this is cold," he laughed, as I linked my arm through his, wheeled him around and marched him off for a circuit around the outside of the church.

"You all right?" I asked pointedly, as soon as we reached the shelter of the church wall.

"What, you mean, about Lou and Jamie? Well, I can't say I'm overjoyed but I'm coping all right and I'm pleased for them. Jamie seems like a nice enough bloke and it would never have worked out between us. We want different things. I want to travel, see the world, live life on the edge. She wants to settle down and have kids. Kids … urghhh."

"Nothing wrong with kids. I would have loved to have had kids … a son like you … or a daughter, but I guess it's too late now," I sighed.

"You're not *that* old," he countered.

"I'm 38, and at any rate, since I haven't got a husband I won't be having any kids in a hurry. I missed my chance, I'm afraid. Do you remember Ray?"

"Wasn't he some Asian guy you used to hang out with years ago?"

"Half-Asian, but yes, that's the one. We broke up when you were … hmmm … seven, I believe. In the end, we wanted different things, only unfortunately it took me 15 years to find that out. He wanted to move to Portsmouth and I wanted to live here … so we parted. It happens, sometimes."

"I can't imagine why you would want to live here. There's nothing to do," he said disdainfully.

"I used to feel like that when I was your age. That's partly why I moved to Manchester in my early 20s but I came back. How about you? Where are you based? Somewhere lively?"

"Harrogate … it's all right as towns go. I'm at the AFC. I've almost completed Phase One … that's 42 weeks. Phase Two is at Catterick … that's just south of Richmond."

As we turned the final corner, we almost collided with Chris. He was half-tucked into an alcove on the north wall of the tower keeping out of the wind and chatting with Alan.

"Hi Vicks, hiya Scott. Doesn't my girl look lovely?" he said, flushed with pride, gesturing towards Louise who was posing for a photograph. "Perhaps Mum will finally forgive us for getting married on the sly, since our daughter's gone for the full works," he grinned. "Look at her, she's in her element."

Mum was indeed 'in her element' arranging her granddaughter's veil assisted by the photographer, who was calling out instructions, while Julie and her father looked on with an air of mild amusement.

As we conversed, I noticed the curate again. He was standing in front of the porch scanning the guests as if searching for someone in particular. By now I was convinced that we had met before, so I stepped out boldly from behind my brothers. He spotted me, smiled and raised his hand slightly.

"I know that man," I announced, "the one that did the service, though I can't imagine where from. Will you excuse me, I'm dying to find out?"

I left Scott expounding on the extraordinary power of military dress when attempting to impress the legion of would-be female admirers who frequented the bars in and around Harrogate. Evidently I didn't have too much to worry about on account of my nephew. I headed across the lawn to talk to the mysterious cleric.

"Hello, haven't we met before?" he said, as I approached him. "I never forget a face."

"I did think you looked familiar. All the way through the service, I kept trying to place you. I still can't. I do apologise, I'll probably kick myself when you tell me."

"My name's Robin. Robin Caswell. I married your friend Sally."

"Oh my God! Yes, I remember now. You were at the school reunion!"

"That's right. I was the 'spotty kid,'" he grinned.

"Oh no! Did she tell you that? I was *so* embarrassed," I shrieked. "I had no idea she was married to you. Me and my big mouth! I'm so sorry."

"That's all right, no hard feelings. It was pretty funny, to be honest, and I did have terrible acne when I was a boy," he smiled.

"Anyway, how *is* Sally? I haven't seen her for absolutely years!"

He hesitated. "Sally … Sally … passed away eight years ago," he said quietly.

For the second time in the presence of this man, I would fain have sunk into a hole in the ground than remain where I was, rooted to the spot in my present state of utter mortification, which was like a blow to the head.

"Oh Jesus, I'm so sorry," I spluttered. "No, no, I didn't mean to say that … the Jesus bit, I mean, you being a cleric. Oh, what *must* you think of me?" I shuffled my feet and stared down at my shoes, too embarrassed to look him in the face. "I'm afraid I've made rather of mess of things. No offence meant," I said awkwardly.

"None taken ... and you weren't to know." He laid his hand on my arm. "Come along Vicky. Don't be hard on yourself. Look, I'm not a puritan. People use expressions like that as part of their everyday speech. It's something I've learnt to accept."

"What happened to Sally?" I asked faintly, "if you don't mind me asking."

"She was in a road accident. She died instantly. She didn't suffer."

"Poor Sally. I-I can't believe she's gone. It must have been a terrible shock for you," I stammered, wanting to offer some words of comfort, but finding none.

"It was a massive blow. I confess I lost my way for a while, but my faith carried me over the abyss and … well, here I am, in my third year of training and due to take orders next spring."

"Oh, you're not ordained then? I assumed you'd been doing it for years, only you conducted the service like a pro … I mean, I wouldn't have expected less, really I wouldn't," I babbled, feeling my colour rise. "Gosh, I do seem to be putting my foot in it, rather."

"I used to be an estate agent," he said, with a wry smile. "After Sally, I was forced to re-evaluate my life. We have to train for four years before taking orders. What do you do for a job?"

"I'm a midwife," I declared proudly.

"Very commendable. Is that your son, over there in uniform," he asked pleasantly.

"No, no … that's Scott. He's my nephew, I don't have any children. As a matter of fact, I never got married."

"Do you live round here?"

"Yeah, I live with my Mum and my brother Michael, a few miles from here. D'you remember Michael? He was in the year above you at school."

"Not sure, to be honest."

Just then, we were interrupted by a call from the photographer, who was summoning the bride's family for a group shot.

"Look, I'd love to catch up," said Robin. "May I have your number?"

"Of course," I blushed, "only I've got nothing to write it on … or with."

"Wait there a moment." He disappeared into the church and emerged a few seconds later bearing a leaflet about upcoming events, and a ball pen.

I wrote down my telephone number, we shook hands and I went about the business of the day with a spring in my step.

At length, the wedding party relocated to the Bridge Inn where a sumptuous meal and an afternoon of merriment awaited us. We dined on broccoli and stilton soup, pan-fried sea bream and Belgian chocolate torte washed down with lashings of champagne.

As I sat sipping my drink with my sister after the speeches, an astonishing thing happened. Liam got up from the neighbouring table and ambled across to us.

"Hello Vicky, hello Toni," he said stiffly. "The food was excellent, don't you think?"

"Gorgeous," I concurred.

"Very nice, Mr. Blane," mumbled Toni, trying hard not to flinch under the gaze of her adversary.

"Now then, please don't call me Mr. Blane. Liam will do just fine," said the old gentleman. "What was I saying? Ah yes, I remember now. Young Jamie is a very pleasant chap, all told. I think he'll do very nicely for my Louise. We have a lot in common, you know."

"You have?" I said with interest.

"Yes. It's like this, you see. Many years ago, before we met, I worked on the railways. I used to drive the West Coast Mainline when I lived in Glasgow with my wife and daughters. Well now, what with our Jamie being a rail engineer an' all, we've got lots to talk about and a jolly time we have of it swapping stories." He hesitated. "It seems I'm indebted to you, Toni."

"That's all right," replied Toni nervously, toying with the stem of her glass.

"It's more than all right. I mean what I say. I might be a cantankerous old stick but I believe in giving credit where it's due. It seems I've underestimated you and haven't been altogether fair. Thanks to you, my Louise not only has a steady job – which she enjoys immensely I might add – she has a charming husband too, who I'm sure will make a splendid son-in-law and an excellent father, when the time comes."

Toni swallowed hard and turned crimson. "It … it was nothing, really," she stammered.

"It was a great deal and I hope we can be friends from now on." He held out a wrinkled hand.

Toni offered hers in return and they shook hands tentatively.

"Thank you, Liam," she said graciously. "That would be very nice."

As I looked on incredulously, I was overcome by a wave of emotion and thought I might cry. I took a gulp of champagne and a few deep breaths and regained my composure. This was turning into quite a day.

The tables had been cleared and moved to the sides of the room in readiness for a performance of Ralph Vaughan Williams' 'The Lark Ascending' by our very own home-grown virtuoso violinist Sarah, accompanied on the piano by her mother. Atop the piano was a huge bowl of peonies. Anne Cowley had been tasked with arranging the flowers. At 63 years old, by dint of her passion for teaching and her kindly disposition, she was still imparting knowledge to keen young minds at our local primary school, where Julie worked as a peripatetic music teacher. Today, she sat alongside Julie to turn the pages. Meanwhile, her son Paul was lining the chairs up in rows, a few feet from the piano. He still played chess with Liam once a week. The private taxi arrangement he had fallen into with Julie had expanded and nowadays we all made use of his services, should any one of the clan succumb to the temptation to drink rather than take the car, as was often the case. We took our seats and listened spellbound to Sarah's exquisite playing, which was met with rapturous applause.

After an interval, the lights were dimmed and the opening refrain from Bryan Adams' '(Everything I Do) I Do It For You' chimed out of the PA. Louise and Jamie swept onto the dance floor for the first dance. Next came Chris and Julie, Alan and Caroline, Toni and Jason and soon the floor was dotted with swaying couples. As I sat against the wall with Mum watching the dancers, I found myself thinking about Robin with a mixture of self-reproach and anticipation. That I had made a complete fool of myself, there could be no doubt. Still, he had asked for my number and that counted for something.

"Dance with me?" said Chris later on, as I was making my way with my sister back across the carpet to our seats, after an emphatic dual rendition of Bo-Rap complete with air guitar, fuelled by champagne and nostalgia.

"Yeah, sure," I panted, tugging off my heels and handing them to Toni. "Here, take these. My feet are killing me."

Back on the dance floor, I clutched at my brother's waist and settled my head on his chest. I felt very small in my stockinged feet, and very, very safe enveloped in the strong arms of my beloved older brother. Rocking like a pendulum to the melody of 'Hey Jude', I thought of Dad and wished he could have been there to witness the marriage of his granddaughter to his neighbour's child.

"Well?" said my brother, presently.

"Well what?"

"Mum says you've got yourself a date."

"Mum is very presumptuous," I rejoined.

"Well, have you or haven't you?" he persisted.

"He asked me for my number, that's all. We were at school together. Personally, I can't imagine why he wanted it, unless he regards me as a soul in need of saving. I made a right hash of things and took the good Lord's name in vain twice in as many minutes!"

"Single?" he pressed.

"Widowed," I replied. "For goodness sake, give over. You'll jinx it!"

Just then, Janice and her father stepped onto the dance floor.

"It's funny how things work out," said my brother. "Dad was always hankering for an alliance with the Duffys, leastways that's the way it looked to me."

"You mean, you and Janice? My goodness, you must be telepathic. I was thinking about Dad not two minutes ago."

"Yeah, sure I do. They were practically putting up the banns before I cut my first tooth. We'd have been sitting on 300 acres by now if I'd been willing to throw in my lot with Gymkhana Jill!"

"Shush, don't be disrespectful. I like Janice," I chided.

"Yeah, me too, but I never wanted to marry the kid, not even when I was a spotty-faced youth. Do you remember how Dad used to browbeat me? He was like a stuck record. '*Who's going to run the farm when I'm gone. my boy*?'" This was uttered in a gruff and austere tone that mimicked Dad to a tee, and Chris chuckled at his own joke. "Why do you think I slunk off to Blackpool with my intended and got spliced on a wet Saturday night in November? Man, he was intractable."

"You shouldn't speak ill of the dead."

"Anyway, it looks like they finally got their alliance," he continued, ignoring my reprimand, "not that it counts for much. It's purely academic now."

He gave me an affectionate squeeze and we na-na'ed our way through all four minutes of the fade-out.

At 10.30, as the theme song from 'Dirty Dancing' played out, the lights came up. Soon after, the newlyweds took their leave and retired to their room for a few hours' shut-eye before an early start and long drive to Manchester Airport the next morning. From there, they had booked a week at a beach hotel in Tenerife before taking up residence in a starter home on a new estate in Kirkby. Thanks to spiralling interest rates, leading to a sharp fall in property prices and subsequent reduction in the base rate, the couple were well placed to buy. In the meantime, Chris and Julie, Sarah, Julia and Liam piled into Paul's Orion and departed for Wasdale Head. Presently he returned to the inn to pick up his mother and shortly after, our seven-seater hired taxi arrived and we headed for home. Alan and Caroline were sleeping in the spare room tonight and 12 year old Leonie with me.

"I hear you made quite an impression on the vicar," teased Caroline, as we jostled for space at the bathroom sink.

"That's one way of putting it," I said ruefully.

"Why else do you think he asked for your number, you cloth-head!"

"Maybe you're right," I conceded, feeling my heart give a little flutter as I found myself daring to hope.

"Are you awake, Leonie?" I asked my niece softly, much later, as she tossed and turned in the bed on the opposite wall.

"No, I can't sleep," she grumbled. "It's *too* quiet … and it's *too* dark."

"Me neither. I feel a bit sick, to be honest," I admitted, fumbling for my glass and taking a large swig of water.

"Ha! Serves you right," she said sanctimoniously. "You were drunk!"

"I was not drunk," I parried. "It's adrenaline," I added self-righteously, after a pause.

"Oh yeah, Ryan told me you fancied the vicar," she giggled.

"Crikey! Is there anyone who doesn't know all about my private affairs? Anyway, I don't fancy him."

"Liar," she quipped. "Night night, Auntie. Sweet dreams."

* * *

Robin was as good as his word and the following Saturday I was sitting opposite the man who had married my niece and neighbour just a week before, at a table for two at the Bridge Inn.

"I must confess," he admitted, after a couple of glasses of wine, "I wasn't altogether honest with you when we met last week."

"Really? And you a man of the cloth!" I said, feigning shock at his startling revelation.

"You see, I didn't really believe that young man in the army get-up was your son. It would have been unusual for a mother and son to take a turn around the churchyard together. In my experience, that's usually what people do when they haven't spoken for a while.

I noticed that the young man in uniform was standing with another lady who I took to be his mother. Then you waltzed up and whisked him off so it wasn't hard to work out who was who."

"And?"

"Well, don't you remember? I asked you if he was your son."

"Oh … I see … yes, so you did."

"A question designed to find out if you were married with children … rather underhand of me, don't you think?" he said impishly.

"Dear God! What would the good Lord say? Oh crikey, there I go again. I must mind my language," I said apologetically.

"I think the good Lord has bigger fish to fry than my machinations … or the occasional profanity for that matter. D'you want dessert?"

"Yes please, I'll have one of everything," I grinned.

From that day on, we were frequently in each other's company. We would go for walks, eat out or go to the cinema. Sometimes he would come over and play board games with the family. At other times, I would make the 45 minute drive up the coast to the Victorian terraced cottage in John Street, Workington, where he lived with his shabby old cat Ben. Once we had got past the initial stage, though physically compatible, it was not a relationship that was governed by passion, rather by common interests and a strong desire for companionship.

* * *

Seven months later, we were sitting at a table for two at Mrs. Wilson's Eatery, situated in the quaint Victorian seaside resort of Silloth, waiting for our lunch to arrive. At the next table sat a couple with two young children, a dark-haired boy, who was sitting at the table colouring, and a little red-headed girl in a highchair.

"I would have loved to have children, wouldn't you?" mused Robin, glancing over at the pair.

"Absolutely. I always wanted kids," I replied emphatically, "but some things aren't meant to be. I have loads of nieces and nephews. They keep me busy. I guess it's my destiny to be the maiden aunt," I added mournfully, casting the bait and wondering if the fish would bite.

"Well, neither of us are getting any younger and we both want the same thing. Do you really think it's too late, only I don't?"

"Blimey, I'm 39! I'm going to have to get my skates on," I laughed, drawing him out.

"Look here, Vicky. I'm no Tom Cruise but if you really want to have a family, I'm happy to assist, though we'd need to make it legal, me being a cleric. Don't get me wrong. It's not just about having children. I think I'm in love with you. I never thought I'd say that again, after Sally."

"Is that a proposal?" I asked, dumbfounded.

"I guess so," he said, colouring.

"I … I don't know what to say. That is, I'm inclined to say yes but I wasn't expecting it, at least, not this soon. Are you sure you're in love with me, only 'think' feels a bit inconclusive. Is it what you really want or do you just feel sorry for me?"

"I've actually thought about it a great deal, though I've kept very quiet, as I wanted to be sure. But I've finally made up my mind." He reached across the table and took me by the hand. "Will you marry me, Vicky?" he said ceremoniously. "I don't have a ring, I'm afraid, as I had no idea whether you'd accept, and I have to be careful with my money."

"Can I think about it?" I said, "just for a couple of days."

"Yes of course. Ah, here's our lunch."

"Do you love him?" asked Mum, as we sat at the kitchen table later that day, sipping our tea.

"It depends how you define love. If you mean, does the earth move every time he whispers my name, then no. On the other hand, if you mean, do I enjoy his company and want to spend the rest of my life with him and grow old with him, then I guess I do. Back in a moment!"

I grabbed my coat, exited the farmhouse, strolled down to the crossroads and stopped on the bridge, where I had stood 18 years ago almost to the day, considering my future, before I had flown to Manchester on the heels of my brother. It was already dark. A keen wind tugged at my hair and whipped at the clouds overhead, sending them scudding across the moon. The plash of the water competed for airspace with the creaking trees that edged the stream below me. It didn't take long for me to make up my mind.

Having neither the means nor the inclination to put on a lavish affair, we decided to hold the wedding reception at home. We set about hiring a marquee and coerced Mum, Toni and Louise into doing the catering, which was to be a simple all-day buffet. Polly was called upon to do the photography and Phil's nephew was tasked with providing the sounds. Janice threw herself into just about everything else.

As I had no intention of getting smashed on my hen night, it made sense to hold the event on the day immediately preceding my marriage rather than a week or so before, as is customary. That way, I could share the occasion with Sarah, who had moved to London and was living in a house-share in South Croydon with girlfriends, and with my various friends from afar. I booked an early evening slot at the Wasdale Head Inn.

Three months later, on the eve of my wedding, I eagerly awaited the arrival of my dear friend and confidante Rose. It was to be her first visit into the county and I was excited to show her my childhood home and introduce her to my folks. Rose had checked into the Bridge Inn with her family earlier in the day. I had arranged for Paul to collect her on his way to the farm, where he was to pick up Mum, Polly and me and drive us to the pub. After a fond embrace, I gave Rose a quick tour of the house while Paul waited in the kitchen. At 66 years old, Rose still looked as young and spry as she had done when we first met 18 years ago.

She had a fine head of bouncing, honey-blonde curls, her make-up was immaculate and she wore an oversized black sweater, leopard-print leggings and black ankle boots. I stared down at my plaid skirt suit and square-toed sandals and felt a trifle deflated. However, I was in a buoyant mood, the moment passed and I quickly regained my high spirits.

When the time came to depart, Mum was still putting the finishing touches on the sherry trifle and Polly was applying her mascara.

"You can go on without us," suggested Mum. "Will you be a dear, pop out back and ask Janice if we could have a lift with her? You'll find her in the marquee."

"In that case," put in Paul, "d'you mind if we stop off for Julie and Sarah on the way. They'll be wearing heels and it looks like rain. Since I've got a couple of spare seats in the car, it seems a shame to make them walk."

At the mention of my sister-in-law and niece, a strange look flitted across the face of my friend but I paid no heed and we went outside together.

"Haven't you done enough for one day, Jan?" I said, standing at the threshold and surveying our afternoon's work. Three neat rows of trestle tables topped with white linen tablecloths and shining cutlery ran lengthways down the interior of the huge tent. A fourth stood on a raised dais at the opposite end. "This is my very good friend, Rose. Would you mind giving Mum and Polly a lift, only they're not quite ready and I can't be late to my own hen party?"

"Sure," smiled Janice. "I'm on my way in now."

When we arrived at Lingmell Old Stead, Sarah came to the door.

"Mum's upstairs," she smiled. "Would you like to come in for a moment? There's someone I want you to meet."

"Ah, would that be the mysterious Emil?" I asked mischievously.

A few months ago, Sarah had announced that she was dating a young saxophonist.

"Yes," she blushed. "This is his first trip up."

"May I bring my friend in? She's come up from Manchester. I've left her in the car with Paul."

"Of course, bring them in."

"Where's Julia? Is she coming with Mandy?"

"Yes, she's gone down to the Bridge Inn," replied Sarah.

"Oh right, yes, I remember now. Caroline went out just before we left. I think she might have gone to pick them up. We'd have had them at ours but we're full up. It's chaos, Sarah. I'm seriously not doing this, ever again!" I laughed, skipped down the path and returned with Rose and Paul.

"Sarah, this is Rose. Rose, this is my niece Sarah."

We went through to the lounge. A log fire was crackling in the grate. A young man sat in an armchair leafing through a copy of the Jazz Journal. His skin was the colour of ebony and his hair was jet black and close-cropped.

"This is Emil," announced Sarah. "We met during a production of Prokofiev's 'Romeo and Juliet', ironically. He's not part of the regular orchestra. He mostly works as a session musician."

"Hello Emil. I heard you're from across the Channel. I'm Chris's sister and this is Rose." I held out my hand and he stood up and shook it warmly.

"Hello, it's good to meet you at last." His voice was rich and melodious and his accent French.

"Have you been living here long … in England, I mean?"

"I came here four years ago when I was offered work. I loved London so much I decided to stay."

"I used to live in London, but I came back," I said diffidently. "It was a bit too busy and crowded for me … and I missed my family."

"That's the very thing I love about London," he said enthusiastically. "There's so much going on. It's a great place to work if you're a musician. What do you do?"

Before I had time to answer, we were interrupted by the sound of clattering china. Liam was standing at the kitchen door bearing a tea tray. Two mugs lay on their sides in a pool of tea, which was streaming from tray to floor. His face was white and his hands were shaking.

"Rosie," he gasped, his eyes glistening. "Rosie, is it really you?"

I turned to look at my friend. She stood transfixed, eyes staring and mouth agape. Liam lurched forward and the tea tray crashed to the ground. Quick as a flash, Rose leapt to his aid, scooping him up before he hit the floor.

"Liam! Oh my poor dear," she cried, staggering to the sofa with the old man in her arms, collapsing alongside him and placing her hand on his brow. By now, Liam's eyes were brimming with tears.

"Mother?"

I spun around. Julie was poised on the staircase, ashen-faced, watching her parents over the bannisters.

"Julie! Oh my darling girl," burst out Rose, looking wildly from one to the other, unsure whether to tend to her husband or run to her daughter.

Barely able to comprehend the scene being played out before my eyes, for my head was reeling, instinct took over. I dashed up the stairs, took my sister-in-law by the arm and conveyed her safely to the bottom, for fear she would miss her footing in her extreme state of agitation.

"Come and sit beside me, child," gulped Rose, choking back a sob and patting the sofa with her free hand.

Julie hesitated, crossed the room and sat down tentatively. Rose flung her arm around her daughter's shoulders, pulled her close and planted a kiss on her pale cheek. Julie flinched visibly. On her opposite side, Liam raised a quivering hand to his wife's face and stroked it tenderly.

"I don't deserve your forgiveness," wailed Rose, who was now crying in earnest. "I should never have disappeared like that. It was unthinkably cruel and selfish of me."

"Whatever possessed you to do it?" said Julie, with a faint note of resentment in her voice.

"After Sarah ... after we lost Sarah," she faltered, "I wasn't myself. Neither of us were ... May I have a tissue please?"

I grabbed a handful of tissues from a box on the sideboard and stuffed them into my friend's outstretched hand, then sat down on the floor, for my legs had turned to jelly. Rose wiped her eyes, blew her nose and took a series of deep breaths.

"After Sarah, I became obsessed with the desire to have another child," she sniffed, "to fill the void, you understand. Liam wouldn't hear of it. I was 36. Back then, you would have been considered virtually past it in terms of childbearing. That posed a risk that he was ill-disposed to take. You must remember, he had already buried a wife and two bairns. Also bear in mind, he was 21 years older than me and ill-equipped at 57 to cope with a new babby. I'm right, aren't I, pet?"

Liam nodded, speechless with emotion, and clutched at his wife's hand.

"Well, we fought like tigers," she continued. "The more I pressed my point home, the more obstinate and morose your father became, not that I blame him in the least."

"I remember all that," said Julie bitterly. "I thought the world was coming to an end."

"I'm sorry, my love. It was never my intention to hurt you. I took temporary leave of my senses. I was crippled by anger and hate, hate at life for taking my child from me. You father bore the brunt, poor dear. You always took his side and rightly so. On the night before I left, we had the most terrific row. Do you remember what you said to me?"

"Uh huh," murmured Julie, colouring.

"You spoke the truth, my dear. Children aren't like cars. They're not so easy to replace. I can see now that in trying to obliterate the past, I was sabotaging the present. You touched a nerve. After that, it didn't take a great leap of the imagination to convince myself

I was the villain of the piece and, believing I was doing you both a kindness, I vanished without trace. I think I knew deep down that I was still Liam's best girl, but in my desperation for a child, I chose not to listen to my better self. Instead, I saw a way out and squared it with my conscience. I launched my campaign and got my wish but it cost me dear. I started to question my motives. You see, Julie, grief is like a spectre. Invite it in and it will run its course and dissipate. Keep it at bay and it will lurk in the shadows and come back to haunt you. Believe me, there is no agony greater than the loss of a child. I feared it so I banished it from my mind. My baby was the instrument. Eventually I saw that it was wilful ignorance that had driven me to act, not my scruples, which were a sham. I was consumed with guilt for the best part of 20 years. Don't get me wrong, I love my Deborah, and after she was born, I did try to contact you both, but you'd moved away."

"Deborah?" exclaimed Julie, startled.

"You have a half-sister. You'll meet her tomorrow. She's 26. She's keeping her father company at the Bridge Inn this evening ... This has all come as a terrible shock. I feel awful," she groaned.

"Oh my God!" breathed Julie.

"There's one thing I don't understand," I ventured, after an uncomfortable pause. "If you simply disappeared, you can't have got divorced, in which case, how do you come to be married to Leslie?"

"Ho, that! We were never married. That was all pretence. Things were very different in the '60s, Vicky. Society took a very dim view of unmarried couples and poor Deborah would have been tantamount to an outcast, had anyone caught on. To all intents and purposes we were married, but not in the legal sense."

"Where did you go, Rosie?" asked Liam, gazing at his wife in wonder and taking up the thread.

"I went to my mother's at Crewe."

"It was the first place we tried. She told me you weren't there," said Julie tersely.

"Well yes, she was sworn to secrecy. As I said, I was determined not to be found," explained Rose. "It was a beastly thing to do but I can't change the past. I got myself a job at Leighton Hospital and took a flat. Soon after that, I met Leslie. He was a casualty of the Coppenhall Rail Disaster and I nursed him back to health, though he lost a leg in the process. He was a military man, like you."

"Ah, Rosie. You always had an eye for a soldier," said Liam wryly.

"He was an airman but point taken," she said, giving him a watery smile.

"I fought in the Second World War, you know Emil," said Liam proudly to his granddaughter's young beau. "That's how I met this lady. My, she was a bonny nurse."

"Look, I hate to break up a family party, but I'm getting a bit jittery about the time. We really should go," I put in.

"Yes, you're right," said Julie briskly, rising and reaching out for Rose's hand in a magnanimous gesture which did her enormous credit. "Come on, Mother."

Julie and Sarah collected their coats and Liam got up and followed us out into the lobby like a man in a daze.

"I'm sorry, Liam," said Rose gently, turning to embrace her husband at the door. "I'm not coming back to live here but I'm glad I found you again and I would love to stay in touch."

"Yes, of course, I understand," replied the old man bashfully, wiping a tear from his cheek. "See you tomorrow at church."

"If only I'd known before," I moaned from my seat in the back of Paul's Orion between Rose and Julie. "I might have been able to save you both years of torment."

"Maybe it's for the best," said Rose, now partially recovered. "I've done a lot of soul-searching in the last 30 years. Had I not made peace with myself, I would never have found the courage to talk so openly about my feelings. To do that, I needed to understand what drove me to act the way I did. By the same token," she continued, leaning forward to address her daughter, "you may have been much less willing to give me a fighting chance to make amends, had you not had more than your fair share of strife." Julie caught her breath. "You see child, Vicky has used me as something of a sounding board, so I do know that things haven't always been easy between you and Chris. It's through suffering that we gain wisdom and learn to forgive. Vicky was very honest with me but it was always with the best of intentions." She noticed my beetroot-red face and acknowledged my discomfiture with apologetic look.

When we arrived at the Wasdale Head Inn, most of the party were already assembled.

"You were *ages*," said Toni. "What kept you?"

"How long have you got?" I sighed, sinking into the seat next to hers, which she had kept free for me.

"Does it bother you getting married to a vicar?" demanded Leonie much later, from the other side of the bedroom, "you not being a churchgoer."

"I respect his beliefs and he respects mine. It's what we have to do in life. As long as we're all tolerant of one another's viewpoints and working for the greater good, I don't see what difference it makes. Now be quiet. I need my beauty sleep, though I doubt it'll make any difference at my age. My head's spinning like a top and I've barely had a drop to drink. Night, sweetheart."

Needless to say, I lay awake staring at the ceiling for at least half the night. Fortunately, it didn't catch up with me till the following night.

Friday 26th March 1993 was a pleasant spring day of sunshine and showers. At 11 a.m. I donned my mother's wedding dress, combed out my hair and awaited the arrival of Paul in his smart, black Ford Orion, accompanied by my brother Chris who was to give me away.

"I almost forgot," said Toni innocently, as she fastened my veil into my unwieldy curls. "I've brought something for you to wear." She dived into her handbag, drew out a scrap of fabric and flattened it on the bedside cabinet. The band had been roughly cut from an old pair of navy tights. Daubed across it, in silver nail polish, were the letters B R I D E.

"Hey, they're Mum's tights … and that's my nail varnish!" I squealed, bursting into a fit of giggles. "I can't believe you kept that thing all these years. I only made it for a joke!"

"Joke or no, I wore it on my wedding day. Now it's your turn!" she said triumphantly, picking it up and waving it in my face.

Downstairs, my four nieces were gathered in the kitchen. They were dressed in simple but elegant tunics, which were belted at the waist and descended to their feet, fashioned from an enormous roll of baby-blue crepe de chine that Mum had picked up at a car boot sale. Scott and Ryan, who was now in his penultimate year at school, had gone on ahead to St. Paul's Church with Jason to run through their ushering duties.

The service went like a dream, though I remember little about it. I do remember that I was blissfully happy. All my friends and relatives were there, along with the usual suspects. Auntie Gwen and Uncle Roger, who had welcomed me into their home during my first year-and-a-half of training, journeyed up from Barrow. Of the friends I had made on the course, Wendy came over from Ulverston with David and their two teenage boys. Donna made the short trip down from Whitehaven. Linda drove up from Manchester with her husband and four children, three boys and a girl. Ray and his family came all the way up from London, as did Nicky accompanied by her boyfriend and young son. We had shared many a meal together in the cafés and pubs in and around London, when Ray had been immersed in his studies. My business associate Karen was there with her partner, ready to depart at a moment's notice should her services be required by one of our little cohort of expectant mums. Thankfully, the day passed without event.

At six o'clock, I removed my sandals and shuffled gingerly with Robin onto the makeshift dance floor, a huge tarpaulin groundsheet which scrunched beneath our feet, to start the dancing. I chose the song 'Maybe I'm Amazed' by Wings, which was a favourite of mine. At the end of the first verse, Michael paraded Mum out onto the tarpaulin and took her in his arms. I was impressed by that. Toni and Jason followed suit. Chris and Julie were next to join the little throng. Then, to my unspeakable surprise, Ray got up and walked boldly over to Deborah. They stepped onto the floor together and I watched with astonishment as he pulled her close and wrapped his arms around her waist. I must have caught his eye, for he grinned at me and winked.

Later in the evening, after a large dose of dutch courage, Rose launched her campaign to salvage her past. Liam had to be practically press-ganged onto the dance floor by his three granddaughters. However, having overcome his initial reluctance, it was heartwarming to witness the couple locked in a friendly embrace, swaying to Simply Red's 'Holding Back The Years' – an interesting coincidence, as I remarked to my new husband afterwards. Meanwhile, Michael trod the boards with just about every single female on the guest list, to wit, Polly, Donna, Janice, his two teenage nieces Julia and Leonie, and even Deborah, whom he stole from under Ray's nose while Ray was topping up her glass. Just before midnight, after well over half an hour of hugging, kissing and fond farewells, we climbed into the Orion to embark on the 45 minute drive to Robin's home in Workington, too tired to contemplate anything other than a good night's sleep.

* * *

Later in the spring, Robin was ordained and took a living in the Vale of Lorton, situated in the north west corner of the county.

On a hot August day, Ben the cat passed away peacefully. He was 18 years old. Robin found him curled up beneath a clump of heather at the bottom of the garden. The following Saturday, we went over to Mum's for a meal and a game of cards.

"We lost Ben this week," I said to Mum, soon after we had arrived. "It's not the same without a cat about the place and Robin's quite cut up about it. Ooh, I do miss you," I crooned, picking up the portly Thomasin and giving her a bear hug.

"Strange you should mention that," said Mum. "Next door's lab's had pups and Michael's desperate to get his hands on one. Of course I said no, on account of the kitties. They're not as young as they used to be and I don't think it would be fair on them."

"I'll take them!" I said eagerly, part serious, part in jest.

"Would you really?"

"Don't be silly, Mum. I was only joking. That's to say, I would, but I wouldn't dream of stealing your babies."

"Well, as a matter of fact, I wouldn't mind all that much. Don't get me wrong, I'm very fond of them, but I've been thinking it would be nice to have a dog again. It will be good for both of us, keep us active, and Michael will finally stop badgering me."

"I would say you're pretty active already, but if you really want me to take them, I'm happy to oblige," I grinned.

"Hadn't you better ask your husband?" suggested Mum.

"Oh, he'll be fine. I don't recall checking with you," I laughed. "I just turned up with the two of them in a cardboard box! Would you like to come and live with me, sweetie?" I cooed, pressing my cheek against my fat friend's furry body. "Seriously, Mum, you should put her on a diet. It can't be good for her … you great lump of lard," I teased, holding her aloft. Gosh, you weigh a ton."

It goes without saying that Robin was delighted by the prospect. As for Michael, he was over the moon. Within a month, the two old biddies were comfortably installed in their new home and the puppy moved into Cinderdale Farm.

At the end of September, I took a trip to the GP, who confirmed my suspicions. I was with child.

"You know, you should wait till your 40th birthday and tell

your family then," said Robin later, as I was about to call Mum and share my glad tidings. "It's only another two weeks, if you can keep it under your hat until then."

"Actually, that's a great idea," I agreed.

On Friday 15th October, all the family gathered in our new home on the lower slopes of Mellbreak close to the northern tip of Crummock Water, to mark my passage into a new decade.

"Not drinking?" said Toni, spying a half-empty tumbler of orange juice standing on the kitchen worktop.

"I've got a headache," I lied.

"You *are* joking? You're as grumpy as hell when you've got a headache," she said archly. "You're certainly full of beans tonight. You're not pregnant, are you?" My response, or rather my lack of one, spoke volumes. "As a matter of fact, I'd put money on it!" she goaded. I felt my colour rise. "Oh my God, you *are* Vicky, you're pregnant! I *knew* it!"

"All right, keep it down. Everyone will hear. I was going to announce it over dinner but please at least let's get the food done first."

"Vicky! Vicky! You're expecting!" shrieked Mum, rushing in and flinging her arms around my neck.

Within seconds, the kitchen was heaving as the various members of our two families flocked in to convey their congratulations. Hugs were exchanged and glasses clinked.

Much of the talk at the dinner table revolved around the coming event.

"Mother's talk," said Sarah wearily to her sister, during a lull in the conversation.

"Huh! That was a great song. Tears for Fears." said Louise. "I used to love that band!"

"Son of a Preacher Man – if it's a boy," volunteered Mum.

"Living on a Prayer?" added Jamie with a grin.

"Rockin' Robin," put in Michael, and everybody laughed including my spouse.

"Take Good Care of My Baby," offered Julie. "Mum used to love that song."

"Here's one," said Chris. "Life begins at 40."

"Never heard of it," I shrugged. "Who sang it?"

"Only the mighty John Lennon," he declared reverently, raising his eyes to heaven.

"Amen to that!" I said, draining the juice from my glass. "Top-up, anyone?"

Epilogue

On Saturday 27th April, almost 30 years to the day since I had first met him, Liam passed away peacefully at home with his wife at his side. He was 91 years old. It was a perfect spring day. The sun was smiling down and the air was warm, with a soft breeze. The rich, mellow notes of a robin punctuated the drone of a distant tractor. The sweet citrus scent of magnolia blossom emanated from the old, gnarled tree that hugged the ancient stone wall running down the length of the plot.

I sat in the ramshackle garden at Lingmell Old Stead, chatting with Rose who had come up for the weekend. The family were gathered to celebrate the second birthday of our twin girls and to welcome the latest addition to the Kelly clan, a baby boy who shared his great-grandfather's name. Sophy and Harriet played at my feet with a newly-acquired Noah's Ark shape-sorter, a gift from my mother. Toni sat a few feet away, reading a copy of 'Cosmopolitan', while Mum was relaxing, her face to the sun and her eyes closed. Liam was dozing in a deckchair next to Rose, who was cradling baby Liam in her lap. His mother Louise was indoors with Julie, preparing the food. In the meantime, the boys had gone down to the Wasdale Head Inn for a swift pint before lunch.

"I do hope they'll be happy," said Rose, referring to the coming marriage between her daughter Deborah and my old flame Ray. "He's so much older than her. It's funny how history repeats itself."

"He's a good man," I replied.

"A very good man," echoed Liam, opening one eye.

"Talking of good men," I called across to Mum, "did you manage to find one?"

"Leave your mother alone," laughed Rose. "She doesn't want a boyfriend at her time of life!"

"I don't mean *that* sort of man, I meant a farmhand to help about the place! She's 69, you know. I've told her she needs to slow down but she won't listen to me."

"As a matter of fact, I have a girl starting in the summer. Her name is Jennifer. Do you remember Avice?" asked Mum, peeping out from under her eyelids and lifting her hand to her forehead to deflect the glare of the sun's rays.

"Remember her? Why of course! She helped me deliver Sarah … and I got the cats from her, if you recollect."

"Yes, that's right, you did. How are my lovely ladies?"

"Thomasin's lost another kilo," I said triumphantly. "I *told* you she was overweight. Elfride's got intestinal cancer, sadly, though cancer's not uncommon in cats. She's had a good innings. We're keeping her comfortable on steroids and we'll decide when the time's right," I sighed. "Who's Jennifer?"

"She's Avice's youngest. She's leaving school this year. Michael's going to show her the ropes. She can take over some of the more strenuous work."

"About time …I suppose he'd rather it was Polly," I added, with a smirk.

"Ah … dear sweet wayward Polly," smiled Mum. "She'll be back for the harvest."

"Lunch is in 10 minutes," trilled Julie from the back door. "Any sign of the men yet?"

"Nah," I drawled, leaning back in my garden chair to soak up the sun.

Rose leant over and prodded her husband's arm. "Liam?" but Liam had fallen into a very deep sleep, one from which there would be no waking. According to the coroner, it was a heart attack and his passing was instant and painless.

I'd like to say that we all lived happily ever after but our story isn't over yet.

Acknowledgements

I would like to thank the following people, all of whom have been instrumental in turning my dream into reality. Firstly, thanks go to my husband Chris for his love, patience and support during the nine years it has taken me to complete this project. To my wonderful parents, Anne and Michael Slatford, for their love, inspiration and belief in my work and for correcting my errors, both factual and typographical! Thank you to my very dear friend Wendy Brown, for sharing my journey and providing me with unceasingly positive feedback every step of the way. Thanks also to my little army of proofreaders, including my husband Chris, sister Sheila Andrews, Mollie Semple, Caroline Thurston and April Joy. Thanks to Andrew Slegg, Sophie White, Maira Javaid, Harriet Cox and numerous others for their interest and words of encouragement during the creative process. Thank you to Fern Bushnell and the team at Matador for taking on this project and doing an excellent job. Thanks to Martin Lawrence for providing the beautiful cover art. My thanks also to the following people for their part in acquainting me with the many and varied locations described in this book, in particular my mum and dad, my uncles Peter, Michael and Ron (RIP), Tina and John Healy and Andy Callen, Caroline Thurston and Adrian Forward, the Semples of Stokesley, Lindy and Dorian Matts and the team at Croydon Crusaders. Thanks to Karen Cutler for use of her dog Bella! To the countless individuals across the UK whose books, posts, photos and videos have enabled me to create a historically accurate account of a bygone era. To the owners of Melbreak Cottage, Loweswater, to whom I am indebted. Your kindness to me that day provided me with the material with which to launch my project. Finally to my three beautiful daughters, Jennine, Lyndsey and Susie, for putting up with my ramblings and for making me so proud! This list is by no means exhaustive and if I've forgotten to mention you, please accept my apologies – it's nothing personal!

Music has always played, and continues to play, a huge part in my life. This book contains numerous references to the music that dominated the airwaves during the latter years of the 20th century. I would like to pay a personal tribute to just a handful of the recording artists, their bandmates and associates – alive or dead – who have peppered my life with extraordinary moments of sheer joy through their songwriting genius and/or performance skills: the legendary Joe Elliott; the inimitable Pete Way and partner-in-crime Paul Chapman; Robin Zander; 'Professor' Neil Peart and Rush; Bob Catley and Tony Clarkin; Rob Halford and Glenn Tipton; Justin Currie and Iain Harvie; Fish; Genesis (pre-1978 incarnation) – especially Tony Banks, for his massive contribution to the pool of songwriting talent, and Steve Hackett, for keeping the music alive in the present day; Jon Anderson and the 'Yes' men! David Gilmour; Roland Orzabal and Curt Smith; Matt Bellamy and Muse; Peter Buck; Don Henley; Simon Le Bon; Dolores O'Riordan and Miranda Lambert. Thank you.

Last but not least, I wish to acknowledge the literary genius of Thomas Hardy, the Bronte sisters and Jane Austen, who set the benchmark so high that I cannot ever hope to attain it!